Frank Ziegl

THE STORY OF
609 SQUADRON

Under The White Rose

9/379334

CRÉCY BOOKS

This revised and updated edition published by Crécy Books Ltd, 1993
First published by Macdonald & Co. Ltd., 1971

© The Estate of Frank Ziegler, 1971

ISBN 0 947554 29 7

Printed and bound in Great Britain by
Hartnolls Limited, Bodmin, Cornwall

FOREWORD

by Air Chief Marshal Sir John Grandy, G.C.B., K.B.E., D.S.O.,
Chief of the Air Staff

The history of 609 (West Riding) Squadron covers the period, with only a brief break, from 1936–1951; this well-researched account faithfully reflects the life and spirit of the Squadron during those years. The author was the Squadron I.O. at a time when pilots were encouraged to regard I.O.'s as their High Priests. It is not surprising therefore that, with his first-hand knowledge of people and events, he has been able to evoke the style of 609 Squadron as well as recording the Squadron's operational achievements. This is important because style, more than anything else, distinguishes one squadron from another.

In some ways this book also highlights how times have changed. The modern Air Force is not as carefree as it used to be. With a Lightning costing forty times as much as a Spitfire at today's prices that is to be expected. The responsibilities are great; the margin for error is small. In what is glibly referred to as a permissive age we have to demand higher standards of self-discipline than ever before; and, what is more, we get them. But the spirit hasn't changed and our young men's approach to life has the same healthy vigour which has been the hallmark of the Royal Air Force for the past 50 years.

This book contains the virtues – and one or two of the foibles – of a famous Auxiliary squadron in war and in peace. I commend Frank Ziegler's history; it is written with honesty and humour. I have no doubt that those who served and fought with 609 will be reminded of much that they can remember with pride.

John Grandy

ACKNOWLEDGEMENTS

This book could not have been written without the help of a great many people, who wrote down their memories, composed assessments, lent books, photographs and private diaries, allowed themselves to be interrogated by post, telephone or in person, or checked the drafts of some of the chapters. Since they are, I think, all mentioned later, it is hardly necessary to name them here – with one exception. That is the devoted Chairman of 609 Squadron Association, David R. Shaw, who wrote personally to every surviving member of the Squadron whose address was known, enlisted their help and put me in touch with them.

I am also grateful to the Ministry of Defence for granting me access to 609 Squadron's official records, to H.M. Stationery Office for permission to quote from Crown Copyright histories, and to the authors and publishers of other works that I have quoted.

Finally, I wish to thank Air Chief Marshal Sir John Grandy, Chief of the Air Staff, for kindly troubling to read the manuscript and for writing a Foreword.

F.Z.
December 1970.

Sadly Frank Ziegler died in 1976, this new edition has been edited and new information added by Flt Lt Chris Goss, 609 Squadron's official historian.

PROLOGUE

A passenger arriving at or departing from Leeds and Bradford Airport in the late afternoon of 29th March, 1968, may well have wondered why the new Terminal Building was packed with about a hundred men locked together in conversation. Their age groups varied : while the majority were in their late forties or fifties, some were in their thirties, and a few were over sixty. And although aeroplanes were the common denominator of them all, none was intending to take off that evening; while if a few of them had indeed landed at the airport a few minutes earlier, they had come by unscheduled flights and presented a pretty mixed bag of skymen. One was a famous test pilot, another a general of the Belgian Air Force, and a third the chairman of Lloyds Bank Ltd. A captain of British European Airways had come by train and bus.

If our passenger was a local man he may have spied amongst the throng the officer commanding the near-by Royal Air Force Station, Church Fenton – Group-Captain Jerry South. It was his uniform, in fact, which may have given the show away. For to all those present Leeds and Bradford Airport will always be Yeadon, and presently they grew silent as a plaque on the wall was unveiled. In gleaming letters this proclaimed :

609

(WEST RIDING)

SQUADRON

ROYAL AUXILIARY AIR FORCE

WAS FORMED ON 10TH FEBRUARY, 1936 AT

THIS AIRFIELD WHICH WAS ITS HOME BASE

UNTIL 1951

609 was here when the War began. Equipped with Spitfires and Typhoons, in continuous operation from wartime bases between 1939 and 1945, the Squadron covered the evacuation of Dunkirk, served

with distinction in the Battle of Britain and supported the Normandy landings. Reformed in 1946, 609 returned to Yeadon in 1947 and continued as a fighter squadron until 1957.

Never in the field of human conflict was so much owed by so many to so few.

WINSTON S. CHURCHILL.

With this unveiling the wheel of 609 Squadron's history went full circle; for the unveiler—now the chairman of Lloyds Bank—was the same man who thirty-two years previously, in 1936, had been appointed, as Squadron-Leader Harald Peake, to raise this squadron and become its first commanding officer. The words which he and his successor in command, Squadron-Leader Geoffrey Ambler, spoke now in retrospect form some of the bones of this book.

The subsequent service careers of both had been meteoric, the former relinquishing command of a squadron to become Director of the Auxiliary Air Force, with the rank of Air Commodore, the latter being the only Auxiliary Officer in the war to attain the rank of Air Vice-Marshal when later he was appointed Senior Air Staff Officer at H.Q. Fighter Command. But both remained 609's 'patron saints'. While Director of Public Relations, Air Ministry, Harald Peake visited the Squadron often during the war, and formally presented it with its Badge in 1941; Geoffrey Ambler became its post-war Honorary Air Commodore, and after disbandment President of 609 Squadron Association, in which the living ghost is still enshrined.

It was under his authority that members of this Association in 1967 approached the Chairman of the Leeds and Bradford Airport Committee with the suggestion that its splendid new Terminal Building would be incomplete without some monument to Yeadon's military history—with the result that this Committee not only agreed with enthusiasm, but promised a contribution towards the cost. The rest of the cost would, it was hoped, be defrayed by former members of the Squadron ... if enough of them could be found.

It was then that a 'crash committee', whose members, among them its inspired chairman David R. Shaw, had ten years before been volunteers flying Meteor jet fighters, began its 'Operation Search'. Those whose addresses were known were interrogated, every clue followed up, telephone directories scrutinized in all parts of the land. In the end, no less than 139 contributors were found, over a dozen of them in Belgium.

And now over a hundred of them had come to do honour to something defunct since eleven years, yet whose spirit evidently still throve. Most of them, especially the oldest and the youngest, were local men; for both in 1936 (when it was formed) and in 1946 (when it was reformed) 609 had been an exclusively Yorkshire squadron. Indeed, some of the original Yorkshire airmen had serviced its aircraft in the war right up till 1944, and pre-war Yorkshire pilots had fought till nearly the end of 1940—by which time they were all dead, exhausted or too old.

By the nature of things there could, in war-time, be no replacements from the original, local, strictly volunteer source. From 1940 till 1945 the West Riding Squadron (as its name remained) became perhaps the most international fighting unit since the Crusades. Under the White Rose—which, with crossed hunting horns and the motto 'Tally Ho!', comprised its Badge—there fought British, Canadians, Australians, New Zealanders, Americans, Poles, Frenchmen, a Norwegian, South African, Armenian, Turkish, Rhodesian and an unnaturalized German, while from 1941 onwards half its aircrew came from Belgium. Though some of them may have had but a hazy idea as to where Yorkshire lay, and no one ever explained to them whether a Riding was animal, vegetable or mineral, they became as proud to belong to the West Riding Squadron as any native of Leeds or Bradford. Together they made it one of the most successful fighter squadrons that any country has produced.

Between inception in 1936 and destruction in 1957 609 had twenty-one commanding officers, sixteen of whom had led the Squadron in war. Of the latter three had been killed in action, four had been taken prisoner, one had been badly burned and one had died just two weeks before the plaque at Leeds and Bradford Airport was unveiled. Despite all this, the crowning triumph of 'Operation Search' was that when, later the same evening, The Hundred sat down to a reunion dinner at the Merrion Hotel,

Leeds, they were confronted by no less than fourteen of the officers who had once commanded them – including two out of three Belgians – from a possible seventeen survivors. Some of these had never met each other before, yet now they sat in a long chronological row along the base of a huge letter E, whose multiple prongs accommodated, in contemporary groups of progressive vintage, the men they had once led.

As Intelligence Officer, I had served under nearly all the wartime commanders, or else known them earlier as junior officers. They had succeeded each other like the notes of a scale or successive images on a roll of film. But now, after a quarter of a century, seeing so many of them together seemed to make nonsense of time, or was as if all had been photographed on a single negative. Yet as each, chronologically again, made a speech – wisely limited by chairman Shaw's decree to two minutes each – he was introduced by a swarthy man with a magnificent handle-bar moustache, who had served under the first and the last of them, and with every one of The Hundred – a man who had witnessed this squadron's dawn, high noon and sunset. To some he was Leading Aircraftman Hanson, the fitter; to others Sergeant Hanson, in charge of 'B' Flight's aircraft; to the youngest he was Flight-Lieutenant Hanson, M.B.E., Squadron Engineer Officer. To all he was 'Darkie' Hanson – the human repository of 609 Squadron's traditions, joys, sorrows . . . and memories.

After such an interval of time one might have expected the speeches to be trite, facetious or sentimental. They were none of these things (I have a tape recording). There was magic in the air this night, and I suspect, as each former C.O. spoke, he sensed that the absent and the dead were listening too. Each spoke with astonishing humility and one gathered that, whatever his achievements since, he considered his brief hour in command of a squadron, *this* squadron, to have been his proudest. Perhaps not so astonishing, really; for though it is a sad commentary on civilization that some of the closest human brotherhoods have been cemented by war, this country today is also the poorer for the fact that such brotherhoods as the squadrons of the Royal Auxiliary Air Force no longer exist.

When the speeches were over, Air Vice-Marshal Ambler pub-

licly suggested I should write this book. Though 'in cold blood' it
has proved a different matter, at the time, amongst all those
familiar faces, it seemed an easy enough task. Amongst those
at my own table were 'Joe' Atkinson, with whom I had shared
bedrooms for two years and whose death I had mourned in error
for twenty; John Skett, 609's only pilot who had served in Bomber
Command; Tommy Rigler, one of the most colourful pilots ever
to join a fighter squadron; while next to me was a cheerful blond
mountain of confidence named John Bisdee, who had left in 1941
and later commanded 601 Squadron in Malta. He is a born organi-
zer, and currently chairman of one of the Unilever companies. In-
directly *he* should take the blame for this book; for when I went
to 609 it was only as *locum tenens* and after a fortnight I left.

'Shouldn't be surprised to see you back again,' he said with a
wink. 'Frankie Howell and I are trying to organize something.'
(Frankie was his flight commander).

Soon afterwards, while with another squadron in Cornwall, I
was informed by Group H.Q. that I had been posted back to 609
by the direct request of its commanding officer.

It was a compliment I did not deserve but have never forgotten.

INTRODUCTION

It was October, 1940. On the train that carried me from London towards Bath I was acutely conscious of the cardboard box which lay inadequately concealed on the rack of the compartment. It contained my gas mask or 'respirator'. Everyone carried one in those days, but because I was now an 'Acting Pilot-Officer on Probation' mine should have been the military version carried in a canvas satchel. That I still had a civilian one marked me out as a 'sprog' – R.A.F. parlance for one who is new and ignorant in his calling.

I was, in theory, an Intelligence Officer. Yesterday I had put on my uniform and peaked cap for the first time, and after practising a few salutes in the mirror until I could infuse what I thought was the necessary air of nonchalance, had reported to a centre in an outer suburb of London. There, with some forty other raw recruits, I had spent the day filling in papers and being sorted out. The highlight had been when a tall and handsome Wing Commander (who was also a Lord) arrived and addressed us on the subject of interrogating air crews with tact and efficiency. He then interrogated each of us with such efficiency that two minutes apiece were all that were necessary to split us up into two groups, one of them assigned to Bomber Command, the other to Fighter. I, he somehow decided, was more suited to the latter.

We of Fighter Command were then appointed to stations ranging from the blitzed airfields of Kent to the somnolent Orkney Islands north of Scotland, with the option of changing if we could find someone who would agree to a 'swap'. With my home in London, I did all but change with someone who had been appointed to Fighter Command headquarters itself at Stanmore – in which case I might have achieved greater promotion, but this book would not have been written. We were to report to our stations and commence duty on the morrow.

I returned for my last night at home just as the familiar bombs began to drop – familiar because until today I had been working amongst them as a member of London's civil defence organization. For the past fortnight they had been raining down nightly. I had seen churches and power stations blazing, dwellings pulverized and the human shambles of a direct hit on a shelter. Outside the shell of St. James's Church, Piccadilly, was pinned a pathetic little notice saying 'No organ recital this week'. Now, as I stepped over the prostrate figures that occupied all but a narrow rim of the underground railway platform and emerged into the glass-strewn streets, I felt a pang of shame that I was leaving my wife, a Red Cross nurse, to go on evacuating patients from blazing hospitals while I in the R.A.F. (though I did not yet know it) would at last be able to sleep.

On the train I thought over the instructions about interrogating pilots with 'tact and efficiency'. Not yet having seen The Few or their Spitfires and Hurricanes except as interweaving smoke trails high up in the sky – the groundsman's view of the Battle of Britain – I was diffident. Striving to hide my ignorance from the airman who met me at Corsham railway station, I asked him what aircraft were in use at the airfield to which he was driving me, but realized I had failed when he replied : 'There aren't any aircraft, Sir. You see, it isn't an airfield.'

Instead, we entered the grounds of a pleasant-looking manor house, suggestive of log fires and panelled rooms. I reported to an officer called the Camp Commandant. Despite this imposing title he turned out to be only a Flight-Lieutenant and I studiously re-frained from saluting him. Rather as a theatrical agent might deal with an actor, he said he didn't think there would be any work for me today, and I filled in some more papers, wondering what the work would be on the morrow. I was then escorted away by a young man with a brassard marked 'O.O.' (for Orderly Officer) who was told to find me a bed – but not before the Camp Com-mandant had followed me out into the passage and gently ex-plained that one should salute on entering *any* office, however junior the rank of the officer in charge.

I thanked him, and realized I had put up my first 'black'.

More were to follow, as was to be expected from an Intelligence Officer who not only knew nothing about Intelligence, but almost as little about the R.A.F. itself. Direct-commission officers who joined it a little later were subjected to a month's course, during which they marched, did P.T., learnt the conventions and courtesies and were introduced to the mysteries of King's Regulations. I learnt by trial and error. Eight months later, while manning the Intelligence Office at Biggin Hill, I knew enough not to return the salute of a very high officer indeed – because I was hatless. The officer was General de Gaulle, who asked me where he could find Winston Churchill. I suggested that, it being 12.45, the Prime Minister might be having a drink in the Officer's Mess.

The Orderly Officer, ignoring his instructions to find me a bed, instead handed me over to two real Intelligence Officers, who took me to have tea. This, far from being served before a log fire in the panelled room of my imagination, was consumed standing up in a draughty marquee. My bed (a camp one) later turned out to be one of several in a damp tent, approached via a sea of mud, barbed wire and trenches, all of which claimed their periodical victims in the autumnal dark. All senior officers lived out in requisitioned houses, and Rudloe Manor itself comprised only offices.

I was therefore surprised to hear, during tea, that this quiet if insalubrious spot was responsible for the air defence of the whole of south-west England. It was, in fact, No. 10 Group Headquarters. The Air Officer Commanding was Air Vice-Marshal Sir Quintin Brand, K.B.E., D.S.O., M.C., D.F.C., who had shot down a German Gotha in the last raid on England of World War I, and been knighted after his pioneer flight from England to the Cape in 1920. His chief of staff (called S.A.S.O.) was an Air Commodore, and the next senior officer was the Group Captain Ops.

My own job would be to do a shift as Duty Intelligence Officer, of which the main burden, I gathered, was to write a thing called a 'Form Y' to Fighter Command. This, consisting first of statistical paragraphs and then a narrative, was designed to supply a complete survey of what had happened in the Group area during the period it covered in the way of enemy raids, the measures taken to combat them and the success thereof. Copies were expected by the

A.O.C., the S.A.S.O., the Group Captain Ops. and the 'Controller'. In return, Fighter Command would circulate to Groups their own 'Form Y', which was the composite of what had happened in the whole of Britain.

'Lot of nonsense, isn't it?' said one of the I.O.s called Heron. He wore a wing on his tunic and had been an Observer in World War I. He seemed far too young, till I remembered that that war had ended only twenty-two years before, when he was nineteen. To be in uniform again, but fighting a war with paper, seemed to him a source of constant mocking amusement. He became my guide, philosopher and friend.

After tea I was taken to the Duty Intelligence Office. The smallest room in the manor, and probably a former larder, it had a stone floor and was heated by a primitive paraffin stove. Theoretically it housed the Duty I.O., a clerk, a teleprinter and its operator. As, however, it was the only place with any warmth for them to go, it was usually crowded out by other junior officers not on duty who used the stove to make coffee. Far more sumptious, but inviolable, was the office of the Senior Intelligence Officer, a Squadron-Leader, and his assistant, a Flight-Lieutenant. They dealt with inscrutable things like 'Gloworms' and 'Flashing Beacons'.

After a lot of shop talk, in the course of which such terms as Forms A, B, G, X-raids, Fading Plots, A.A.L.O.s, R.C.L.O.s, and even W.A.A.F.s, were confidently bandied about, Heron (who was on duty) decided it was time to write his Form Y to Fighter Command. This he did by consulting Forms A, B, etc., and a lot of charts, borrowed from the Operations Room, on which were traced the course of hostile raids, and which, by the time they were spread out, filled the entire room. Finally he looked through a sheaf of teleprints from Sector stations marked 'Composite Combat Reports' – and for the first time, as I read that Red 2 of a certain squadron had shot down a Junkers 88 into the sea, and that Red 3 was missing, I became dimly aware, amidst all the paper, of real squadrons somewhere fighting real battles. Then the teleprinter began to chatter, and Heron's story was simultaneously spewed forth by another teleprinter at Fighter Command.

After a day or two, it was decided that I had learnt enough to try a shift myself. First, however, a pass had to be obtained to admit me to the Operations Room, which was housed in the manor's barn, and very secret. Though not so exciting as a Sector Ops. Room, where one could hear airborne pilots being directed to interceptions, and their sometimes revealing comments, this was, in fact, the hub of the whole Group. From a sort of Royal Box a row of officers, with the Controller in the middle, looked down on a large board resembling a giant game of halma, and consisting of a lot of squares superimposed on a map of south-west England. Round this a number of attractive W.A.A.F.s wearing ear-phones (their beauty varied, I was to learn, with the importance of the station and reached its zenith in the Ops. Room at H.Q. Fighter Command) moved red and yellow counters across it with magnetic croupier's rods as if in obedience to the play of the officers above. In fact, of course, the yellow counters represented the play of officers of the German Luftwaffe – i.e. hostile aircraft whose positions were being plotted electronically by radar or visually by the Royal Observer Corps.

Sometimes there would not be any counters, and everybody from the Controller downwards would be relaxed and the W.A.A.F.s would be reading or knitting. Then one of them would quietly stand up and place a yellow counter at the bottom edge of the board, where the English Channel was, and the tension would increase as it moved northwards. Usually it was followed by more and more, each counter labelled to represent a number of air-craft, till perhaps there were several raids of up to '100 plus' on the board. If they came right up to the point on the map where Group headquarters was situated, one could sometimes hear bombs, and going outside see flames rising into the night sky from the stricken city of Bristol. But whatever was happening outside, the game on the table was the only thing that mattered to those playing it.

At the far end of the room was a vertical board showing all the squadrons in the Group, and their states of Readiness. As the yellow counters advanced, the Controller would give an order, transmitted by the W.A.A.F. on his left, and soon afterwards a red light would go on opposite a certain squadron to show that it, or part of it, had left the ground. A red counter would then appear on the board and draw nearer and nearer to a yellow one. If this represented a single raider which was shot down, the counter would stop moving, and presently a W.A.A.F. with an expressionless face would unobtrusively take it away. Or it might happen to one of our own counters. It was as robot-like as that : nothing to indicate the human drama that somewhere was being enacted in the sky – except occasionally when a dissatisfied squadron commander got through via his Sector Controller to the Group Controller. Then it was as if a dissatisfied shareholder had got through direct to the floor of the Stock Exchange.

Into the 'Royal Box' the Duty Intelligence Officer would, at intervals, creep to hand the Controller the 'colours of the day' – i.e. the recognition signals that aircraft were supposed to flash or fire in case of need (the sequence of which he had painstakingly worked out from two top-secret Admiralty code books) – plus signals and combat reports that had come off the teleprinter; and also to get miscellaneous information from the Ack-Ack or Observer Corps liaison officers in the 'pit' downstairs about bombs, crashes, flares and other phenomena for his Form Y. From the number of yellow counters on the board he would also be able to judge how onerous a period of duty lay before him, and (if it was a night period) whether he would get some sleep on the office camp bed and so be fresh enough next day to visit London. For the I.O.s had so adjusted their duties that after one man had done three fairly concentrated eight-hour periods he was free to leave the uncomfortable camp for the better part of two whole days. Meanwhile, to watch the board, he had to stand self-effacingly behind the Controller, who, if there was something important on, might be the A.O.C. himself. Then he would stand even stiller than usual, with the result that on every I.O.'s trousers, in exactly the same place, was a brown mark where the electric stove to the right of the Controller had scorched them.

One or two of these early Controllers I got to know. Ex-flying men themselves, and somewhat querulous that age or rank now confined them to a ground role, they forgot their basic contempt for the non-flying officers (alias 'Penguins') that the war was bringing increasingly into the R.A.F. to the extent of visiting the Duty Intelligence Office for a cup of coffee before going on duty. They seldom, however, condescended to discuss 'ops' with their host, and that untutored individual (at least in my case) found himself writing about these in terms he very imperfectly understood, and occasionally I used the wrong one. Once, for instance, instead of referring to a certain squadron which had just arrived in the Group as 'not yet operational', I described is as 'not yet organized'. This caused the A.O.C. to send for the S.I.O. (the Squadron-Leader who dealt in 'Gloworms') and point out with some asperity that he had personally 'organized' this squadron in 1917. But one little 'black' of mine remained unnoticed. A report from one of the Sectors stated that two Spitfires had chased a supposed 'Hun' over several counties only to find it was a 'Miles Master'. 'That I.O. doesn't know his Latin,' I said to myself, triumphantly altering the report to read 'Miles Magister' – an aircraft I had heard of, but didn't then know was far too small and slow ever to be mistaken for a Messerschmitt 109. (There was of course, though unknown to me, the much faster Miles Master as well.)

Strangely and untimely enough, the first pilot I personally ever had to interrogate was the A.O.C. himself. The Intelligence system, admirably geared to acquaint 'top brass' with the doings of ordinary pilots, seemed to break down completely if a member of the brass decided to fly operationally himself. So when, one night, our Air Vice-Marshal took off alone in a Hurricane to combat the enemy, Fighter Command demanded a report. Vainly I asked 'Ops.' what he had been up to : no one knew or had dared to ask him. I rang up Sectors : for all they knew the pilot was missing. Finally, in great trepidation, I lifted the telephone receiver.

'A.O.C.'

'D.I.O. here, Sir. Fighter Command want to know what you were doing last night.'

To my surprise he seemed rather pleased. 'Oh, just tell them . . .' and I wrote : 'One Hurricane (Air Vice-Marshal . . .) took off at . . . from . . . and patrolled . . . No enemy contact made.' And Fighter Command was satisfied.

Another absurd moment was when the ops. staff became paralysed by the discovery that some highly secret operational orders in course of being retailed to Sectors were also being heard loud and clear on the B.B.C. one o'clock news bulletin. 'Obviously a matter for Intelligence,' said someone, and the Controller asked me to investigate. I was still wondering how to set about this task when fortunately some Post Office engineers took over.

The daylight Battle of Britain by now was nearly over. Hoping to sap civilian morale, and thus the war effort, the enemy had switched his bomber strength to raiding cities by night, and against this there was at this time little effective defence. Anti-aircraft fire, though massive, was hardly yet scientific. If it minimized any bombing precision there might otherwise have been, and boosted civilian morale by its sheer noise (while simultaneously subjecting those on duty to a cascade of falling shrapnel), any hits it achieved were a matter of luck. Effective defence by night-fighters had to await the development of airborne radar pioneered by John Cunningham. But meanwhile the A.O.C. of No. 10 Group was one of those (as we have seen from his personal example) who believed that single-engined day-fighters could be adapted for the role, and I think it was he who invented a new tactic whereby Hurricanes and Spitfires would patrol over a target city at staggered altitudes above those reserved for the guns.

The code name for this operation was *Fighter Night*, and it was on the occasion that it was tried out for the first time over Bristol that I put up what was judged to be an '*imperial* black'. For the fact was that, whereas the name of the operation was doubtless known to the S.I.O. and his assistant, neither had considered it necessary to pass it on to the night Duty I.O.s at Group or Sectors. The result was that, although all sorties were duly reported by Sectors to me, and by me to Fighter Command, the magic phrase *Fighter Night* never appeared, and there was nothing specifically to indicate that it had ever taken place. This was too much for the A.O.C., probably already riled by the complete failure of the operation, and it was decided that someone had better 'carry the can'. When it was discovered that on duty had been the same I.O. who had not known the difference between 'organized' and 'operational', it became pretty clear who was going to carry it. Sent for by the S.I.O., I was handed an Adverse Letter which the S.A.S.O. had written about me to no less an authority, I seem to remember, than the Air Ministry itself. With some embarrassment the S.I.O. explained that he had twice intervened with the S.A.S.O. on my behalf, but that he was adamant; so would I please sign the letter myself to show that it had been read and understood.

After a mere ten weeks as an Acting Pilot Officer on Probation, it was evident that my war-time career in the R.A.F. was already about to end in a 'bowler hat'. I wrote a report in my defence but no reprieve came, and to my colleagues I became an object of muted sympathy, like a man about to go to the gallows. However, I decided not to go without a final fling. Next day, contrary to all advice, and ignoring the rules whereby a junior officer can only obtain an interview with a very senior officer through the medium of his immediate boss, I knocked perfunctorily on the S.A.S.O.'s sacred door (it was a jar), entered with the letter in my hand, and demanded a word with him. To my great surprise he was most pleasant, listened to me, asked about my previous life, gently scolded me for upsetting the A.O.C., and said the matter was forgotten. I asked him what I should do with the famous letter.

'Keep it as a souvenir,' he said.

The S.I.O. was flabbergasted. And now I can't even remember the S.A.S.O.'s name.

*

9/ 379334

One result of the unwelcome attention that had been focused upon me was the discovery that I was 'supernumerary' at Group H.Q., and should have been sent to a squadron long ago. On a cold day in January, 1941, therefore, I found myself embarked on a complicated train journey: destination, Warmwell airfield in Dorset. There I was to be attached for a fortnight to No. 609 ('West Riding of Yorkshire') Squadron, while its regular I.O. went on a course. For the first time I was to meet fighter pilots and their aircraft face to face.

Though at Group all squadrons to me had been distant cyphers, I had noticed that the one which sent in more reports than most, because most frequently engaged with the enemy, was the very one I was coming to. Three days before I first put on uniform it had distinguished itself by claiming its 'hundredth Hun' – the first Spitfire squadron in Fighter Command to do so and the more remarkably, it was said, because it was an 'Auxiliary' squadron (R.A.F. equivalent of 'Territorial'). A month later, one of its flight

commanders—Flight-Lieutenant J. C. Dundas, D.F.C. and Bar—
had been lost while shooting down the German ace Major Wick,
a pilot who had claimed to have shot down 56 aircraft. Finally,
one of my coffee-drinking visitors of late had been a D.F.C. squadron-leader called MacArthur, the first Battle of Britain pilot I
ever spoke to. He was now, he told me, doing a 'stooge' job as
a rest, and hated it. When I mentioned that I was going to 609
as I.O. his whole face lighted up.

'But that's my old squadron!' he cried, rather as if he should
have been consulted. '*Please* give 'em all my love!'

It was my first experience of that blood-brotherhood which
united the members of certain war-time fighter squadrons with
bonds stronger than those of country or even family.

At Dorchester I was met at the station by a tall and rather awesome Flying-Officer who turned out to be 609's regular I.O.

'Tomorrow,' he informed me, 'you will be looking after 152. On
Friday you will have both squadrons, and when 152's I.O. comes
back you will be 609's body till I return.'

It was a simple way of putting an immediate future which
seemed fraught with difficulty. I thought once more of those
initial instructions about interrogating pilots with tact and efficiency as they returned battle-scarred and exhausted from the
skies, and of the parting reminder of the S.I.O. at Group that combat reports *must* come in quickly. What if both squadrons were
engaged simultaneously and repaired to their separate dispersal
points with me the only I.O. on the station? Such was my diffi-
dence that when we arrived at the gates of the aerodrome I half
hoped that the sentry who inspected my identity card would
refuse to admit me.

'Better come and meet some of the chaps,' said my guide, as
we drew up at a small encampment of tents situated in a sea of
mud. 'This is our Dispersal.'

Outside were a number of young men in leather jackets, whom
I took to be pilots, kicking a football around.

'Sergeant Boyd! Sergeant Palmer!' They reluctantly desisted
from their game, viewed me with quizzical interest, and waited.

'This is Pilot-Officer Ziegler, who has come to take my place
for a fortnight. He's rather new, so be kind to him.'

They shook hands good-naturedly, then went on with their game. Next moment the flap of a small marquee opened and, followed by derisive shouts from within, two bodies wearing Mae Wests precipitated themselves into the open and lay struggling on the muddy grass. Others followed more leisurely, and we all watched till they had finished.

'This is Aggie,' said the I.O., indicating the larger body as it regained the vertical. 'The other one's Novo.'

'Officers of the West Riding squadron,' added the one called Aggie. 'I'm half Armenian, half French, and Novo's a dirty old Pole. How do you do.'

He was a tall, powerfully built young man – he had been a boxing blue at Oxford – with a small Errol Flynn moustache and a soft honeyed voice with just the right tinge of foreign intonation to make it irresistible to girls. His real name was Noël Agazarian. The other, Nowierski, was slightly bald and much older—he was thirty-four. He wore the D.F.C. ribbon and looked tough and experienced.

In the marquee was a confusion of flying kit, books, playing cards and papers marked 'Secret'. Two pilots were playing chess, three were arguing and one was asleep. There was a little, monkeyish, wise-cracking Canadian named Keith Ogilvie; three more Poles known as Post, Zura and Big Enough (for Ostaszewski, Zurakowski and Olenski); some Englishmen; a Welsh sergeant named Hughes-Rees (the sleeper); but no Yorkshiremen. They were all, I was told, at Readiness.

'And this is Leading-Aircraftman Kay, the man who really runs the Squadron,' said Aggie, indicating an airman clerk manning a couple of telephones in the corner. 'He's our liaison with Ops.'

The Ops. clerk (who, like many of the ground staff, *was* a Yorkshireman) beamed and declared he had found Aggie's Mae West; whereupon the latter whipped off the one he was wearing, marked 'Johnny', and threw it to one of the chess players. 'You can have it, Sidney,' he said. 'Johnny's wearing yours anyway.'

At this remark Sidney Hill, a drily humorous young man with a twitching eye that made complete strangers think he was winking at them, affected immense pained surprise. His opponent, Johnny Curchin, a short stocky lad with no neck, though patently wearing a Mae West marked 'Sidney', merely grunted, and the game went on. But not for long, because presently Leading-Aircraftman Kay, after answering the telephone, suddenly leapt to his feet and at the top of his voice shouted, 'Blue Section SCRAMBLE!'

Immediately there was pandemonium. Playing cards, books and papers fell to the floor as the two chess players rose to their feet, swearingly sorted out bits of equipment from the débris around them and bolted for the exit, amidst caustic references from their colleagues to snowballs in hell.

'Don't forget it's my move!' cried Sidney as they fought their way through the tent flap – and one felt that the game was the thing they were here for, and the 'scramble' an irritating interruption, like the Spanish Armada to Drake's game of bowls. Shortly afterwards I noticed, suspended on the wall, a piece of a Junkers 88 with the legend 'The 100th Hun destroyed by 609 (West Riding) Squadron.'

Outside, Sergeant Palmer had left his football and was also running. At each of three Spitfires stood two airmen, waiting like grooms to mount their masters for a fox hunt. As each pilot gained his cockpit, one of them was up on the wing, buckling him in. Another was plying the mobile starter battery, and each Rolls Royce Merlin engine turned slowly and painfully before bursting into life with an angry roar. Next moment the airmen had jumped from the wings, the chocks were jerked from the wheels, and the three Spitfires went sailing straight down the aerodrome, faster and faster, till with a final bounce they took the air and their wheels went up sideways like a swimmer completing the breast stroke. Just as I thought they must hit the hangar at the end, they pulled up, turned to port and began climbing – perhaps two minutes from the time the Ops. clerk had spoken. It was the first time I had seen Spitfires taking off, and I was impressed.

'Like birds, aren't they?' said Aggie, answering my thought. 'However long I fly, I shall never tire of watching Spits take to the air.' (Sadly, fate had ordained that he wasn't to fly or watch much longer.)

'How do they know what to do?' I asked him. The I.O. had long since disappeared, and I feared I might already be on duty when they returned.

'Ops. will give 'em a vector. 'Steer one-eight-zero, fifty bandits approaching Weymouth, angels 20 – I don't think! It's probably only a bogey. Times aren't what they were. Scramble, scramble, scramble – and never a sausage.'

I gathered there had not been a combat since Christmas, and that the pilots were 'browned off' at having to observe a state of Readiness all day, punctuated with eventless patrols. For it was much the same team which had been accustomed, not long before, to being 'scrambled' sometimes two and three times a day as a whole squadron to combat the hordes of Dorniers, Junkers, Heinkels and Messerschmitts in one of the vital battles of history. These survivors of 'The Few' did not yet know that they and their dead comrades had already won it by day. Such was their morale that they appeared actually to have enjoyed it, and were expecting and hoping that, as soon as weather permitted, it would recommence. Meanwhile, they resembled restless, unexercised race-horses.

Most restless horse in the stables was Aggie, in the cockpit of whose beloved Spitfire I had been seated for the last half-hour while he, standing on the wing, explained the mysteries of the numerous buttons, levers and dials. He had, he told me, already applied for a posting to North Africa, where Wavell's campaign against the Italian army momentarily provided the war's sole military news. Within a couple of weeks he was gone, and soon afterwards was killed.

We returned to the marquee and in due course the three Spitfires landed. I watched as, one after the other, they taxied to a standstill outside the tents. Apart from their camouflage and four wicked little holes in each elliptical wing – the muzzles of eight machine guns – there was nothing outwardly to indicate that they were engines of war at all. Yet without a few hundred of these graceful birds of the air the history of the world would already have been changed.

Now, even before the pilots had climbed out, their crews were up on the wings to refuel and rearm them in time for the next emergency.

Rearming, on this occasion, was not necessary, the machine gun muzzles still being covered by canvas patches. As the three pilots re-entered the tent no one looked up, and the Welshman was still asleep.

'Just a bloody old Hudson,' said Johnny, reseating himself at the chess table. 'The silly clot went into cloud, and we chased him for ten minutes before we could see it wasn't a Dornier.'

'Better get the new Brains to teach you some aircraft recognition,' said Keith Ogilvie, the Canadian, slyly. 'Did you know you were supposed to do that thing, Brains?'

'I didn't,' I replied, appalled at the idea, 'and for heaven's sake don't call me Brains.'

Presently the Ops. clerk, after another call on the 'phone, rose to his feet and, with the air of one presenting a penny to a child, said: 'Gentlemen, Squadron released!'

If he had said 'Squadron scramble!' there could have been no more immediate response. Everyone leapt to his feet, chairs and tables fell over, the Welshman woke up, and with cries of 'Who's pinched my hat?' 'Where's the bloody transport?' they all made for the exit. Outside stood a large Humber brake, into which the majority piled – the remainder, including myself, being accommodated in two privately owned cars. Just before we set off a serious-faced, good-looking young man who (like Johnny and Nowierski the Pole) wore the D.F.C. ribbon, emerged from another tent and joined us. He was a flight-lieutenant, and the tent was evidently his office.

'Frankie, meet our Brains reinforcement,' said Aggie. 'Brains, this is Frankie Howell, commander of "A" Flight, and a mighty man of valour.' (I had seen his name, coupled with that of Sidney Hill, inscribed on the bit of Junkers 88 claimed as the Squadron's hundredth 'Hun').

'That'll do, Aggie.' To me he said, evidently knowing all about me: 'You'll find fighter pilots a bit conceited and a bit difficult, but at heart they are all children. Coming to our party tonight?'

I learnt that the mayor of Dorchester was holding a dance at the Corn Exchange in honour of the Squadron, and that the whole of it, including the 150-odd ground staff would be present. Touched at being accepted so soon as a member, I said I would like to.

For sleeping quarters, junior officers of the two squadrons

occupied the adjacent corridors of a long low wooden building adjoining the Mess, and Frankie found me a cubicle belonging to a pilot on leave. The regular I.O. (who lived 'out' with his wife) had kindly delivered my bags, and while the pilots competed for the bath, I unpacked, then strolled over to the Mess. Here I found a colleague from Group who for the past fortnight had been doing *locum tenens* for 152 Squadron. He seemed to be *persona grata* with everyone and introduced me to pilots of both squadrons. 'And here's your C.O.,' he said, leading me to the bar, 'Squadron-Leader Michael Lister Robinson.'

Before me stood a tall, fresh-faced and extremely handsome young man, immaculately dressed in a uniform of whipcord, on which even the D.F.C. ribbon seemed to have been made to measure. He was engaged in conversation with the commanding officer of 152.

'I'm afraid I shan't be much use to you, Sir,' I said on being presented, 'as I've still everything to learn about the job, and am only staying a fortnight.'

'But my dear fellow, of course I am *delighted* you have come. You must have a cocktail at once. Ernest, three champagne cocktails!' And without another word he went on talking to the other squadron-leader, leaving me to wonder how much the charm had been tinged with sarcasm, and to marvel at the assurance that successsful command in battle had bestowed on such young men, giving them authority not only over the personnel of their own squadrons, but over other officers much older than themselves.

Admittedly such young men were about the only warriors in Britain who at this time had any justification to feel assured, but this one was almost too good to be true. He seemed to speak with the mocking staccato voice of Noël Coward – a comparison I would never have thought of had not Noël himself, arriving some months later at Biggin Hill after an extended propaganda tour in favour of Britain's war effort, actually said to me: 'Having just completed 24,000 miles in the air, I feel positively embarrassed to be on the ground.'

There were quite a lot of other officers in the Mess, and I was told that most of these were pupils of Warmwell's Central Gunnery School, which also owned most of the hangars and other facilities, as well as a number of Wellington, Whitley and Hampden bombers. It seemed that in the eyes of the station personnel, from the Group-Captain downwards, the two fighter squadrons were only there on sufferance, and in the Mess there seemed to be total non-fraternization. Even the two squadrons automatically sat down for dinner at separate tables, and with my Intelligence aura about to spread over both, I hesitated, then sat down with 609.

After dinner, instead of proceeding direct to Dorchester, most officers of 609 decided to warm up first at a party given by officers of the Royal Armoured Corps. My chauffeur was the same tall blond character we have already met in the Prologue – Pilot-Officer John Bisdee. He was also known as 'Bishop' or 'The Bish', partly owing to his name, partly to a somewhat episcopal manner of speech. With supreme confidence he drove at great speed up and down the country, not at all perturbed that it was dark and that he had only a hazy idea of where the camp was.

'Funny, you know,' he said, 'how lost one can become on the ground. I've pin-pointed the place often from the air.'

We found it at last, and though it appeared that no one in 609 Squadron knew any of the hosts, it did not seem to matter – fighter pilots seemed to be welcome anywhere. After they had consumed considerable quantities of the excellent champagne cocktails, and danced with anyone they found, the flight commanders reminded their C.O. that 609 was expected elsewhere, so we left for Dorchester. At the Corn Exchange the N.C.O.s and airmen were already dancing with gusto – partly with local girls but mostly with W.A.A.F.s from the station. Soon the officers were dancing too, though not nearly so well, or were being plied with beer. After a somewhat frivolous and inarticulate speech by the C.O., the mayor followed in more stentorian tones, and one gathered that the citizens of Dorchester genuinely looked upon this party of seemingly irresponsible young men as their protectors.

Next morning I was expected to begin my duties. After leading me through a maze of hangars and other buildings, some of which had been gutted by bombs, the Squadron's regular I.O. brought me to a wooden hut which housed the twin Intelligence offices of the two squadrons. There, after some mystifying instructions, he left me with the words that he must go and pack, and I suddenly became aware that now I *was* the only Intelligence Officer on the station, and that on me devolved the reporting of its entire war effort. The hut was half a mile from the nearer squadron's Dispersal, and as much again from the other, and I pictured both squadrons landing from a major battle, and Group ringing up impatiently to know the result before I had reached either of them and spoken to the first pilot. Lonely and perplexed, I took turns sitting in each office, without the slightest idea what I should be doing in either of them. Models of 'friendly' and 'hostile' aircraft, none of which I recognized, depended from the ceiling as in a toy shop; papers and files, whose import I tried vainly to understand, lay heaped upon tables and shelves, and in an outer office was a clerk. I had him in once or twice with a view to gaining instruction in the filing system, but in this I was unsuccessful. His interests inclined more towards music, and whenever I left the office, I returned to find him playing the clarinet – which, as I had no idea of what he should be doing otherwise, was hard to criticize.

It would not have been so bad had the papers remained static. At intervals, however, they were augmented by seemingly urgent teleprinted signals which informed me of the letters various beacons would be flashing in the night; warned me that balloons would be springing up, mushroom-like, all over the country; that the Army was shooting off guns into the air in a score of places, and that all sorts of new or modified aircraft were flying about which pilots, presumably, might easily shoot down. Later I was to learn that the sending of a signal is the time-honoured method of relieving oneself of responsibility – in other words, of 'passing the buck'. But at the moment I grew hot under the collar as I thought of pilots flying into balloons, being shot down by practice anti-aircraft gunfire, or themselves shooting down a Blenheim because its nose had been shortened – unless I, their Intelligence Officer, took action.

From time to time I would hear the sound of Spitfires taking off or landing, and each time would ring up the two Dispersals to see whether there had been a combat – only to be told by the kindly voice of the Ops. clerk that it was a section doing practice flying or an eventless patrol. And all the time I waited nervously for the telephone to ring and the voice of the Station Commander to ask some question which I should be totally incapable of answering. Once it did ring, and a voice said, 'In five minutes a loud gong will sound – take no action', leaving me wondering what I should have done had it said, '*Take* action!' Occasionally a pilot would come in, ask for some information, and withdraw, obviously not quite satisfied. In the afternoon the regular I.O. reappeared to say goodbye, and was angry because I had not taken certain books and files out to the tents. These consisted notably of two massive tomes weighing 5lbs. each, one for each squadron, marked 'Pilots' Order Book' – full of warnings and instructions, each of them signable by all pilots against their names on the typed list opposite. In addition there were files containing Air Ministry, Fighter Command and Group Intelligence Bulletins, the contents of which it was thought pilots ought to know about.

With a feeling that no time was to be lost, I hurriedly pasted into the Order Books a selection of the signals, etc., which had come in that day, and with arms and wrists aching from their burden, set off on foot for the Dispersals. A high wind was blowing, the files fluttered, and secret documents all but escaped in flocks over the county of Dorset. To lessen the distance, I took a short cut over a corner of the airfield, and a Wellington of the C.G.S., coming in to land, missed my head by what seemed like six feet, but was probably twenty. After leaving half my burden with 152 Squadron, it then took another miserable twenty minutes to reach 609. (Later I learnt the technique of tracing by 'phone the whereabouts of the Squadron's transport, and summoning it – at present I did not even know I was allowed to use it.)

Arriving at 609 Dispersal, I announced to Frankie my proposal to read all the latest entries in the P.O.B. aloud – and he, being a responsible young man, unwilling to discourage this first show of initiative by the new I.O., promptly called all pilots to silence. Tolerantly, but in growing amazement, they listened while I solemnly warned them of balloons flying over Scapa Flow, target practice in Norfolk, and an experimental aircraft that might be seen flying over Northern Ireland. I then passed the book around for signature; after which, unmoved, they went on with their poker. All, that is, except Sidney. Addressing me with his involuntary wink, he said : 'I put it to you, Brains, the whole thing's just a lot of bull.'

He was, of course, perfectly right. This extraction of reluctant signatures was the *Intelligence* Officer's way of 'passing the buck' in case something *did* go wrong. Looking back through the book, I found 'orders' dating back to the previous June and opposite each a ghostly list of pilots, many of them long dead, for whom signature was now too late. Two of the Poles had not signed any orders at all, because they could not possibly be expected to understand them. Yet some of the items were presumably important, and I wondered then and subsequently at the nonchallant way in which most fighter pilots of World War II treated information which might affect their own lives, yet nearly always contrived to get hold of information which might contribute to their success against the enemy. If the latter was sound, it was 'pukka gen'; if unsound, 'duff gen'. For the rest, life was too short – or it might be. The pilots who sat around Dispersal on this wintry January day must have known, if they thought, that before the year was out some of them would have won new laurels, and some would have taken off for the last time. But they did not think about it much, and while waiting it was more fun to play pranks anyway.

'Yes, their lives are too short for bull,' I decided, as I wandered back to the office. I was beginning to see where the 'tact' came in. As I approached, the strains of a clarinet grew louder.

In a day or two the I.O. of 152 Squadron returned from leave. Guided by his experience I learnt that much of the unsorted paper that cluttered my office could safely be consigned to the w.p.b. I also began to learn what the role of a squadron I.O. was supposed to be. Basically it was to act as a two-way channel of information : on the one hand to receive and absorb different kinds of intelligence from higher authority, finally presenting the operative parts of it in digestible form to his pilots; on the other hand to extract (by any means in his power) all relevant operational intelligence *from* his pilots, and serve that in digestible form back to higher authority. 'A good Intelligence Officer,' wrote the authors of *Coastal Command*, 'must have something of the qualities of Herodotus, Socrates and Voltaire. He must be tireless in collecting facts, expert in checking them, concise in presenting them'.

If I showed none of the attributes of these masters during that first fortnight I spent with 609 Squadron at Warmwell, there were perhaps fortunately no operational facts that needed collection; while if the indigestible assortment of information I tried to inflict on my pilots was understood by them, it certainly was not by me. I, in fact, was being educated by them. Listening, I was slowly learning the meaning of such expressions as 'flying on a reciprocal', 'two circles deflection', 'pushing the tit', etc., without which new vocabulary I should in the future be lost.

When the weather precluded any flying at all, I found I really was expected to instruct my pilots in aircraft recognition. So might a dabbler in football pools be asked to train a soccer team – it was not till I had been supposedly instructing for three years that I myself was sent on a recognition course. Now, instead, I gave them a talk, illustrated by slides, on canoeing down the Rhone. I even drew up a list of lectures to be given by the pilots themselves, and found amongst them experts on subjects ranging from diesel engines to mushroom-growing, though only one – an impressionistic talk by the C.O. on his early experience of the French air force – was actually given. Occasionally he expressed concern that they were not getting enough exercise, and once I rashly offered to lead them on a cross-country run. Quite a number started, but presently I found myself quite alone, and dressed as I was, with no proof of identity, had great difficulty in being readmitted to the station.

Aggie took exercise by wrestling with anyone he could provoke, including the temporary I.O. One evening, after some of the Squadron had returned from a house-warming party in the new W.A.A.F. Officers' Mess, Novo the Pole was found to have gone to bed and bolted his door. Aggie disapproved.

'Come on, Novo, open up ! We want you !'

Silence from within.

'Open up, you Polish bastard, I say !'

Still no reply.

'Right !'

Entering the cubicle opposite to get a run, Aggie hurled his powerful frame three times against the slender obstacle. At the third impact it splintered and Aggie was inside. Then, not having fixed the next part of the programme, he was suddenly sheepish, especially when Novo, putting aside the letter he had been writing, rose from his bed, found a screwdriver, and without a word disappeared. Presently he returned carrying a door from 152 Squadron's corridor. This he substituted for his own, fixed the broken door where it had come from without waking the occupant, and returning to bed with a polite 'Good-night,' resumed his letter, leaving Aggie speechless with defeat.

Useless I might be, but at least I was obeying the precept, 'The Intelligence Officer shall live with his Squadron'.

Next evening, Michael Lister Robinson called all his officers together and apologetically told them some terrible news: the Station Commander had ordered a 'gas parade' for all units at first light the following morning. The crisis lay in the fact that, whereas all pilots had once been issued with tin hats, respirators and even gas clothing, few now knew what had become of these items, and none had ever thought of putting them on. Fully aware of this, Michael now introduced the Flight-Sergeant Discip, who demonstrated (a) how to tie the gas cape to the back in a neat roll, and (b) how, at the command 'GAS!' to drape it about the person by pulling a certain string. Rightly suspecting that this 'gen' had not been fully absorbed, Michael then ordered that all batmen be briefed how to dress their officers.

With only about half a batman per officer, there was a wild scramble at dawn next day to get the West Riding Squadron on parade in a guise it had never assumed before. Particularly impressive were the Poles, who – having been ordered to 'Bring everything you've got' – appeared festooned with guns and ivory-hilted knives. But mine was the only tin hat, and while the rest of the officers walked self-consciously up and down before the serried ranks of the airmen, I hastily secreted this in the corner of a hangar. Then the command 'Officers fall in' was given and everything – the numbering by squadrons, the inspection, the alternate standing at attention and at ease – went off satisfactorily until suddenly the word 'GAS!' was shouted. At once there was an undignified scene as dusty respirators were torn from satchels and donned for the first time. And then came the *moment célèbre*. As one man the officers of the West Riding Squadron pulled the designated string, and as one cape the capes fell ignominiously to the ground, just as a station N.C.O., with obvious sadistic pleasure, began to hurl tear-gas bombs to windward. There was nothing for it but to bend down, pick up capes, unroll capes and drape them on the person by hand – all facial confusion being happily concealed beneath the expressionless respirators, among which that of Squadron-Leader Robinson was leaking.

After the gas exercise that followed, officers were instructed to have their tin hats painted blue. A certain corporal had ordered someone to decontaminate a Spitfire, and 'look smart about it', and the 'someone' had turned out to be the Station Commander.

Besides an Intelligence Officer the Squadron had an Adjutant, an Engineer Officer and a Medical Officer, who were responsible respectively for its administration, its aeroplanes and its health. Being as ill-acquainted with the intricate relationship of 'boost' and 'revs' as I was with the effects of '*g*' on the nervous systems of pilots I was in no position to talk shop with the second two – they were professionals, I was an amateur. I therefore concentrated on seeking the acquaintance of Halliday Tidswell, the Adjutant. His amateur status was however impugned by the fact that he shared the C.O.'s office, and made no bones about parading as the *fuehrer's* deputy. If any pilot queried his authority, he would point to his sleeve and say, 'See this ring? Well, as far as you're concerned, it's equivalent to two and a half'. If further proof of power were needed, he had merely to raise a hatch in the wall to command the services of the Orderly Room, without whose co-operation no one joined or left the Squadron, or even went on leave. The president of the Orderly Room was a taciturn but highly efficient corporal, assisted by a sergeant. Both were Auxiliaries, while the former at least had been there since long before the war, and knew more about King's Regulations than the Adjutant himself. Probably both felt that, no matter how many pilots came and went, it was really themselves and their fellow Yorkshire colleagues who formed the core of 609, and it was no uncommon sight for a junior pilot-officer to be seen pleading for an extra ration card while Corporal Simpson sat and weighed the merits of the case.

But when I first arrived, Hal Tidswell was also on leave, and I only met him during the second of my two weeks as *locum tenens*. Then, on entering the C.O.'s office, I found a tall, quite handsome man of about my own age, clad in a leather flying jacket. Slightly surprised at the attire (I myself was wearing a great-coat) I asked : 'Are you the Adjutant of 609?'

'You, I suppose, are from C.G.S.,' he replied with some contempt.

A little hurt that he should be unaware of the arrival of a new Squadron I.O., however temporary, I pointed out that so far from being a member of the Central Gunnery School, I had nearly been written off by one of its aircraft on my very first day. Though not obviously glad that I had escaped, he did at this disclosure offer me a cigarette.

'Take a seat,' he said. 'I suppose you realize you've come to one of the best squadrons in Fighter Command – personally I consider it *the* best – and that it's a great honour for you to have come at all'.

Unable to dispute the Squadron's reputation, and unwilling to suggest that the honour might not apply to me alone, I responded by asking questions. He answered them all and then, warming to his subject, added : 'Perhaps you would like to read the Squadron diary. Corporal Simpson!' he called through the hatch. 'Bring in the Form 540 for Pilot-Officer Ziegler.'

And so, while Hal interviewed airmen and signed railway warrants and passes on this bleak day of January 1941 – a month when the war seemed to have fizzled out – I read the first sentence in the history of No. 609 (West Riding) Squadron. It ran :

Yeadon, 10.2.36. No. 609 (West Riding) (Bomber) Squadron due to form (A.M.O. N.6/1936)....

I

THE WEAPON IS FORGED

A.M.O. N.6/1936. . . . By the stroke of a pen a squadron had been created. Yesterday it did not exist; today it did. Even if it was only on paper, the genesis suggested an almost biblical omnipotence. Yet the first day in the life of a great squadron is baldly summarized in its diary: 'Owing to bad weather conditions, building was delayed. Squadron-Leader Harald Peake was granted a Commission in the A.A.F. and appointed to command the Squadron (London Gazette dated 10.2.36).'

Thirty-two years later this founder of 609 recalled:

'I remember the day very well. For the first time as C.O. I visited Yeadon to meet Colonel Sullivan, Secretary of the West Riding Territorial Army and Air Force Association, and Flight-Lieutenant Norman Odbert,* the regular officer appointed as our first Adjutant. There was some snow on the ground, it was bitterly cold, and what we saw was far from encouraging. The first section of a small group of huts was going up, and some canvas bales containing our first Bessoneau hangar were lying vaguely about. We were glad to be offered shelter and hot coffee in the Yorkshire Aeroplane Clubhouse. Flight-Lieutenant Odbert got accommodation at the hotel down the road, and I went straight up to London to protest about the pace at which the promised buildings were going up.'

No wonder that a photograph taken on this day shows all three of the officers mentioned above wearing civilian dress. For the

* By a happy coincidence this same officer was an R.A.F. commander in Malta when 609 went there in 1956 for its last summer camp. There were still two members of the Squadron – Darkie Hanson and D. H. Andrews, by then respectively Flight-Lieutenant and Flying Officer – who as airmen had overlapped with him before the war.

commander of an Auxiliary Squadron to have worn uniform when, like Adam, he was as yet its only flesh and blood, might have looked both premature and eccentric. In any case the only uniform he owned at this moment was that of a retired subaltern of the York- shire Dragoons Yeomanry, which he had joined after having served in World War I with the Coldstream Guards.

Why, then, was it that a man aged 37, with no previous experi- ence of air force service, was chosen to raise and command a new squadron of the Auxiliary Air Force?

The answers are several, the first at least connected with the word 'Yeomanry'. For just as this body of mounted volunteers had come into being as a home defence force against the threat of Napoleon, so did the later squadrons of the Auxiliary Air Force directly owe their existence to the threat of Hitler. Nor does the parallel end there; for if concerning the former it has been written,

Recruiting, organisation and command were upon a county basis, the county gentlemen officering the force, the farmers and yeomen serving in its ranks, and all alike providing their own horses,

the only respects in which this did not apply to the latter were that the ranks were no longer restricted to farmers, and the new volun- teer force was not expected to provide its own aeroplanes. Since the foundation of the Yeomanry, Yorkshire had of course been industrialized, and though it still included some of England's big- gest estates, 'the 'gentlemen' about to become officers were less strictly 'county', and more the descendants of the textile and col- liery families who had led the industrial revolution. Their com- manding officer, Harald Peake, was both : late Master of the Rufford Hounds on the one side, and a member of a Yorkshire colliery-owning family on the other – while the M.P. for North Leeds was his elder brother Osbert, destined later to become minister of the Crown and the first Viscount Ingleby. (In April 1938 the latter was to save 609 a serious set-back when, as the result of a question he arranged to be asked in the House of Com- mons, the posting of its Adjutant and chief flying instructor, Norman Odbert, was cancelled.)

The person mainly responsible for Harald Peake's appointment had been Major-General The (10th) Earl of Scarbrough, Chairman and driving force of the West Riding Territorial Army Association. Looking for a man of local influence to attract and select the best human material for its new winged offshoot, he was no doubt pleased to find that no one was better qualified than his own neighbour whom he had known for many years. For Harald Peake had been a Territorial already, flew an aeroplane, had rowed for Eton, Cambridge and England, and possessed a drive and ability that later would win him the Chairmanship successively of the London Assurance, the Steel Company of Wales and Lloyds Bank Ltd.

In fact 609 Squadron might never have existed had not Harald Peake, some years previously, persuaded Lord Scarbrough to write to the Secretary of State for Air, saying that if and when further Auxiliary squadrons were required, the West Riding Territorial Association would undertake to recruit two – one in the Leeds, the other in the Doncaster area. But though the seed was thus sown, it took a long time to germinate; and Peake, who hoped to serve in one of the squadrons, became increasingly depressed at the delay in forming them:

'In 1934, seeing no future for troops mounted on horseback and armed with swords and rifles, I had resigned my commission in the Yorkshire Dragoons, and as I was working hard, preferred to spend my short holidays flying my aeroplane on the Continent rather than at a Yeomanry camp. But now I was already approaching the upper age limit for training as a service pilot. Consequently it came as a complete surprise when, in the late autumn of 1935, I received a telephone call from Air Commodore J. C. Quinnell, commanding No. 1 Air Defence Group, R.A.F., asking whether I would accept appointment as first C.O. of No. 609 Squadron when it was formed. On consulting Lord Scarbrough I was urged to accept, and have little doubt that the proposal came from him. Meanwhile the decision to form the Squadron was to be kept dead secret until the Secretary of State for Air made a statement in the House of Commons.'

There followed 'hush-hush' conferences between Quinnell and Peake, both at the former's London Headquarters and also at possible airfield locations. So far the Association was only authorized to recruit one squadron, and when, of the two most favoured locations, Yeadon near Leeds was chosen in preference to Doncaster,

Harald Peake, who lived near the latter, thought seriously whether he should after all accept command. For not only was he now too old ever to lead the future squadron in the air, but Yeadon was sixty-two miles fom his home, Lound Hall, Tuxford, just over the Nottinghamshire border. In summer this presented no great problem, since near Bawtry Hall, his parental home only fourteen miles from his own, he had a private airfield and could commute to Yeadon by air; but in winter or at night it was a long and tedious road journey through built-up areas. In the end, happily for 609, he decided he would make the effort for a year or two. By then, with luck, the second squadron might be due to form at Doncaster and he could transfer – provided his friend Squadron-Leader Geoffrey Ambler, at present C.O. of 608 (North Riding) Squadron and who lived near Yeadon, could then be persuaded to take over 609 and raise it to an operational standard.

The second part of his plan duly came off; the first, as we shall see, not quite. Meanwhile, if not all future members of his Squadron knew Harald Peake personally, they all knew of him; and even if to some of them he seemed a bit of a feudal magnate, he doubtless understood, and possibly shared, the feeling that unites all Yorkshiremen of moor and mine and field and factory : that of slight superiority towards their neighbours under the Red Rose of Lancaster, and of infinite superiority towards the South.

*

The Auxiliary (or Territorial) Air Force was of course no new thing. It had been fathered by the then Chief of Air Staff, Lord Trenchard, as long ago as 1924, when (assisted by Grosvenor, the founder of 601 Squadron) he had sold the idea of 'Winged Terriers' to the Cabinet as a means of increasing the number of Home Defence squadrons with the minimum of expense. By 1926 the first four Auxiliary squadrons – 600 (City of London), 601 (County of London), 602 (City of Glasgow) and 603 (City of Edinburgh) were in existence, despite the scornful doubts of Winston Churchill and others that 'week-end fliers' could ever make an effective contribution to air defence. Close on their heels followed 605 (County of Warwick), and in 1930 604 (County of Middlesex), 607 (County of Durham) and 608 (North Riding).

Besides founding the A.A.F., 'Boom' Trenchard encouraged it in the only way of life possible for its successful continuation. When the first C.O. of 603 rang up to complain about the 'regulations', Trenchard replied. 'You're running your own show. If you don't like the regulations, rewrite them.' His biographer, Andrew Boyle, adds in his book *Trenchard* (Collins 1962):

To squadron loyalty, a tenuous thing sometimes in a service that spanned the winds of heaven, was being added that stabilising element in all human concerns which matter – attachment to one place that men could cherish and would defend to the death because their human roots were there.

In such a 'club', Trenchard is further quoted as saying, 'regulation is only for the fool to keep and the wise man to break.' And the important feature of the A.A.F. was that it was not a 'Reserve' for the R.A.F., but a separate air force altogether. A member of the R.A.F. might be posted from one unit to another; a member of the A.A.F. stayed in his own – where his roots were.

In 1936, to match the expansion of the R.A.F. provoked by Germany's rearmament and Hitler's first military demonstrations outside his frontiers, the A.A.F. was doubled – if one included the four R.A.F. 'Special Reserve' squadrons (500, 501, 502 and 504) which were transferred to it and re-formed in that year. Besides 609 there rose out of the ground: 610 (County of Chester), 611 (West Lancashire), 612 (County of Aberdeen), 615 (County of Surrey) and later 616 (South Yorkshire). In addition 613 and 614 were formed at Manchester and Cardiff almost on the eve of hostilities and assigned to 'Army Co-operation', but as that role disappeared during the war their subsequent history is less well known. In the end – and despite the fact that all A.A.F. Squadrons were initially described as Day Bombers – all became Fighter Squadrons bar six: the two 'Army Co-op' ones just mentioned, plus 608, 612, 500 and 502 assigned to Coastal Command. That left fourteen fighter squadrons, of which 600 and 604 became night-fighter squadrons almost from the start, together forming about one quarter of the total fighter strength available when Britain faced her moment of truth in August, 1940.

Besides the basic difference between R.A.F. and A.A.F. squadrons, time wrought its own difference between A.A.F. squadrons formed in 1926 and those formed ten years later. The former, when the hostilities started, had already a distinguished peace-time history and tradition behind them, but most of their early officers and airmen were by then superannuated. The latter, on the other hand, went to war with the bulk of their original teams intact, and formed their own abiding traditions from then on. Though it is impossible to say which was the better idea, it is interesting to note that at a moment when the rival airborne pranks of the perhaps over-aristocratic 600 and 601 Squadrons were occupying headlines in the national press, 609 Squadron was gingerly putting its first pilots into the air.

The first 'amateur' pilot posted to the Squadron was Stephen G. Beaumont, junior partner in a firm of solicitors which numbered the Peake family amongst its clients. This conscientious and intelligent man of twenty-six, already since three years responsible for a widowed mother and two younger brothers, had a year previously felt obliged to do something about Hitler as well. One day on a bus the Town Clerk of Wakefield, referring to the newspaper headlines of yet more Nazi processions and parades, had said to him : 'You can't make people play at being soldiers indefinitely without them one day wanting to *be* soldiers.'

The germ of unrest had been injected – 'the vague feeling that there was going to be trouble in Europe, and I personally was doing nothing about it.' Stephen was an Oxford graduate, and his upbringing had taught him that those who in the past had enjoyed educational and financial advantages had a special obligation to defend the country that had given them their way of life. But how? Become an officer in the county Yeomanry – Hussars, Dragoons? Too expensive, and surely anyway the horse was obsolete. Changing three times, he travelled by bus to the West Riding Aero Club at Yeadon. 'A general smell of alcohol pervaded the place and it was raining, but eventually I was taken up in a Gipsy Moth.' Though civil flying was pretty expensive too, he had flown solo already when next spring he heard that Harald Peake, on the same airfield, was founding a squadron of the Auxiliary Air Force. 'I wrote to him offering my services, and was told my application would be considered along with the other applications which he had received.' In the end his commission preceded his marriage by a few weeks.

Posted to the Squadron on the same 24th of April – though they do not appear to have met for another two months – were an Auxiliary Adjutant (Flying-Officer the Earl of Lincoln, now the ninth Duke of Newcastle), a medical officer (Flying-Officer T. McM. Boyle), and two Flying-Officers from the Volunteer Reserve, who already had their 'wings': Bill Humble and P. R. Nickols. The following year Nickols and ten Auxiliary airmen formed part of the Street-Lining Party in London at the Coronation of King George VI, whereas Humble soon departed because his destiny lay as a test pilot with the Hawker Aircraft Co. Earlier still Harald Peake had applied for the services of Commander Roger Burges (R.N., retired), who was duly posted to the Squadron as a Flight-Lieutenant in the Equipment Branch, and during the first four months of 609's existence he and Norman Odbert supervised the construction by contractors of buildings, roads, drains, etc., and accepted delivery of stores.

According to the Formation Scheme initial accommodation mainly comprised one hangar for three aeroplanes, four lecture rooms, offices, guard room, medical quarters, living accommodation for permanent staff, officers' and airmen's messes, and a games room, with messing arrangements under the control of the N.A.A.F.I. All these buildings, including the canvas-covered hangar, were made of wood, and were referred to as 'temporary quarters, which will house the Squadron till such time as a site has been selected on which to construct an aerodrome and permanent buildings'. The Air Estimates of March 1938 were more specific: £65,000 to be spent during the next twelve months on providing 'permanent accommodation' for the Squadron. But it was all a mirage: war was too near, and when 609 Squadron was reformed at Yeadon in 1946 back it went into the old 'temporary quarters' of ten years (or was it a century?) before. Only after the war was there a Town H.Q.

Meanwhile the newly formed Squadron was not far from losing even the *pied-à-terre* it had. This was when the Leeds-Bradford Aerodrome Committee, which then as now controlled Yeadon on behalf of the two municipalities and wanted to expand its facilities for civil aviation, gave the Air Ministry notice to quit. 'It was stated that because of the presence of the No. 609 (West Riding) Bombing Squadron the Committee was put to extra expense.' What 'monetary contribution' was the Ministry prepared to make? In the end the Air Ministry agreed to lease some acres for fourteen years at an annual rental of £1,500 rising to £1,750 – and things were amicably settled.

'The battle for equipment would have provided most people with a full-time occupation, yet Squadron-Leader Peake fitted this into his already more than busy life. . I do not know in terms of hours how much time he expended on the struggle to get just one more Avro Tutor, Hawker Hart, or piece of workshop equipment. At a time when hardly anyone had anything, and everyone needed more than was available, he battled incessantly and successfully.'

So says the Duke (or Earl, as he then was), who evidently worked very hard too, spending day after day at the camp. By 1937 he was promoted to Flight-Lieutenant and was virtually second in command. He also helped officers' morale by inviting them over to his magnificent home, Clumber Park, now demolished.

The regular Adjutant, N. C. Odbert, and his assistant, Flight-Lieutenant A. W. S. Matheson who arrived in July 1936, were the flying instructors. They also supervised the work of the Regular personnel, comprising about a third of the total, whose job it was to teach the Auxiliary airmen their trades – to become fitters, riggers, armourers, 'wireless' mechanics and the rest – and to look after the aircraft and equipment when the latter were engaged in their civilian occupations. 'They suddenly found themselves,' says the Duke, 'in a most unbelievable, unaccustomed and uncomfortable situation. They started us in the right direction, and one can only hope they felt we continued on course'. No doubt they also taught the 'amateurs' something of the service way of life. One corporal instructor is referred to admiringly by one of his pupils as 'a hard-bitten Regular who knew every trick in the book and every fiddle going'. There was also a Territorial Association Clerk, Mr. David Dunn, who handled correspondence with Auxiliary applicants, acted as the C.O.'s secretary, and became a trusted and respected channel of communication between him and them.

By the end of June most of the Regular element were in residence, there were three Avro Tutors for *ab initio* flying training, three Hawker Harts for service training, and recruiting and training of Auxiliary personnel was in full swing.

'There was no shortage of recruits,' says Harald Peake, who with Odbert interviewed them at week-ends, sleeping Saturday nights on a camp bed in his office. 'We had sufficient applicants to form three or four squadrons. The difficulty was choosing them' – the only obvious criteria for rejection being excessive age (thirty-eight was the limit) or excessive distance to travel (preference was given to applicants residing within a ten-mile radius of the centre of Leeds or to those 'outside the radius who possess motor cars or motor cycles to enable them to get to their training'). The Duke adds:

'We junior officers who arrived for training in our own varied and often unreliable means of transport were invariably amused and delighted each Sunday evening to watch a certain Auxiliary airman being collected by his Rolls-Royce and chauffeur.'

Evidently the quality was good too. On 8th June 1936 Odbert told the *Yorkshire Evening Post* that, judging from preliminary interviews, the general standard of prospective recruits was 'excellent'. At the Squadron's first annual dinner, held at the Hotel Metropole, Leeds, one year and a day after it had been officially created, its commanding officer stated that some eighty applications for commissions and nearly 200 for enlistment had already been dealt with. As a result fourteen Auxiliary officers were now either commissioned or undergoing training, and 'two flights, comprising ninety Auxiliary men, were receiving instruction in trades'. On the back of a surviving menu card is printed the first Nominal Roll, from which such names as D. H. Andrews, J. M. Fitzgerald, G. E. Ingall, A. P. Rabbidge, and the brothers A. G. and K. A. Walker became familiar to the writer years later as senior N.C.O.s. It also includes the name of A. Haslam Wood, said to be the very first airman in 609, and who during the war became an armament officer at H.Q. Fighter Command with the rank of Squadron-Leader.

609 being at this stage classed as a 'bomber' squadron, the most sought-after 'trade' was that of air-gunner. It was also the most short-lived, for when 609 changed Commands and in December 1938 became a fighter squadron, its air-gunners had either to re-muster as armourers or move to other squadrons. The first M.O., Tom Boyle – now an ear, nose and throat specialist and a Governor of Leeds General Infirmary – recalls one recruit, Gerry Brown, was desperately keen to fly despite being colour-blind.

'He therefore approached the Medical N.C.O., Corporal Williams, who was one of the characters of the Squadron, and persuaded him to loan him Ishihara colour fuse testing pictures which he proceeded to learn by heart, so that he could give the proper answers at his medical examination. He passed his medical, under my supervision, by this subterfuge, but fortunately for his safety and that of others did not subsequently take up flying duties.'

Another airman, R. F. Burgess, was greatly flattered on apply-ing to join the Squadron when the Clerk asked whether he wished to take up a commission or was content to join the ranks. He said he was quite happy to sign on as AC2 ACH (GD).

'My medical was conducted in a sketchy manner by the N.C.O., who passed me A.1, including 6/6th vision. As I couldn't see much without glasses, this entry on my documents caused amazement to M.O.s in the years to follow, who were hard put to it to find a reason for my sudden decay. In 1943 it even prevented me getting a com-mission in a ground branch, because according to my documents I was fit air crew, and for a long time it was thought I was malingering to avoid such duties ... until full tests showed that without my glasses I could not tell the difference between friend and foe at any distance over three feet. However, I am glad the N.C.O. let me through – I would have missed a lot if I had not been able to join the Squadron.'

At another medical, when the N.C.O. indicated a bottle on the shelf which a less co-operative airman was ordered to use for the purpose of producing a 'specimen', he got the answer, 'Wot, from 'ere?'

The first airmen of 609 (according to the very first, Haslam Wood) wore R.F.C. puttees and riding breeches, with 'choker' –

collar tunics. Their C.O., being proud of his Squadron, arranged for even the airmen's uniforms to be tailor-made, whereas officers were sent to Gieves. Smartness on parade was – according to contemporary newspaper accounts of official inspections – not the least successful facet of their training, and immediately responsible for this was Warrant-Officer Faux (Discip.). One day Haslam Wood incurred his wrath by wearing his peaked cap (forage caps were things of the future) jauntily on the side of his head :

'Mr. Wood, who do you think you are? A bloody admiral?'

'No, sir.'

'Then why do you think His Majesty gave you a bloody hat? It was not to look like a bloody admiral, but to keep your bloody brains warm!'

Whether admirals did (or do) wear their hats (or caps) in the manner referred to is immaterial. According to Darkie Hanson, Harry Faux (who died soon after attending the 1968 reunion), was greatly loved in 609 despite his discipline. The fact was, of course, that he could only impose it at week-ends and one or two evenings a week, and to a man with twenty years' experience in the Regular service the idea of his charges serving other masters during the rest of the week must have called for some mental re-orientation. How, for instance, was he, or for that matter the Auxiliary Adjutant, to impose discipline in an actual case when one Auxiliary airman who (not without some provocation) assaulted another by hitting him over the head with a plate that still contained N.A.A.F.I. bacon and two eggs – knowing that in a few hours time the culprit would be a perfectly free civilian? The Auxiliary Adjutant (the present Duke) sums things up :

'Such was the background and basis on which our astonishing Auxiliary Air Force was built – a basis of mutual respect and understanding and devotion to the cause, reflecting the mysterious power of the mad Englishman to produce a military force based on an entirely volunteer concept.'

He remembered it in 1945, when as a member of the liberating force in Norway, a special effort at turn-out and deportment seemed to result in the population hiding away in the belief that the blue uniforms were German. 'Oh no,' said a Norwegian lady when the Duke put forward this idea, 'it is not possible. You see, the Germans are militarists. You are civilians in uniform.'

Meanwhile a few of 609's civilians in uniform were, by some oversight, never 'attested' – i.e. they failed to take the oath of loyalty – and later, presumably, could have deserted to the enemy with impunity.

At the first annual dinner in February 1937, the Squadron's potential Auxiliary flying strength had consisted of two Flying Officers (Nickols and Humble), four Pilot Officers (S. G. Beaumont, L. H. Sagar, P. Drummond-Hay and D. Persse-Joynt), and two civilians (Messrs. P. H. Barran and J. R. Rylands) – another civilian being Mr. G. G. Robinson, soon to be commissioned in the Accountancy Branch. By the time of the first Summer Camp, six months later, Humble had departed, Beaumont, Persse-Joynt and Drummond-Hay had got their 'wings', and A. R. Edge, J. C. Gilbert and B. W. Little had joined the Squadron and been commissioned. Of all these Nickols would be obliged on medical grounds to remuster as Armament Officer, Rylands would before long relinquish his commission in the Squadron, and Sagar would be unable to go on flying because of first an operation, then a motor smash. The remaining seven – Beaumont, Persse-Joynt, Barran, Drummond-Hay, Gilbert, Little and Edge – would comprise over half the twelve pilots who went to war in August 1939, and four of them, including the two future flight commanders, Persse-Joynt and Barran,* would be dead before August 1940. As the original warriors of 609, they deserve such introduction as it is possible for the writer, long afterwards, to give.

Stephen Beaumont, already mentioned, modestly describes himself as 'a poor pilot with defective eyesight', but 'as conscientious as the rest.' A man of great intelligence and integrity, with an unusual understanding and sympathy for his fellow humans, he be-

* The original commander of 'B' flight was Stephen Beaumont. In early 1939 he suggested to the new C.O., Ambler, that in view of increasing legal practice, age and responsibility for a wife and two small children, he should leave the Squadron and join the A.A.F. Reserve. 'You can't – war's coming!' said Ambler. As a compromise Stephen handed over command of the flight to Pip Barran.

came a corner stone of the Squadron, and 'a walking encyclopedia' of its history.

Dudley Persse-Joynt – known as 'Presser' from the moment his batman addressed him as 'Mr. Press-'er-Joints' – is described as 'a delightful wild and volatile Irishman who would attempt anything' – including captaining the Squadron's very competent rugger team ('he made me play,' Beaumont recalls a trifle ruefully). Bisdee, who met him later, says he always flew in an Irvin jacket with the collar turned up, and wondered whether this impaired his rearward vision. In civilian life he worked for an oil company.

Philip ('Pip') Barran is described by Air Vice-Marshal Ambler as 'the very best type of A.A.F. officer – a born leader, who communicated his enthusiasm to others'. A trainee mining engineer and manager of a brickworks at a colliery owned by his mother's family (Briggs), he was a local man who seems to have been universally liked and respected. He evidently also invented most of the officers' nicknames.

Peter Drummond-Hay – 'a good pilot with lots of guts,' though evidently thought of as something of a snob. 'The name is *Drummond*-Hay,' he once corrected a young officer who had addressed him as 'Hay', hearing which, Stephen Beaumont told the young man he was lucky not to have been required to say 'Hay-Drummond-Hay'. In late 1938 he married 'well' – his wife was a niece of Lord Baden-Powell – and transferred to the A.A.F. reserve, but rejoined the Squadron at its first war station after some refresher training.

Bernard Little and John Gilbert are inevitably mentioned in one breath, firstly because they were inseparable in the air as on the ground, secondly because they were known to their comrades respectively as 'The Black Boozer' and 'The Pink Boozer', or just 'Blackie' and 'Pinky'. These names reflected their contrasting colouring and complexions as well as their capacity for downing beer, and were of course also invented by Pip Barran – who, Bernard protests mildly, was no mean performer himself. As a fellow solicitor in Wakefield (was in 1970 coroner of Halifax and district), Bernard was introduced to the Squadron by Stephen Beaumont, at whose house I met him over thirty years later. He had a reputation in the Squadron for being ready to tackle anything, however dangerous or unpleasant, to help someone, but says he only got his 'wings' in June 1939. His close friend Gilbert he describes in retrospect as 'a gay and cheerful extrovert, highly successful in charming members of the opposite sex.'

To the surviving contemporaries of 'Paul' Edge it may come as a surprise that 'Paul' was not his name at all, but a derivative of the Barran corruption POAR (his rank plus initials). Alternatively called 'Gramps' because, aged twenty-nine in 1937, he was 609's oldest pilot, he had already done some pre-Squadron flying thanks to Amy Johnson. Her 'Get Air-minded' campaign after her famed solo flight to Australia had been backed by the *Daily Mail* to the extent of paying for the training of one individual up to 'A'-licence standard at every flying club in Britain. Edge promptly applied at the Yorkshire one, and was taken up for an aptitude test by Captain Worrall, who had been Alan Cobham's co-pilot on the trail-blazing flight to the Cape (and lost part of a finger by poking it into the propeller while drawing attention to some stampeding elephants). 'I can only assume,' concludes Edge modestly, 'that the other applicants were incredibly inept, for I was selected'. After getting his 'A'-licence, however, the charge was thirty-five shillings an hour, so when 609 was formed on the same airfield, 'I decided that it would be more logical to fly far superior aircraft at no expense to myself'. And in the Squadron he may have had more opportunity to fly than some, because he took up permanent quarters in the Mess. As technical representative with I.G. Dyestuffs Ltd., Bradford, but without a home in the area, he found this more convenient and cheaper than living in 'digs'.

The first Summer Camp, at Ramsgate Municipal Airport during the first fortnight of August 1937, was attended by twelve Auxiliary officers and ninety-three Auxiliary Airmen, two Regular officers and thirty-four Regular airmen. Nine aircraft are recorded as having been flown from Yorkshire to Kent for the period, two of them presumably by the Adjutant-instructors Odbert and Matheson, which leaves seven. As only eight of the twelve Auxiliary officers belonged to the General Duties branch, this implies that all but one of them flew the 'planes down – astonishing considering how inexperienced some of them were. But now the Camp provided the first opportunity for pilots and ground staff alike to train for more than a few hours at a time. The former, who when limited to week-end flying averaged only some five–twelve hours a month, could now fly each day. As regards the latter, though in the previous April there had already been a Trade Test Board for some airmen on the initial Flight, the progress gained during this fortnight made possible a further Board in December for both 'A' and 'B' flights.

These fortnights spent under canvas seem to have been very popular, and virtually regarded as holidays with extra pay. For however hard the Regular staff had to work, it appears that the Auxiliaries at this stage were not overstrained. Bernard Little, for instance, comments that flying was limited to the mornings, with afternoons and evenings free. With typical honesty he recounts that on the second morning, after a night out in London with his great friend Pinky Gilbert, he was unable to judge his height and approach, and with the watching Squadron 'making a book' made some thirty attempts before getting the Avro Tutor down. Afterwards, he confesses, 'I had my first experience of a monumental strip from Flight-Lieutenant Matheson' – an Australian who did not mince his words.

But even if the flying was restricted to the mornings, it still evidently exceeded local tolerance. The Duke recalls 'being instructed to deal with some local officials from Ramsgate corporation who were complaining of the noise created by our few Tutors and Harts'. One wonders whether they regretted their complaint when they saw the shambles the enemy made of their town three years later. Six years later the same Squadron would be fighting against enemy fighters and fighter-bombers just above its rooftops.

By August 1938, when the second Summer Camp was held at Thorney Island, 609 was a complete squadron, if not yet completely trained. Besides 'A' and 'B' flights there was a 'C' (or 'T') flight to train the newer volunteers; and the last three pilots of the initial, all-Auxiliary, war-time team had been accepted as officers after adequate flying and social tests. To pass the latter, it seems, a prospective candidate would be invited by the commanding officer to take Sunday lunch in the Mess with himself and the other officers. These would gravely watch as he drank several glasses of sherry, and listen to the effect these had. If his parlance was no longer that of a gentleman, he would presumably be black-balled. If they, and particularly the C.O., approved of the candidate, the latter would recommend his acceptance to the Territorial Association, who would forward the recommendation with their comments to the Air Ministry for commissioning.

No objection could have been raised to the three officers who joined in the summer of 1938. The first, Desmond ('Dizzy') Ayre, was a mining engineer in one of the Peake family's collieries. A Newfoundlander by origin, he is described as quiet, competent, conscientious, likeable and 'a true gentleman'. According to his great friend 'Paul' Edge, he could have made a living as a veterinary surgeon, such was the trust he inspired in animals.

The second, Joseph Dawson, son of Sir Benjamin Dawson, Bart., sprang from one of Yorkshire's leading textile families, and used to arrive for training in a Lagonda. He is generally considered to have been one of the best pilots the Squadron ever had – 'absolutely steady and reliable', as well as 'very, very charming'.

The third, John Dundas (sometimes known as 'Dogs' for reasons that are obscure), was an aristocrat, intellectual, athlete, humorist, and journalist on the editorial staff of the *Yorkshire Post*. Though related to the heads of two powerful Yorkshire families, the Marquess of Zetland and Viscount Halifax (he was also a cousin of Harald Peake), he sometimes shocked the 'Establishment' by his criticism of the pre-war Conservative government. Though extremely carefree and untidy (even to the extent of taking out a girl without first shaving), his academic record was brilliant: scholarship to Stowe at twelve, school certificate with six credits at thirteen, scholarship to Christ Church, Oxford, at seventeen and a First in Modern History before he was twenty-one – thereafter winning an award that took him to the Sorbonne and Heidelberg university. As a specialist in foreign affairs, he was sent at the time of Munich to report from Czechoslovakia, and later accompanied Chamberlain and Halifax to Rome. By then he was already a member of 609, in which he was destined to become one of its most famous warriors. With Dawson he formed another pair that was seldom split either in the air or on the ground.

Finally, at the end of the year, there came another ex-Stoic, Jarvis Blayney, who, having been already in the Volunteer Reserve, achieved his 'wings' within half a year. Member of another textile family, he also was a humorist but, unlike Dundas, very well dressed.

'By the summer of 1938, with the aid of much blasting, pneumatic drills and mechanical diggers, a real hangar was taking shape.'

So runs one of the earliest entries in an unofficial journal that Sergeant (later Flight-Sergeant) 'Tich' Cloves began to write early that year. Though the idea of such a journal had been launched by the C.O. himself, the job of writing it had 'somehow landed in the lap of a recently posted-in Regular sergeant' – who proceeded to reveal his devotion to the Auxiliary squadron he served by continuing to write it till he was finally posted away again in April 1941. In 1969 its worn and mildewed pages were resurrected by their author, exactly copied in his own fair hand, and sent to the present writer – a fascinating record, wittily caustic though kindly, of the fortunes of a squadron's individual aircraft at the hands of the pilots who flew them, by one of the men responsible for their maintenance and repair.

It is probably well that the pilots, being officers, were absolved from reading what was being written about them – for they suffered enough already from the outspoken comments of their own professional instructors, especially those of Flight-Lieutenant Matheson. To this tough Australian, Auxiliary pilots were 'real Pommie Bastards' – particularly when, as was usually the case, they failed to attain his own high standards in the matter of flying. 'None of us has ever before or since been so thoroughly cursed,' says Stephen Beaumont, remembering the aftermath of a formation flight when 'Mat', after dealing with the others, finally turned sadly to him with the words, 'And you, Beau, were just bloody.'*

Still worse befell Bernard Little, who in May 1938 had to face the wrath of both Odbert and Matheson simultaneously after getting hopelessly lost as a result of industrial haze. 'At last I saw a racecourse, and on examining maps was convinced it was New-

*Alister Matheson was later killed in 1943. Previously Mrs. Beaumont had been appointed god-mother to his first-born, and widow and children still visit from Australia.

castle. After landing on the five-furlong straight, however, I was horrified on being told by members of the gathering crowd that it was Pontefract, only some twelve miles from Yeadon.' Being still without his 'wings', he was not authorized to take off again after a forced landing, and had to wait for the two Regular officers to come and pick him up and fly the Avro back – his own unpopularity being emphasized by the fact that his escapade made them both late for an important party.

'Paul' Edge also strayed amongst civilians in embarrassing circumstances. Equally lost, in a Hawker Hind, he was about to be overtaken by darkness.

'With no night-flying experience I decided I had better get down quickly, and touched down on the only open ground I could find. The Hind finished its run on the edge of a putting green on which a belated foursome were actually putting. With remarkable courtesy they ignored the deep ruts I had made in what turned out to be Temple Newsome golf course and pointed out the approximate direction of Yeadon. Deciding there was no time for taxying into wind I turned and scraped off over some trees down-wind, and a few minutes later was back at Yeadon confessing my "gaffe". However, the Secretary accepted the Adjutant's apology for one temporarily ruined fairway in a most gentlemanly manner.'

Since these incidents involved no damage to aircraft, they did not feature in Cloves' journal.

'But sooner or later we knew someone would open the account. It turned out to be Flying Officer Beaumont, but being a decent bloke he did it in 'T' Flight's Hind trainer L7232. He landed rather fast and seeing Mr. Walker's form getting a bit close, gave the "kite" some brake. The "kite" didn't go much on this and decided to tip up on its nose – port bottom plane and airscrew written off. Flying Officer Beaumont sustained no injury, but mentioned he had some difficulty in descending from the elevated position. The necessary repairs were carried out and the aircraft was "S" again in quick time.'

This was in early 1939, and it is only fair to mention that a major reason for the tip-up (the same thing happened to a new Adjutant-instructor, Flight-Lieutenant Golledge) was that another stroke of the pen had suddenly transformed Beaumont and his colleagues from bomber into fighter pilots. This meant that though they still went on flying the Hawkers Hinds that had replaced the earlier Harts, these no longer had an air-gunner in the rear cockpit to hold down the tail on landing. Soon afterwards sand ballast was substituted, unless someone wanted a 'flip'. (Darkie Hanson recalls that on his own first 'flip' the pilot looped the loop, only to confess on landing that it was the first time he had done so without an instructor.)

The change from Bomber to Fighter Command, in December 1938, virtually coincided with a change in command of the Squadron when Harald Peake was appointed Director of the Auxiliary Air Force, Air Ministry, and raised to the acting rank of Air Commodore in one step.

'This habit of leap-frog promotion,' said his successor slyly during his speech thirty years later, 'seems to have stuck to him in his industrial and commercial life ever since.'

Though Harald Peake was the first and only holder of the post, its creation was overdue after the A.A.F.'s rapid expansion, and followed from an enquiry set up by 'Stuffy' Dowding after, so it is said, a quite lowly Auxiliary officer had bypassed all the 'usual channels' by airing some complaint directly with the Secretary of State for Air, who also happened to be Hon. Air Commodore of his Squadron. So now, just as the Territorials had always had a Director General at the War Office to look after the interests of 'Citizen Soldiers', the A.A.F. had a Director to look after those of 'Citizen Airmen'. Though the post was necessarily abolished at the outbreak of war, and Air Commodore Harald Peake then became successively Director of Public Relations, Air Ministry, and of R.A.F. Welfare, he continued to maintain close contact with the A.A.F. squadrons, and particularly with the one he had founded and commanded, 'whose standards and code of behaviour', to quote Bernard Little, 'he set and moulded'.

Almost simultaneously there departed the Squadron's Auxiliary Adjutant, the Earl of Lincoln, to command No. 616 (South Yorkshire) Squadron, whose formation at Doncaster had at last been approved – and whose buildings had already been planned, and first applicants for membership interviewed, by Harald Peake! Already twenty-nine when he joined 609, the Earl had been ineligible for flying training at its hands, but still contrived to get some by joining a civil flying club. As a result, two years later, the rule was waived and he was allowed to transfer to the General Duties Branch, becoming the first pilot in 616 to get his 'wings'. In 1944, soon after D-Day (by then he had inherited the dukedom), he was commanding a Signals and Radar Control unit off the American beaches, when the L.S.T. from which it operated was blown up by a torpedo from a Ju 88. Later Group-Captain James McComb, C.B.E., D.F.C., told Stephen Beaumont:

Fished out of the Channel, dressed in an ordinary seaman's gear and very dirty, he was taken to Naval H.Q. in Portsmouth, where the C.-in-C., observing a figure resting in the sunshine on the grass outside his office, said to me: 'What is that filthy object? Bring it in!' I duly obeyed and made the presentation: 'Wing-Commander His Grace the Duke of Newcastle, Sir.'

*

Geoffrey Ambler, who succeeded to the command of 609 Squadron only ten months before the outbreak of hostilities, was another true Yorkshireman whose family had been worsted spinners in the wool textile industry since the eighteenth century. Another graduate of Cambridge and a rowing blue (for two years he had been President of the C.U. Boat Club), his experience as an aviator went back to 1926, and (like Peake) he owned a succession of private aeroplanes. Add the fact that he had been an officer in No. 608 (North Riding) Squadron since its formation in 1930, and had commanded it since it changed to the fighter role in 1934, and it is easy to see that in getting him as its commanding officer at this vital moment the West Riding Squadron could not have done better. It was in fact obtaining the services of one of the most distinguished Auxiliary officers there ever were, and (as mentioned earlier) the only one who during the coming war was to reach the rank of Air Vice-Marshal.

Soon after he took over, Darkie Hanson remembers, Ambler had the Squadron on parade and said, 'There's obviously going to be a war, and we're going to work like hell. Any dead wood – we shall cut it out.' And it was so. All those who continued to serve under him are agreed that but for his single-minded devotion, force of character, and shining personal example, 609 could scarcely have been converted into an effective fighter squadron in time.

Whereas in the early days of the A.A.F. twelve hours per officer
per year were the minimum required, the hours now flown sometimes exceeded those of their R.A.F. counterparts. It required an
effort from both air and ground crews, but it was made. 'The
enthusiasm and dedication of all A.A.F. personnel was quite amazing,' their C.O. recalls. Already the experiment of recruiting a
squadron of volunteers from a cross-section of the local population, with mutual loyalties, respect and comradeship as its driving
force, was succeeding.

By January 1939, Cloves records, there were two new hangars,
'A' and 'B' flights were classed as operational flights under Auxil-
iary flight commanders and with six Hinds each, while basic training was now restricted to 'T' (Training) Flight, whose aircraft
consisted of 'the faithful old Avros, a Hind trainer and four Hinds'.
Of the original instructional staff Flight-Sergeants 'Chiefie' Harris,
'Ben' Bennett and 'Taff' Hughes had departed, leaving only
Flight-Sergeant Coakes (later to become a Group-Captain) and
Sergeant Tucker (later to become a Squadron Leader). Hughes was
replaced by Flight-Sergeant 'Taff' Evans, 'Sergeant Henry Roberts
arrived complete with a large tool box, which instead of tools con-
tained a "squeeze box",' and Warrant Officer Harvey arrived to take
up a new post of Engineer Officer. Although each flight still had a
Regular N.C.O. in charge (Cloves himself and Roberts), Auxiliary
N.C.O.s now took over at the week-ends.

Bachelor officers now lived in the Mess, which however 'temporary' by this time included 'a Billiards Room, a Ladies' Room, a
Mess Steward and necessary cooks and services'. Even the Auxiliary airmen's billets were paved with lino – for R. F. Burgess recalls a week-end fetching 3-cwt. rolls of this in a 1917 Leyland
truck and trailer which refused to ascend the final hill till they
unloaded them.

The Regular flying instructors, Odbert and Matheson, had also
departed, and any successor they had seems to have confined himself to 'T' flight. 'A' and 'B' flights now began to learn fighter
tactics, partly from their C.O. himself, partly with the help of
72 Squadron. For in the last months before the war each A.A.F.
fighter squadron was taken under the 'wing' of a parent R.A.F.
squadron, and 72 at Church Fenton proved both handy and help-

ful. On a Sunday morning 609 would take off in formation, land at its 'parent's' base, then take the air again under operational tuition. But previously the very first squadron take-off in 609's history had produced a 'prang' that evoked a fine example of Sergeant Cloves' descriptive powers:

'Hind K6848 was being flown by Pilot Officer Dundas, with Leading Aircraftman Hunter as human ballast. It happened to be the C.O.'s plane, but that was no deterrent. Forming up took some time, and the old Kestrel V engines were just wondering if they would be required, when bang went the throttles and twelve aircraft became airborne. But the engine of K6848 opted to cut. Deciding he couldn't clear the houses in Victoria Avenue, Pilot-Officer Dundas put it earthwards. He touched down, braked, but the wheels skidded and the aircraft carried on unperturbed. Breaking through the aerodrome fence and chopping down a wind-sock that enveloped a boy on a pushbike, it finally came to rest with its nose in a back garden and its tail resting on the roof of a house. The lady occupant was restored from her hysterics with the aid of brandy, the pilot and passenger then had a sip, and an unidentified airman finished the bottle. Aircraft a write-off.'

The then editor of the *Yorkshire Post* wrote some time afterwards that Dundas, going on night duty with this newspaper just after a court of enquiry had found the accident to have been due to a mechanical defect, hinted archly that he had performed a public service in discovering the defect with such slight consequences.

Church Fenton, inevitably, became the location of the last prewar Summer Camp – this time no holiday, but a fortnight of ceaseless work and transition. For it had been announced that 609 Squadron was to be re-equipped with Spitfires, which for pilots accustomed to flying biplanes with fixed undercarriages was something like changing from a family saloon to a racing car. For conversion flights two dual-seat Battle light bombers were allocated, after which those who qualified, after one aerodrome circuit only, made their first solo flights in 72 Squadron's Spitfires – Dundas after only sixty hours' flying all told. Shortly afterwards Squadron-Leader Ambler flew back from Southampton 609's first very own Spitfire, L1082, which was destined to survive in Squadron service till near the end of the Battle of Britain.

'On August 13th we struck camp and returned to Yeadon, thinking we had done a good job and earned a spot of leave. There was none to be had, only a long week-end. We were nearing a crisis.'

So wrote Cloves. On August 24th airman R. F. Burgess was lying in bed, idly wondering what suit to put on, when the arrival of a long blue envelope made the decision for him. He was to put on uniform and report to Yeadon forthwith, complete with kitbag. 'Going on leave, mate?' asked the bus conductor innocently.

The blue envelope meant mobilization: it contained a Form of Embodiment, 'embodying' the A.A.F. with the R.A.F. for the duration of hostilities. As Auxiliary airmen staggered up with their kitbags to the main gate, says G. E. Bradbury, they were met by the Regular Warrant-Officer Discip., who chortled, 'Now, you bastards, I've got you!'

He had, but still with some slight reservations. The status was: 'An Auxiliary officer or airman serving with the R.A.F.' – i.e. still not part of it. He could not be posted away from his unit nor sent abroad without his consent, and when the R.A.F. won in the end it did so by sheer blackmail. If, unlike the VR of the Volunteer Reserve and the T of the Territorials, the A remained on survivors' lapels till the end of the war, I am told this was because Winston Churchill, himself Honorary Air Commodore of an Auxiliary Squadron, had no intention of removing his own.

For Stephen Beaumont a much needed holiday at Birling Gap, Eastbourne, was cut short by a telegram: REPORT DUTY FORTHWITH – AMBLER. After driving through the night, at 5 a.m. he stopped for a moment at Wakefield to say goodbye to his wife, and later wrote in his diary:

'She was downstairs, the children of course asleep. Can see her standing there in white, so plainly, and am conscious of a similar scene between my parents on an August afternoon in 1914 – my earliest recollection, when I was four. Feelings of "Relief that it's come at last", mixed with "It's probably only a false alarm".'

It wasn't. On August 27th, equipped with just two Spitfires and one Battle, and leaving its Hinds behind, 609 Squadron moved off by road, with officers' and some airmen's cars stuffed with gramophones, golf clubs and other sporting equipment, to its first war station, Catterick, forty miles to the north.

Also left behind were Flight-Lieutenant Roger Burges, Equipment Officer, and Pilot-Officer G. T. Dodgshun, assistant Regular Adjutant who had been largely responsible for the Squadron's mobilization scheme, and was now left in charge of six Auxiliary pupil pilots and a number of Auxiliary airmen. The officers were Michael Appleby, David Crook, Geoffrey Gaunt, Gordon Mitchell, J. R. Newsome and Pat Womersley. The first four rejoined 609 in time for the Battle of Britain, while Womersley diverged to Coastal Command but became 609's first C.O. when it was reformed in 1946. Now, after a month that included rugger, mixed hockey against W.A.A.F.s chosen, wrote Crook, 'for their decorative rather than their athletic qualifications', but no flying, he, Appleby, Mitchell and Womersley found themselves members of the first 'war' course at Flying Training School, Little Rissington, Glos.

Here, for the very first time, Auxiliary officers were expected to conform to Regular R.A.F. standards of discipline, which included drill, bed at 10.30 and no private cars. Men in their mid-twenties actually found themselves being ordered by an N.C.O. to have their hair cut before the next parade, and the whole confrontation probably gave rise to a remark overheard by Appleby many months later at Northolt:

'Auxiliaries are gentlemen trying to be officers; Regular are officers trying to be gentlemen; V.R.s are neither trying to be both.'

It was an aphorism that can only have appealed to a pre-war mentality, for when the battle was on, origins became of no account. By then 609 included officers *and* gentlemen from all three sources as well as from abroad.

Meanwhile the impact of service life was mitigated by the fact that the entire intake for this particular course consisted of Auxiliary officers and like-minded former members of university air squadrons. When Peter Dunning-White of 601 Squadron drove up in a Rolls-Royce complete with valet, John McGrath of the same squadron in an Alvis Speed-Twenty, and even Michael Appleby of 609 in a drop-head Hillman, the rule about private cars was quietly waived by the sensible Welsh station commander, Group-Captain ApEllis. In the end, says Appleby, 'it was the best time I had in my whole service career – highlights of schooldays and university rolled into one.' And they received probably the best service training of any Auxiliary pilots to date, on that noisy American monoplane trainer, the Harvard. For air-firing instruction they were detached to the Central Gunnery School at Warmwell in Dorset – later not the happiest of 609 Squadron's wartime locations – where Appleby for the first time was appointed by his brother officers as their somewhat cynical advocate with Authority. For Warmwell also had a 10.30 p.m. curfew, and when some of the students were not only caught 'out', but actually talking to some W.A.A.F.s outside the latter's billets, a very adverse report was forwarded by the station commander to the culprits' own C.O. at Little Rissington. Hot on its heels came Appleby, who promptly sought an interview.

'This girl Elizabeth,' he informed the Group-Captain (her name was mentioned in the report), 'she is a nice and intelligent girl, and incidentally a great friend of my family.' 'Thank goodness,' said the C.O., clutching at this convenient straw and certainly not checking with Michael's family. 'Charge dismissed.'

Such precedents were useful, for when the course was finally over it was made clear to Authority that the only onward posting that interested Appleby, Crook and Mitchell was back to 609 (West Riding) Squadron.

That left just twelve pilots to go to war, and ten days after reaching Catterick it was declared. Beaumont wrote : 'Pip Barran had a portable radio, and we listened to the sincere but tired and melancholy tones of Neville Chamberlain. As we did so the sun shone, practice flying went on overhead, and the green grass of the aerodrome and the russet woods beyond were completely peaceful. Nobody said a thing,' (even if one or two glanced surreptitiously towards the east). But when the speech, rebroadcast in the Mess on the B.B.C. one o'clock news, was followed by the National Anthem, 'everyone suddenly sprang to attention – then somewhat shame-facedly went in to lunch.'

Airmen's accommodation at Catterick was overcrowded owing to the presence of other squadrons and of recently called-up Class E reservists who, says Darkie Hanson rather patronizingly, 'hadn't seen an aircraft since 1918, and whose warrant officers didn't know as much as our A.C.2s'. One of them, R. F. Burgess recalls, infuriated an R.A.F. police sergeant who asked for his 'last three' by answering '56' – till it turned out that really was all of his num-ber. As a result of the pressure on billets, some of 609's airmen were quartered in the old Officers' Mess. This also had historical connections, for it had not been used since World War I, and empty wine bottles from that war were still stacked in the back yard. However the Squadron only remained at Catterick for five weeks, during which time it collected the rest of its Spitfires and received more training on them with the help of 41 Squadron, whose Regular pilots were, on average, five years younger. Yet despite the novelty of flying modern fighters – and especially of having to wait for a gap in the traffic before taking off uphill over the Great North Road – there was only one 'wheels-up' landing. The culprit was Paul Edge – 'the only time I saw him lose his temper', says Darkie Hanson. Edge himself remarks :

'Spitfires being in very short supply, it called for a personal rasp-berry from the A.O.C., delivered by Squadron-Leader Ambler in the kindest possible way. But during my week's Duty Officer, with no flying, I had a sympathetic visit from the Black and Pink Boozers, who informed me that whatever the A.O.C. had thought, they per-sonally thanked me for demonstrating so splendidly that their private fears about a genuine forced landing in a Spitfire were totally un-founded and that as a result their own confidence in the aircraft was vastly increased !'

In collecting its Spitfires 609 benefitted from its C.O.'s previous command of 608, for this squadron, now in Coastal Command, obliged its former chief by flying his present pilots to the source of supply in their Ansons. Stephen Beaumont, one of a party of five so conveyed to Ternhill in Shropshire, records their 'silly glee' on being ordered by the station commander there to fly the Spits all the way back with 'wheels down' to show everyone on the ground that they were 'friendly'. They refrained from pointing out that the order was impossible to obey because the engines would boil !

Next stop was Acklington in Northumberland – the second in 609's progression to the north. On October 5th and 6th the two flights landed there 'gunned up' for the first time, and from then on began to observe an operational defensive 'state' that with few changes would be its pattern for several years, namely :

One section at Readiness (airborne in five minutes)
One section at Available (airborne in fifteen minutes)
One section at 'Released' (airborne in thirty minutes)
One section stood off for training, weather permitting, or even allowed off the camp provided the C.O. knew where they were.

With only twelve pilots in the Squadron (later the establishment was twenty-six), pilots had to be around most of the time, and the C.O., Ambler, being one of the twelve, flew as much as anybody, besides coping with all the planning and administration – and air controlling – that came his way. In fact, though there were a few so-called operational patrols 'to investigate unidentified aircraft', flying consisted mainly in the practice 'scrambles' he organized to see which section could get off the ground quickest (record two and a quarter minutes). And here, in passing, is the Twelve's 'order of battle', in which each pilot had his own Spitfire, with a nickname (or effigy thereof) painted on it :

'A' FLIGHT		'B' FLIGHT	
Red Section		*Blue Section*	
F/O D. Persse-Joynt	'Joy'	F/O P. H. Barran	'Pip'
F/O A. R. Edge	'Dingbat'	P/O J. C. Dundas	'Squeak'
P/O G. D. Ayre	'Ariel'	P/O J. Dawson	'Wilfred'
Yellow Section		*Green Section*	
S/L G. Ambler	'Gambler'	F/O S. G. Beaumont	'Groucho'
		F/O P. Drummond-	
P/O B. W. Little	'Boozer I'	Hay	'Chico'
P/O J. C. Gilbert	'Boozer II'	P/O A. J. Blayney	'Harpo'

Reserve aircraft : 'Susan' and 'Meteor'. Adjutant (on sick leave) : F/O L. H. Sagar. Acting Adjutant : P/O A. G. Sudworth.

But on October 16th 609 took a small part in the first serious defensive 'flap' in the western war. 'Patrol Acklington, angels 15,' came the voice of Usworth control on the phone. It was meant for 'A' Flight, but somehow 'B' took off instead. Directed first to Alnwick, then Berwick-on-Tweed, they were told to look out for four enemy aircraft headed south, but these failed to appear and they landed wondering what it had all been about. Later there was a rumour about an attack on the Forth Bridge.

It was in fact the first occasion since 1918 that enemy aircraft had flown over British soil, and their target was not the Forth Bridge but the largest battleship in the British Navy, H.M.S. *Hood*. Shadowed by German reconnaissance planes as she entered the Firth of Forth, this great ship was in the act of docking at Rosyth naval base, beyond the Bridge, when a force of Junkers 88s of the anti-shipping *Geschwader*, KG 30, found her. 'She was a sitting target,' the German leader, *Hauptmann* Pohle Gruppen Kommandeur of I/KG 30 reported, 'but orders robbed us of our prize.' Before take-off he had received a personal order from the *Führer*: 'Should the *Hood* be already in dock, no attack is to be made.' For at this stage of the war the *only* legitimate targets for both British and German bombers were warships at sea or in roadstead—simply because neither side wanted the stigma of being the first to kill civilians.

With the *Hood* out of bounds Pohle concentrated his attack on the cruiser *Southampton* (in Rosyth roads), and would have sunk her had the vital bomb which penetrated three decks exploded. In the event cruisers *Southampton*, *Edinburgh* and one destroyer were slightly damaged, and the Kommandeur's and one other Ju 88 were shot down by Auxiliary Air Force pilots of 602 and 603 Squadrons, Pohle himself being rescued from the sea and becoming perhaps the first German Luftwaffe prisoner of war in British hands. (He reportedly told his captors that he was a personal friend of Goering's, and asked them to arrange for a Red Cross plane to fly a doctor over from Germany to treat his injuries).

Though the details of this enemy operation were evidently too secret for 609 Squadron to be told about, they in fact largely determined its future for the next half-year. Two days previously *Leutnant* Prien had taken his U-boat *U 47* into Scapa Flow and sunk the *Royal Oak*, and one day afterwards four more Ju 88s of

KG 30 flew over and tore the side out of the training-cum-depot ship *Iron Duke*. Both these aggressors had been unlucky not to find more quarry at Scapa, but in fact the three attacks had achieved much more than was immediately obvious. To quote the official history, Royal Air Force, 1939–1945 : 'By two or three boldly executed strokes, and at a total cost of four aircraft, the German Air Force and the U-boat service between them scored a resounding strategic success.' And Basil Collier, author of *The Defence of the United Kingdom* (H.M.S.O.) adds : 'The Home Fleet for five months was compelled to use remote anchorages on the west coast of Scotland . . . Control of the North Sea had been lost.'

For perhaps the first time in its history the British Navy was 'eating humble pie'. Cynically its admirals had noted the complete failure of the R.A.F.'s attempt, one day after the war started, to strike with Blenheims against the *Admiral Scheer* off Wilhelmshaven and Wellingtons against the *Scharnhorst* and *Gneisenau*. Triumphantly they had also noted the equally complete failure of the Luftwaffe, during two attempts on September 26th and October 9th, to make any dent on the Home Fleet at sea – despite the reiterated claim of German propaganda to have sunk the aircraft carrier *Ark Royal*. Only now, with the Navy's invincibility against air attack at last in question, did they become seriously concerned about air defence – for northwards of Edinburgh no system of control and interception existed. When, in March 1940, the Home Fleet did feel able to return to Scapa Flow, it was due in large measure to Geoffrey Ambler in a new capacity.

Meanwhile the 'flap' was really 'on'. At 11 p.m., only hours after units of the Home Fleet had been attacked in the Forth estuary, an officially non-mobile squadron, No. 609, received orders to move itself at dawn next day to Drem, in East Lothian, 'for immediate duty'. It was a challenge to the ingenuity and improvisation even of Geoffrey Ambler, which he solved by requistioning civilian transport that included two White Horse whisky trucks for the less urgent personnel and stores, while the 'greasers', as Cloves termed the flight servicing crews, 'were transplanted in the bowels of Whitley bombers, up to twenty and more at a time'. At 13.40 on October 17th the Squadron reported itself to Turnhouse control as 'fully operational' at its new station.

Four days later precisely the same thing happened, with yet another northward stride to Kinloss on the Moray Firth. This time the 'greasers' travelled *de luxe* in two Ensigns, late of Imperial Airways, supplied by H.Q. Fighter Command. For the Spitfires, with the mountains of Aberdeenshire in between, maps were essential, but were obtained only just in time owing to the relevant station officer, who had been drinking, declining to issue them the night before. Next afternoon, despite bad weather, 609 was once again ready for action – though this time there was no fighter operations sector to which to report. Next morning the sun shone on all the magnificence of Scottish autumnal foliage, with blue sky and blue sea setting off a mountain background, 'and warm enough for June', as Beaumont wrote in his diary. It was a station so remote that even the instructors of the F.T.S. who shared it had never before seen Spitfires, and came over to see 609's with interest and envy. When, a little later, Beaumont's Green section was sent on patrol by Pip Barran, following was the only operations preamble :

'The C.O. of 41 Squadron rang up from Wick to say two unidentified aircraft had been seen 150 miles out to sea (presumably by the Navy), and would we patrol 50 miles out from Kinnaird's Head, and they would do the same from Caithness.'

Despite the fact that beyond Elgin the section was completely out of radio touch with land, it still remained on patrol far over the North Sea for one and a half hours, in the course of which Peter Drummond-Hay spied their colleagues from the north and Beaumont led him and Blayney in an attack on what were surely some Heinkels – till, just in time, they turned out to be Skuas of the same Royal Navy it was their mission to protect. 'Well done,' said Ambler after they landed, 'but don't do it again. Fighter Command instructions are that no pilot is to fly more than five miles out to sea, and you ought not to have been sent.' He had been much worried, Persse-Joynt reported, about possible engine failure.

For the moment Kinloss was a 'flash in the pan', and after only two days the Squadron returned to Drem – where personnel of its Servicing Section were still arriving from Acklington. For the first night 609 was joined by 41 Squadron on its way back to Catterick, whence it had made its first 'kill' on the seventeenth off Whitby. Though it was rumoured that 609 would also be returning to Catterick, Drem was to remain its parent station until May 18th, 1940.

As an airfield Drem was 'small, hilly and soft in patches'. Till now it had been the home solely of a Flying Training School, and it was plain that the staff (unlike that at Kinloss) resented an intrusion that impaired both its comfort and code of discipline. Officers of 609 had no sooner dispersed their aircraft and entered the Mess than they were reprimanded by the station commander for walking on the grass. Finally, after a fight for offices and billets had gone in favour of Squadron-Leader Ambler, the F.T.S. moved away and Drem became a fighter station only, shared by 609 with 602 (City of Glasgow) Squadron – 'a grand lot of chaps though casual by our standards and usually late for everything', wrote Beaumont – and finally 603 (City of Edinburgh). On October 28th these two squadrons together brought down the first enemy aircraft of World War II to crash on British soil – a Heinkel 111 which force-landed only ten miles from Drem, beside a village that appropriately bore the same name as Flight-Lieutenant Gifford, the leader of the section of 603 that was involved. If their colleagues of the West Riding Squadron were a little jealous, it was after all the Scottish squadrons' 'home beat', and having taken a good close-up look at this one on the ground the former should be quick to recognize future Heinkels in the air. Meanwhile survivors of the enemy crew are said to have expressed disgust at having been shot down by mere 'Auxiliary amateurs'.

Unfortunately such events were rare, and though during the first seven months of the war more interceptions were made in Scotland than in either France or England, the squadrons based there made no more 'kills' before the end of the year. Whenever, after hours of waiting in dispersed caravans, 609 had a section 'scrambled', the unidentified aircraft either turned out to be friendly or was not seen at all owing to the badness of the weather. Once, when Green section reached for their safety catches as the designation actually changed from 'unidentified' to 'enemy', their target turned out to be 'Presser' and his Red section on a practice flight. Meanwhile 609's thirty-five-year-old C.O. went on tire-lessly coaching his pilots at every opportunity till they had learnt every form of attack in the book. Circling the airfield one day on returning from a flight during which R.T. silence had been en-joined, Little and Gilbert watched in growing amazement as he led them round and round for ten minutes while he apparently fought a losing battle to adjust his helmet. At last he broke R.T. silence with the words, 'For God's sake get into bloody line astern!,' and they were sternly reminded on landing that placing one's hand on one's head was the *visual* sign for line astern.

As the long Scottish winter set in, the billets became very cold. Airman Waterson recalls that water spilt during an evening 'brew-up' soon froze to the floor, and that half 609's personnel went down with flu. To keep the grass runways serviceable, snow had to be cleared by hand, and during gales the Spitfires had to be tied down. Once, according to Bradbury and Burgess, a Short Scylla, late of Imperial Airways, was torn from its moorings and blown upside down with its protesting radio-operator still inside. As its fuel poured out there was a scene as in *Whisky Galore*: 'All the car owners on the station, led by Charlie Harvey, the engineering W.O., hared across the 'drome with anything that would hold petrol.'

Compensations also included E.N.S.A. concerts, even if these tended to be drowned by the rival chanting of *Scotland the Brave* by 602 and *There'll Always be an England* by 609. Futhermore, the capital of Scotland itself was only some fifteen miles to the west, and North Berwick half that distance to the east. The Black and Pink Boozers, Little and Gilbert, returning late from Scotland's capital, would find little notes on their pillows, thoughtfully put there by their squadron (and section) commander, Geoffrey Ambler, reminding them that the three of them were on dawn Readiness. Officers and airmen are agreed that 'the hospitality of the locals was fabulous'. John Bisdee, who joined the Squadron on Boxing Day, 1939, is still ecstatic about 'The Hostesses of North Berwick – and their daughters, with whom we had two months of mixed hockey on a near-by lake.' In the end Drem became one of the Squadron's most happily remembered stations of the war, and one can imagine the feelings of G. E. Bradbury, revisiting it thirty years later, on finding it is now a turkey farm. But in North Berwick he reports, 609 is still remembered, and the former proprietress of the County Hotel now welcomes its survivors at the Redlands.

In late November 609 received its first Regular pilots, and notably three who were to become household names: Flying-Officer F. J. Howell, who had been stationed in Egypt; Pilot-Officer C. N. 'Teeny' Overton, a tall and curly-headed youth of hardly twenty who came from No. 17 (Hurricane) Squadron, and Flying-Officer I. B. N. Russell. The last, known to his fellow-officers as 'Hack', and to the ground staff apparently as 'Hank', was actually an American who had held a short-service commission in the R.A.F. in the early thirties, had later become a commercial air-line pilot in his own country, and returned to Britain at the outset of hostilities. Though he evidently felt the cold, and flew wrapped up like an Eskimo, he is described as 'an unscareable tough guy' – an impression perhaps enhanced by the fact that he never stopped smoking even while flying a Spitfire ('I reckon its O.K. as long as your Kigass is screwed up tight'). He was also the first pilot of the Squadron to use his parachute – when one leg of his undercarriage refused to descend – and his colleagues were as grateful for the demonstration that this was feasible from a Spitfire as they had been to Edge when he landed without wheels.

A month later there arrived the first war-time V.R.s – Pilot-Officers John Bisdee and J. R. 'Buck' Buchanan, and Sergeants Beard and Bennett. Though they came from an S.F.T.S., they somehow short-circuited the full course and had not even flown monoplanes. So a Harvard trainer was obtained, and for a brief spell 609 again became a training, as well as an operational, unit, with the 'very professional' Frankie Howell as chief instructor first on this, and later in formation flying on Spitfires.

'We were conscious of being the first adopted children in a family – everyone else had known each other for years,' says Bisdee. A scholar of Marlborough, and an exhibitioner of Corpus Christi, Cambridge, he would doubtless have been an Auxiliary himself had he joined the university air squadron instead of the cavalry, but made up for it by remaining with 609 until July 1941. Meanwhile his first job was as assistant Adjutant to Gordon Sudworth, because for the moment there was no one to teach him on the Harvard. On December 5th 609 had departed again to Kinloss.

The signal from H.Q. Fighter Command that sent it there, and 64 Squadron (Blenheims) to Evanton near Invergordon, referred to the transport of 'essential personnel and stores for one week's detached operations'. Though in the event it was five weeks, at least the C.O.s of both squadrons knew what it was all about owing to a warning signal of a month earlier which had referred to standing patrols in defence of 'shipping' in Loch Ewe on the west coast. The 'shipping' (dare I now reveal it?) was of course the Home Fleet, over which 64 was to provide a standing daylight patrol, with 609 manning the eastern approaches and supplying reinforcements if required. Significantly, in view of the complete absence of any area operations control unit, the signal concluded its orders (to the *squadrons*): 'R.T. transmission and receiving stations will be provided at Evanton and Kinloss.' Their own Group H.Q. (No. 13, far to the south in Newcastle), could only be reached even on the telephone via another Command.

Geoffrey Ambler, as usual, was equal to the challenge. Like all pre-war squadron commanders, he had been fully trained in interception control and operations room procedure – the 'control' consisting in giving the pilot vectors, speeds and heights from a 'dead-reckoning' track maintained with the aid of a grease-pencil on a perspex map. Now, within hours, he had rigged up an operations room in the Kinloss signals section with simple equipment obtained from station stores, and trained some 609 clerks * and others for the various jobs.

'Happily we had an airman, LAC Hartley, who had followed me from 608 and was a fully trained radio mechanic in the R.A.F. sense, as well as being a radio 'ham' and engineer in civil life. He was quite brilliant, taking the R.T. transmitter and receiver to pieces and modifying them. By means of some poles we also extended the height of the aerials and thus improved substantially the range and clarity

---

* In his diary Stephen Beaumont drew a diagram of this 'ops room', showing the radio and telephone network and the duty positions of the C.O. and LACs Hartley, Andrews and Cohen.

of communications. All this had to be done at night when the rather stupid stations signals warrant officer was away !'

In addition Ambler arranged a land line to *H.M.S. Curlew* anchored at Invergordon, on which radar plots were obtained from the Navy, and enrolled the Coastguards as an 'observer corps'.

'In the conditions of mountains, winter snow showers, low cloud, etc., I found the controlling very exacting and did not dare delegate it to any young officer since the responsibility was too great. In any event there was no time to train another controller.'

The responsibility was indeed great, and the conditions – snow showers, cloud down to 500 feet, the Cairngorm mountains up to 4,000 feet – were terrible, for the pilots had to fly 'without any Radio Direction-finding equipment or homing facilities'. Yet there were no accidents whatever, and if all the aircraft intercepted turned out to be 'friendly', it still showed that Ambler's masterpiece of improvisation worked.

From the Squadron's point of view he was *too* successful, for on 1st January 1940 they lost him as their leader. Promoted to Wing-Commander, he was sent north to help evolve an air defence for Scapa Flow, and became commander of a new Sector covering North Scotland, Orkney and Shetland – an independent command under the general operational control of 13 Group at Newcastle. He was again successful. In early March 1940 the Home Fleet was able to return to Scapa Flow, and after two defeats in April the Luftwaffe left it alone for the rest of the war.

Geoffrey Ambler's subsequent posts included Commandant of the Royal Observer Corps (which he overhauled), Senior Air Staff Officer, Fighter Command, and A.D.C. to King George VI. Typically, when the war ended, he completed a conversion course on jet fighters at the age of forty-one. One of the last things he did for his Squadron at remote Kinloss when no pay came through for the men, was to pay them out of his private bank account. 'Our accountancy shocked Fighter Command,' says his Adjutant, Gordon Sudworth.

It was still Air Ministry policy at this time to fill a vacancy in the command of an Auxiliary squadron from another Auxiliary squadron or from the A.A.F. Reserve, and as Geoffrey Ambler's successor in 609 Squadron Leader J. A. Vick, formerly a flight commander of 607 was appointed. But the fates were against him: on his way to Kinloss he had a serious motor accident and was taken to hospital. That left the second alternative, and M. V. Avent, once of 605 (County of Warwick) Squadron was appointed. His posting, straight from the Reserve, without first giving him a conversion course from biplanes to monoplane fighters was as unfair to him as it was to the Squadron, and the Scottish Highlands in winter were hardly the ideal location in which to start flying Spitfires. The consequence was that the new C.O., through no fault of his own, was obliged for the duration of his command to delegate leadership in the air to his flight commanders. In the words of Air Vice-Marshal Ambler, 'the Air Ministry policy was mad'.

On 12th January 1940 the West Riding Squadron, the Home Fleet being no longer at 'Port A' (Loch Ewe), returned to Drem, and on the 29th it had its first engagement with the enemy. Red section – 'Presser' Persse-Joynt, Desmond Ayre and 'Paul' Edge – were practising 'circuits and bumps' when they were ordered by Turnhouse control to intercept a Heinkel 111 bombing a merchant ship off the mouth of the Tay. Edge, flying the Squadron's oldest Spitfire L1082, was on the wrong side of the circuit and never caught up. The other two found and attacked it before it darted into cloud, Ayre doing so twice more as it briefly reappeared. Though at the time no results were seen, months later the same Heinkel was shot down near Wick, when its pilot reported that though on 29th January he had managed to regain his base, his aircraft was riddled with bullets.

Convoy patrols now became a regular duty, and in the course of one of them, on 27th February, 609 at last made its first 'kill'. It was Red section again, this time with Buchanan as No. 3. Below, only 500 feet above the sea, an aircraft approached them down the line of ships. Not having spotted the usual patrolling Anson, 'Presser' went closer and identified a Heinkel which at once went full-boost for cloud 1,500 feet above, where 'Presser' lost it. His followers, however, being lower, saw it reappear and brought it down on to the water – though not before Ayre's machine had suffered return fire that punctured oil and glycol tanks, hit both mainplanes and severed the elevator trimming tab control. Despite a flat tyre he landed safely, and the enemy crew took to their rubber dinghy.

It was a great pity it had not happened the day before, while Drem was being honoured by a visit from King George VI, accompanied by Air Chief Marshal Dowding, Commander-in-Chief Fighter Command, and the Air Officer Commanding No. 13 Group, Air Vice-Marshal Saul. Then 609 only just had time to remove a blot on the landscape in the shape of one of its aircraft standing on its nose in a ditch, and as its airmen at this time only possessed one uniform, those involved were not quite as clean on parade as they would have wished. Though 609 was duly inspected – 'H.M. certainly gives one a good hand-shake and look-over,' wrote Beaumont – the hero of the day was Squadron-Leader Farquhar, C.O. of 602, who became decorated with what was presumably Fighter Command's first D.F.C. of the war after playing a leading part in his squadron's victories. Recently (Beaumont goes on) he had even force-landed beside a Heinkel that he had brought down single-handed in an effort to stop the crew from setting it on fire, but failed when his Spitfire turned over. At least the Germans helped him out!

With two squadrons to share the numerous standing and investigation patrols, the individual pilot now had one day on and one day off. Beaumont: 'On the "on" days we average five hours flying each (enough for anyone) and burn about 2,000 gallons of petrol. On the "off" days we are supposed to do practice attacks, but if we go on at this rate we shan't have any aircraft left.'

With enough pilots now to form a spare section for each flight, leave at least was (for a short time) assured. Regular days off, however, were threatened in March by the decision of the authorities that day pilots should become operational by night as well. Spitfires were quite unsuitable for night flying in the black-out, and Cloves, as one of the two leading 'menders', has a series of choice comments on the many misfortunes that inevitably occurred. Examples:

'F/O Dundas in L1084 made a perfect three-point landing – on two wheels and airscrew . . . some explanation like "I was landing uphill"!'

'P/O Bisdee appeared to land L1082 about twenty feet in the air before the aircraft fell the remaining distance with a distinct crunch . . . two oleo legs, port mainplane, airscrew and tail unit written off.'

'Ambulance and fire tender ordered to search for aircraft reported by police to have crashed in flames at N. Berwick. It was never found. It was merely Sergeant Bennett in L1058 losing a parachute flare. "It just dropped out" was his story. Maybe. Shame to blame the pilot – it might have been the fault of those b— armourers.'

But perhaps the most memorable 'prang' in 609's whole history occurred in daylight and involved a colourful Regular attached from 65 Squadron, 'Cannon George' Proudman. Like 'Hack' Russell in that he smoked (a pipe) while flying, he was unlike him in being 'impervious to cold', once while playing billiards astounding Bisdee by removing his jacket and 'revealing underneath simply a shirt-front attached to a collar and a pair of cuffs – no sleeves, no vest, just George !' His nickname derived from his aircraft, which was the first Spitfire to be fitted experimentally with cannon. This he flew, first with 602, then 609, in the hope of trying it out against the enemy, and having demonstrated his marksmanship by shooting a pheasant stone dead from a moving car with a service revolver at a range of thirty feet, he could hardly have missed. Unfortunately 'Cannon George' was also a cowboy of the air who liked to cut his landings fine. On the day of the 'prang' Edge recalls :

'He was giving us a demonstration of a 1914–18 Sopwith Camel landing by "blipping" his ignition switch on and off as he came in. Unfortunately the Rolls Royce Merlin did not like being treated like a Bentley Rotary and elected to stop altogether at the precise moment when George needed power.'

Jarvis Blayney adds : 'He landed slap on top of my aircraft "Harpo", which I had flown for eight months. Both aircraft caught fire, and the resultant firework display of flying shells and bullets was most impressive.' Yet George stepped out unscathed, and Cloves coined a Squadron motto : 'Two before breakfast.'

Earlier the night-training programme had been interrupted by an extraordinary order : to disperse 602's and 609's aircaft each night at Grangemouth on the other side of Edinburgh in the expectation of reprisals for Bomber Command's attack on Sylt. When, after two nights, this enterprise had resulted in numerous aircraft tipping up in boggy ground and pilots becoming unfit to fly due to sheer exhaustion, it was decided the Germans could scarcely do worse if the Spits were dispersed locally.

It was typical of the growing nervousness. If in April Persse-Joynt made Squadron history by actually being 'scrambled' at night, it was in fact the only 'scramble' of any sort during the month. For on the ninth the enemy had invaded Denmark and Norway. In the ensuing lull and the spring weather that accompanied it 609's pilots played golf and tennis and drank beer in pubs with uneasy determination. When, just a month later, the Low Countries were invaded, the Blenheim and Hurricane squadrons went south and once again all leave was stopped, there remained little illusion about the seriousness of the war to come. If, so far, the West Riding Squadron had accounted for only one of the enemy, it could at least boast, unlike many squadrons, that in over eight months it had shot down no aircraft of its own side. Nor, in four years of flying, had it suffered a fatality.

2

THE WEAPON IS TEMPERED

In retrospect the 18th of May, 1940, was for 609 Squadron an historical watershed. On that date the ways of life and thought that characterized a peace-time Auxiliary squadron – and which so far had somehow been prolonged into what the British called 'the phoney war' and the French *la drôle de guerre* – were suddenly and rudely interrupted, and the West Riding Squadron headed for the ordeal by fire from which, seared and cauterized, it was to emerge three months later as one of the finest (if most composite) fighting units of all time.

At 18.00 hours Stephen Beaumont, John Gilbert and 'Buck' Buchanan were observing the normal state of Readiness in Scotland when the section leader was called to the telephone. 'Ops' was relaying a message from H.Q. 13 Group, posting 609 to Tangmere (it turned out to be Northolt) in 11 Group with immediate effect.

'Much telephoning ensued,' Stephen recorded in his diary, 'to get the C.O. and other officers *into* the camp and to keep the air-men *on* the camp. I eventually contacted the C.O. on Muirfield golf course at the tenth hole.' (It seems that, unlike Drake, he did not deem it essential to complete his game). By 22.00 hours all personnel on pass had been recalled, packing-up was in full swing, and the first rail party of fifty men had left Drem for Northolt.

It was just four days since, in the attempt to stop the German break-through at Sedan, the French bomber force had ceased to exist and the British bomber force had lost 60 per cent of its strength. With the Luftwaffe supreme in the sky, Guderian's *Panzers* had begun their race for the Channel ports, and in another four days they were there. News was scant and the fate of the

British Expeditionary Force still unknown. With the coming role of Fighter Command itself not yet established, a fighter squadron from remote Scotland could be forgiven if – with other squadrons left *in situ* – the significance of its own posting south was not at once apparent. Thirty years afterwards 'Teeny' Overton, then at the age of twenty its youngest pilot, recalls : 'I don't think I had a clue what was happening, and feel that was a position many of us were in. From being a small, semi-isolated unit, we suddenly found ourselves part of a big and often baffling circus. Abruptly we were really in the war.'

To convince them, they would need just one look from above at the swirling, smoking misery of Dunkirk.

By 07.30, 19th May, the first rail party under Pilot-Officer John Bisdee had reached Kings Cross, and by 15.00 fifteen pilots and their aircraft, having refuelled en route at Church Fenton (nostalgically near homes to which many of them would never return), had already reported themselves available for action at their new base. The speed of the move, indeed, earned the Squadron its first message of congratulation from A.O.C. No. 11 Group, Air Vice-Marshal Park. By the following day all but a small servicing party, left behind to complete repairs to unserviceable aircraft, had arrived by rail and road.

In the event, ten days were to elapse before 609 was called into action. It was a pause from which both pilots and aircraft to some extent benefitted. Gordon Sudworth, 609's Adjutant, recorded in wonder : 'A considerable number of pilots on this station have had actual experience of fights with the enemy, and pilots of this Squadron seek all available information . . . Practice fights based on actual ones are now being tried out each day.' This seems to have been a reference mainly to the Hurricane pilots of No. 111 Squadron, who had won a good deal of fame fighting over the continent while refuelling there. But writing in his diary on 24th May, Beaumont recorded that 609 was at that moment the only squadron on the station. 111 had gone to Debden to refit; 600 (City of London Squadron) was reforming after losing the whole of its 'B' flight bar one machine, while the Spitfires of the newly reformed 92 Squadron (a year later to become 609's 'blood brothers' at Biggin Hill), had done very well, but also suffered severe loss, including their C.O., Bushell.*

On the 27th 'a very important modification to our aircraft' was received, in the shape of armour plating to be fixed behind the pilot's head and back. While 609 had been in Scotland, out of range of enemy fighters, this had hardly been necessary, even if the fact that it was now delivered minus the necessary fittings suggests that it was also not available. These only arrived two days later, and if a shining example of an Auxiliary ground crew's devotion in war-time was needed, it was provided by the men who, led by Flight-Sergeant Evans, worked day and night for twenty-four hours to get thirteen Spitfires equipped with the vital armour.

It was in the nick of time. The last screw and wing-nut had scarcely been set in place when the orders, received the night before via the station commander, Group Captain Vincent, to stand by for action over the French coast, became orders to take wing. At 12 noon on 30th May, 1940, twelve aircraft of No. 609 (West Riding) Squadron left Northolt to refuel at Biggin Hill, and thence – quite unrehearsed, it seems – take off on its very first squadron patrol of the war.

'I wonder how it will turn out,' Stephen Beaumont wrote in his diary just before leaving. 'My love to all the family if I'm unlucky.'

It was a bit like sending a football eleven, whose members had never played together before, against a crack team that had never tasted defeat. Indeed, though 609 was fully sensible of the honour of having been picked, it is by no means clear why it was. The official war history of the R.A.F. records that Dowding, C.-in-C. of Fighter Command, was not prepared to strip the entire North and Midlands of their defence, 'nor, with one eye on the greater struggle that lay ahead, was he anxious to expose squadrons incompletely trained or recuperating to the heavy wastage entailed in fighting over the Continent.'

And in the end it was less than an 'eleven' that crossed the sea,

---

* Roger Bushell, whom I knew when he was a member of the Cambridge University ski team in the early 'thirties', had recently come from 601 (County of London) Squadron, which he had joined long before the war. Contrary to what was thought at this time he was not killed at Dunkirk, but was taken prisoner and later shot after leading The Great Escape.

for Squadron-Leader Avent, who on this historic occasion included himself as 'Green 3', was obliged to land with the rest of his section at Manston. This was the team that started :

Red Section	Blue Section
F/Lt. D. Persse-Joynt	F/Lt. J. H. Barran
F/O G. D. Ayre	F/O S. G. Beaumont
F/O A. R. Edge	F/O J. C. Gilbert

Yellow Section	Green Section
F/O F. J. Howell	F/O I. B. N. Russell
F/O J. Dawson	P/O C. N. Overton
F/O J. C. Dundas	S/L M. V. Avent

All but three of these were Auxiliary pilots from before the war, two of them – Dudley Persse-Joynt and Stephen Beaumont – having been foundation members in 1936. Amongst them only Persse-Joynt and Desmond ('Dizzy') Ayre had momentarily been in action, and it is a poignant thought that the latter and 'Paul' Edge, who were each other's closest friends on the ground, also flew close together in the air till tragedy struck. The same was soon to apply to two other pairs of inseparables, Gilbert and Little, Dawson and Dundas.

'Operation Dynamo' – the evacuation of the British Expeditionary Force from Dunkirk – had been in progress for three days. The destruction of the B.E.F. by the Luftwaffe alone – that was the feather Goering wanted in his cap, and to oblige him Hitler halted the German armour for two and a half vital days. At the outset it looked as if Goering would win his feather, for already on the first day of the evacuation, 27th May, it had become impossible (for the moment) to go on using the bomb-torn quays, and of 340,000 men only 7,669 got away. Where, the British soldiers asked, was the R.A.F.? Yet 200 Spitfires and Hurricanes had been operating (in relays), and one German air corps reported that its losses this day exceeded the combined total of the previous ten.

For the next day and a half the weather had come to the aid of the British. Low clouds, fusing with the black smoke from Dunkirk's burning oil tanks and bomb dust, blotted out the whole area and the Luftwaffe could not see where to aim its bombs. Moreover the Senior Naval Officer now signalled: 'Fighter protection has been invaluable,' and this reflected the change in fighter deployment that Air Vice-Marshal Park, A.O.C. 11 Group, had sought. Having flown over Dunkirk himself in a Hurricane, he believed that the use of up to four of his eighteen squadrons at a time, sometimes in two separate formations albeit with some intervals between patrols, would be more effective than constant cover by only one or two squadrons during the whole seventeen-hour daylight period. On the 28th it worked, but on the 29th, when the clouds cleared, the Luftwaffe sank five large passengers ships and three destroyers, with seven more destroyers damaged – largely in the intervals when no fighters were present.

Though on 30th May the weather again favoured the evacuation, it and bad planning killed one of 609 Squadron's pilots and might have killed many more. After taking off again from Biggin Hill with 213 Squadron at 14.20, 609 spent forty minutes and some 25 per cent of its fuel making rendezvous with other units and reaching the Dunkirk area. There it patrolled at 15,000 feet for a solid hour. There was no enemy, but down at 2–3,000 feet was a layer of thick haze; and just as this had prevented the Luftwaffe from operating, so now it menaced 609 Squadron's homecoming. Already short of petrol, Yellow section lost its way. Each with just two gallons remaining, Howell got down at Rochford, while Dawson and Dundas force-landed at Frinton-on-Sea, happily at a joint cost of only one damaged mainplane. But Desmond Ayre of Red section also lost his way. Though somehow his fuel carried him to Harwich, he there spun in to his death in the grounds of an explosives works at Oakley.

The remainder of the Squadron managed to put down just in time at Manston, the airfield nearest to the continent on the southeast tip of Kent. ('It was not funny,' recorded Beaumont, whose own fuel gauge had ceased to register over Dunkirk). Manston, though a valuable advanced base for the Dunkirk and later operations, at this moment, so far from being equipped to handle a continual influx of squadrons, scarcely possessed the personnel and equipment necessary to handle a single one with any speed. There were, for instance, just seven starter batteries. Yet from Manston, at 18.30, half of the original team grimly crossed the Channel again. This time they spent only half an hour on patrol and returned after sixty minutes direct to Northolt. There, no doubt, their colleagues told them about the first casualty the Squadron had sustained since its creation – the same man who had shared its first victory, back in February. After nine months of war, the score was a dismal one-all.*

According to the Germans, 31st May began with fog, but this cleared by the afternoon, and intercepted signals indicated that ships, not Dunkirk town and harbour, would be their target. Though in fact the *Stukas* (Ju 87 dive-bombers) were grounded all day, horizontal bombers assailed the shipping at half-hour intervals right through the afternoon, even if on this occasion they were so effectively engaged that only one ship was sunk by direct air attack. As for 609, this time it was ordered over to North Weald, whence it took off at 14.00 to act as 'top patrol' at 20,000 feet. That is to say ten of them did, for one of the flight commanders, Pip Barran, failed to start up and another pilot returned with engine trouble.

From the subsequent report it would seem that either the Squadron had been badly briefed, or else did not carry out its orders. And indeed the tragedy during all the days of the Dunkirk operation was that 609 was a team without a captain – sections and sometimes even individuals apparently acting quite independently. In normal parlance 'top patrol' (or cover) meant protection of lower formations from enemy fighter attack; yet now, it was reported, 'Red Section dived to 10,000 feet to investigate two bombers.' Of the three of them Red 2 (Russell) attacked a Heinkel 111, disabling one of its engines, and Red 3 (Overton) climbed back to patrol altitude, understanding he had been ordered to do so. Perhaps it was indeed the last order of his section leader and flight commander, Flight-Lieutenant 'Presser' Persse-Joynt, who was never seen again. Could it be that in these pre-mirror days the high turned-up collar of his Irvin jacket had really masked his

*Desmond Ayre's funeral was marked by the participation of the R.A.F. Central Band and by reversed arms—'the only full ceremonial funeral I was to see', comments R. F. Burgess, one of 609's Auxiliary Leading Aircraftmen. 'On later occasions there was neither time nor opportunity.'

attacker? 'Possibly,' says Overton, 'but I think the weather was too hot to wear one.'

Yellow Section was again composed of Howell, Dundas and Dawson, and it was one of the latter, probably Dawson, who after peeling off to investigate yet another aircraft down at 10,000 feet (which turned out to be friendly), had his attention directed by bursting A.A. shells to a Heinkel dropping bombs some way above him. This he probably destroyed after a full-throttle dive, finally losing it far out to sea beneath low cloud.

For the second patrol, starting at 19.00, only nine Spitfires were still serviceable. This time 111 Squadron provided the top cover while 609 accompanied 264 Squadron's Boulton-Paul Defiants at 10,000 feet. And on this occasion 609 tangled with enemy bombers and fighters simultaneously, with every one of its nine pilots engaged.

Leading the Squadron now, though only a Flying-Officer, was its American, 'Hack' Russell, and what he achieved during this evening action made him one of the heroes of the whole Dunkirk affair. That he was with the Squadron at all was a mystery, for according to the meagre records of the time he had, on 8th May, been posted away to 245 Squadron at Leconfield, only to rejoin 609, just a fortnight later, from 607 Squadron 'on instructions given to him by the Air Ministry'. He apparently spent that fortnight fighting the enemy very profitably in France, where 607 had been, so that now his combat experience as a pilot of 609 was unique.

This time there was no patrolling at all. As Russell and his eight followers approached, the air over Dunkirk was plumed with naval anti-aircraft shells bursting in a thick layer all the way between 10,000 and 15,000 feet. One had only to follow the main concentrations to locate the enemy bombers in sections of five or three, each escorted by fighters 1,000 feet above them. Russell, counting a formation of fifteen Heinkels and twenty Messerschmitt 109s,

* 264 Squadron. Just before and during the Dunkirk operation this squadron's Defiants enjoyed, if at considerable cost to themselves, a moment of glory thanks to taking the enemy by surprise. Thinking they were Hurricanes, with normal forward fire-power, he found himself being shot at from all angles by a gunner in a power-operated turret amidships.

led his little team round in a 180-degree climbing turn till it was alongside the bombers – all of which at once jettisoned their bombs. What followed was a truly magnificent display of air fighting by Red Leader (Russell) and his No. 2 ('Teeny' Overton).

First they quickly destroyed a Heinkel by making simultaneous beam attacks from opposite sides. Then Russell, finding a second Heinkel which had broken formation, sent this into the sea in flames. He was about to continue the slaughter when he saw his No. 3, Sergeant Bennett, attacking the same enemy plane. And by now the German fighters had come down, with one of them on Bennett's tail. At once Russell changed targets, and as soon as this Me 109 came into his sights, he fired from 100 yards range, allowing two rings deflection. It worked : his opponent lost six feet of his port wing and dived straight in. Meanwhile young 'Teeny' – so young, Stephen Beaumont told me thirty years later, that he 'still had puppy-fat' – had noticed just in time that he too had a 109 on his tail. There ensued the first dogfight in 609's history. Despite 'rolls off the top' and other aerobatics, neither contestant could get into a firing position for six minutes – when just for a moment the Messerschmitt turned too steeply to gain superior height, and Overton in a stall turn got him in his sights for a single second and opened fire from seventy yards range. It was enough : smoke poured from his opponent's engine and the plane dived into that insatiable sea.

Frankie Howell's Yellow section and Blue section, led by Peter Drummond-Hay, both climbed up to attack the Heinkels, but then Howell spotted a single Junkers 88, and Drummond-Hay a single Dornier 17, both in the act of bombing, and both went down again to attack these quarries. The Ju 88 in fact opened fire first, but this had ceased when Dawson attacked, and both its propellers slowed right up. Yellow 3 (Dawson or Dundas) reported : 'When we first saw the enemy, they were 5–7,000 feet above us and it took fifteen minutes to climb above them. Me 109s came up on our quarter but did not attack, and first I thought they were Hurricanes as I am sure they had R.A.F. roundels' – with small black crosses in the middle. After that he went off on a private investigation.

Drummond-Hay was credited with the destruction of his Dornier, and may himself have been saved by his No. 3, Buchanan, who hit one of three Me 109s as it came straight towards him, and immediately afterwards assailed a Heinkel 200 feet below and apparently already slightly damaged. After a full beam attack this jettisoned its bomb-load and headed for the coast with one engine out of action and undercarriage now fully down. But suddenly Buchanan's own engine juddered and almost stopped, and he lost 1,000 feet. Thinking it had been hit in his encounter with the Me 109, he himself was already headed for a forced landing at Dunkirk when the engine obligingly picked up again, and turning round he flew home and landed at Manston – undamaged.

But Blue 2 ('Pinky' Gilbert, the pal of 'Darkie' Little) was not saved.* However loath the Me 109s may have been to attack Yellow section, they picked off a Spitfire each from both Red and Blue. No one saw what happened to Gilbert, but saving the life of Red 3 (Sergeant Bennett) was the crowning achievement this day of the heroic 'Hack' Russell. Not only did he literally shoot an Me 109 off Bennett's tail with his last rounds of ammunition, but then seeing that the latter's engine was hit, he tried to nurse him all the way back to Hawkinge. Though Bennett did not quite make it, and landed in the sea three miles from the coast, Russell circled till he saw him floating in his Mae West, then 'flew to Dover and secured a rescue launch, which went out and picked Red 3 up'. (It was actually the minesweeper *Playboy*).

'Never was the cool splendour of an early summer morning less appreciated by the men on the beaches,' write the official R.A.F. chroniclers about 1st June. For the evacuation this was perhaps the worst day, and perhaps the most successful one for the Luftwaffe, which threw in all its serviceable aircraft and sank at least ten vessels, including three destroyers loaded with troops, apart from heavy casualties caused by newly positioned artillery batteries. 'Though many squadrons of Spitfires and Hurricanes were put up

---

* Bernard Little tells me: 'I have often wondered whether Pinky had a premonition. The night before he was killed he suddenly asked me if I had a Bible. This surprised me, for all the time we had roomed together he had never previously shown any interest in religion. However, I did have one, and tossed it across. Quietly he read through the psalm, *The Lord is my Shepherd*, and tossed it back. Then we went to sleep.'

... most of them tangled with Colonel Osterkamp's Me 109s and Lieutenant-Colonel Huth's Me 110s. Thus the *Stukas* were able once again to dive on the evacuation fleet.' So writes the author of *The Luftwaffe War Diaries*, which I recently translated.

It was also a black day for 609, which lost two more of its most cherished men. Down to nine aircraft, the Squadron again went on patrol in the afternoon and evening, though on each occasion just one section was engaged. In fact, on the first it was just two aircraft – 'Hack' Russell and 'Paul' Edge, for their No. 3 (Mitchell) had lost them on a turn.

'I was searching the sky for him,' Edge recalls thirty years afterwards, 'and momentarily drew abreast of Hack. In that precise moment an Me 110 must have crept up astern. I saw Hack, surrounded by bursting shells and tracer, pull up in a near-vertical climb, then fall off in a stall and commence a long slow spiral into the sea. I followed him down till it was obvious he was not in control, and then climbed hard. The Me 110 was still there, flying in a wide circle. I pulled the Spit hard round and tried a deflection shot, but its nose swung violently off-target because the four guns in the port wing failed to fire.' Despite this grave hindrance he repeated the attack, but then : 'Suddenly the Me 110 turned sharply and attacked head-on. It seemed he was deliberately trying to ram me, and with a closing speed of at least 400 m.p.h. a collision seemed imminent. I had only a split second to decide whether to pass over or under. Some intuition forced me to ram the stick forward, and he flashed overhead with only feet between us. Feeling less than semi-operational I went for the sea, and steering due west flew over several little boats ...'

This was 609's first dogfight with one of Goerings much-vaunted *Zerstörer* ('destroyers'). What no one seems to have told Edge till now is, that at the time *he* was credited as the destroyer, and his leader's avenger. For as the two planes hurtled towards each other 'Paul's' finger was on the firing button, and immediately afterwards the Me 110 turned on its back and plunged vertically into the haze just above the sea.

The second patrol once again saw the engagement of the Howell, Dundas and Dawson team, and it can be summarized sadly. The first two attacked and crippled two Heinkels, and Dawson was last seen doing the same. Then the Me 110s came down, and just in time the other two saw the Very lights, fired presumably by the Navy. Evidently Dawson did not.

After this day the evacuation was restricted to the hours of darkness, and finally ended on 4th June. Fighter patrols were thus only required at the vulnerable periods of dawn and dusk, and 609's last effort was in the evening of 2nd June by three complete novices led by Peter Drummond-Hay. One of these was John Bisdee (last service i/c rail party Scotland–Northolt), the other two Gordon Mitchell (who had flown operationally the day before for the first time), and Michael Appleby (who had not yet done so at all). Though these two had, with David Crook, been about the last pre-war Auxiliary officers to join the Squadron, they had only recently flown Spitfires for the first time on rejoining it from Flying Training School. And this afternoon the three had landed with their leader at Gravesend with the prospect of a perfunctory 'stooge' patrol of the Thames estuary – till the order was suddenly changed, and only they were available.

The day before, Marshal of the R.A.F. Lord 'Boom' Trenchard had appeared and given a pep talk. 'It made all the difference,' Bisdee recalls. 'Suddenly we were all in the R.F.C., "Boom" was behind me and nothing could go wrong.'

And nothing did. The war diary reports that with the four as 'above guard, 72 Squadron was able to attack the enemy bombers successfully, while the enemy fighters above our squadron (*sic*) did not dare go down to their rescue'. Perhaps they too sensed the presence of a fifth aircraft, invisible and invincible!

The 'miracle' had happened. So far from Goering winning his feather, 225,000 British and 112,000 Allied soldiers had been brought back to form the essential nucleus of an army of the future. For the first time since the German assault began, sixteen to eighteen R.A.F. fighter squadrons, though greatly outnumbered, had, by concentrating some 300 sorties a day in one area, helped to achieve a decisive result. They had done so at the cost of rather more than a hundred aircraft and eighty pilots. If their claims of 262 enemy aircraft destroyed was at least twice the actual figure –

and those of one squadron in particular were pure fantasy – at least it gave them confidence for the future.

As for 609 Squadron's claims, its existing intelligence reports omit to mention them, though in the day-to-day war diary they amount to three He 111, two Me 109, one Do 17 and one Me 110 'definite'. No one seems to have cared greatly, for people's minds were on the friends who had suddenly been removed for ever. To quote 'Paul' Edge: 'I have often felt since, that as pilots of an Auxiliary squadron we were unable to accept their loss with quite the same detached professionalism as most pilots of Regular squadrons would school themselves to do. After all, they had not only been fellow pilots, but also personal friends in civilian life over a long period. The war quite suddenly became grim and tragic.'

Of the eleven Auxiliary pilots who had followed Geoffrey Ambler to war station in August 1939, over one third – 'Presser' Persse-Joynt, Desmond Ayre, 'Pinky' Gilbert and Joseph Dawson – had been wiped out within three days. So had the American 'Hack' Russell, who was posthumously awarded the Squadron's first D.F.C. The man he helped to rescue, Sergeant Bennett, was taken wounded to an emergency hospital at Abbots Langley. 609's loss was one-sixteenth of Fighter Command's total. In all, eighteen of its pilots had helped the great procession of ships and boats to bring the army home to England. Before a comparable procession of ships could take an army back to France, four years were to elapse. By then only seven of the eighteen would still be living. Meanwhile Beaumont wrote home: 'We appear to be losing the war, though eventually, of course, we shan't'.

609 remained at Northolt for another month – a month of uncertainty about the enemy's plans, about the final outcome in France, about the coming fate of Britain. On 3rd June 92 Squadron joined 609 at Northolt, which now became provisionally linked with North Weald as a four-squadron Sector. Orders were for one squadron to be at immediate readiness, two at fifteen minutes availability, and the fourth at thirty. This meant no squadron had a release day, and all personnel had to be on the station from dawn till dusk. There was no privilege leave for the airmen, who had to spend most of their time at Dispersal, and both

they and their officers found that, compared with Scotland, the food in this 'Inner Austerity Zone' was poor.

'The main snag,' says one-time Leading Aircraftman Ron Burgess, 'was the time it took to get it – constant queues. The S.W.O. finally got tired of chasing erks dashing to the mess with no headgear or in overalls, and gave up the struggle to try and make Auxiliaries behave like his own Regulars.'

There were also alarums and excursions. Another 609 airman, Stan Waterson, reports : 'One of our first jobs at Northolt was filling sandbags to protect the Spitfires, which were three to a bay, and constructing a firing step at the back. Each of us was issued with a rifle and fifty rounds of ammo, and whether for practice or for real we were suddenly called out of bed at two a.m. and taken down to the bays in the truck. There we stood shivering on the firing step till the tannoy sounded the "all clear". We heard afterwards paratroops were expected, but whether this was "pukka gen" we never found out.' (Evidently *someone* in authority believed it, for Frankie Howell was sent up to look for them in the air.)

Despite all the Readiness, no action resulted, though on 9th June three sections of 609, after refuelling at Tangmere, escorted 'important' convoys in the direction of Cherbourg and Havre' – sent, it would seem, to try to take off the ill-fated 51st Division. Then, between 11th and 13th June, Winston Churchill flew twice to France in the hope of persuading the French Government to go on fighting, and on both occasions the West Riding Squadron had the honour of being picked as his aerial bodyguard. (I think I am right in saying that these were the only times that Spitfires, unlike Hurricanes, landed in France before 1944).

On the first occasion the P.M. took with him Anthony Eden (then Secretary of State for War), and Generals Dill (C.I.G.S.) and Ismay. With the enemy almost at the gates of Paris, the French Government was in process of leaving the capital, and the Prime Minister, Reynaud, offered to receive the party at Briare, not far from Orleans.

'The German aircraft were now reaching far down into the Channel,' Churchill records in *The Second World War*, and we had to make a still wider sweep . . . The Flamingo had an escort of twelve Spitfires.'

In fact there were only nine, flown by Flight-Lieutenant Barran, Flying-Officers Howell, Drummond-Hay, Dundas and Blayney, and Pilot-Officers Overton, Buchanan, Mitchell and Appleby.* The previous day they had flown to Warmwell near the Dorset coast, where they now made rendezvous with the Prime Minister's Flamingo from Hendon – cruising speed 150 m.p.h.

'The Spitfires did not like the low revs,' recalls Jarvis Blayney, 'and from time to time we had to break away to clear the engines. Eventually we landed at a small airfield, where the aircraft seemed to sink up to the wings in a lake of grass. After a long delay a vehicle with a white flag appeared and indicated where we were to park.'

'There were a few Frenchmen about,' Churchill continues, 'and soon a colonel arrived in a motor car . . . dull and unresponsive. I realised immediately how very far things had fallen even since we were in Paris the week before. After an interval we were conducted to the château, where we found M. Reynaud, Marshal Pétain, General Weygand, the Air General Vuillemin, and some others, including the relatively junior General de Gaulle . . . Hard by on the railway was the Headquarters train, in which some of our party were accommodated. The château possessed but one telephone, in the lavatory. It was kept very busy, with long delays and endless shouted repetitions. At seven o'clock we entered into conference.'

Fortunes of war had deprived 609 of the night out in Paris enjoyed the week before by the Hurricane pilots of that senior Auxiliary squadron, No. 601 (see *The Flying Sword*, MacDonald 1964). According to Blayney, all they could find on the airfield was 'a wooden hut festooned with nude pin-ups and lots of champagne bottles, all empty'. Appleby, however, recalls that the nine pilots discovered not far away a wayside *bistro* catering to the needs of an endless stream of refugees in mattress-covered cars. 'Full of *vino* we then returned to the train.' It seems well that they did so before those in conference, for according to one of them

* Evidently Churchill's aircraft recognition was not very good. In the original edition of *The Second World War* he referred to his escort as 'Hurricanes', which he had had previously. Michael Appleby put this right for subsequent editions by writing to the publishers.

'there were no blankets for the pilots, but plenty for the generals and politicians. 609 soon put that inequality right.' One of the politicians sharing the train was Anthony Eden, who greeted the pilots next morn *without* apparently having suffered from cold.

'Lack of suitable petrol made it impossible for the twelve (*sic*) Spitfires to escort us . . . It was urgently necessary to get back home. Accordingly we started alone . . . As we approached the coast the skies cleared and presently became cloudless. Eight thousand feet below us on our right was Havre, burning . . . Presently I noticed some consultations going on with the captain, and immediately after we dived to a hundred feet or so . . . I learned later that they had seen two German aircraft below us firing at fishing boats. We were lucky that their pilots did not look upwards.'

In the absence of any official 609 record confirming its failure to protect the Prime Minister and the other war leaders on this occasion, I have closely interrogated the three of the nine fighter pilots who are still alive as to the cause. Jarvis Blayney supports Winston :

'Total lack of fuelling facilities on the spot caused us great concern. Eventually in the dim distance we spied a bowser moving towards the little landing ground, but the driver promptly put this into the ditch. Was he, we wondered, a Fifth Columnist?'

Though a supply of 100-octane petrol (also some champagne, later appreciatively shared by ground staff N.C.O.s) was eventually obtained from an R.A.F. unit * still in France, Michael Appleby states that another trouble was a total lack of starter batteries, with the result that, to get off at all, the pilots had to act in pairs to start each other's engines with cranking handles. 'Frankie Howell and I were the last off,' he says. 'I got his engine going, then he cranked mine and rushed back and took off before his own engine overheated. Had my engine stopped . . .' Clearly the Squadron could only get away in driblets – which accounts for the fact that the recollection of my third pilot, 'Teeny' Overton, is limited. 'I personally put up rather a "black",' he says, 'by losing the Squadron and having to land on Jersey to refuel –

* Probably No. 73 Squadron, the last fighter squadron to be withdrawn on June 18th.

inferior petrol from four-gallon cans, but superior brandy stuffed into cockpit spaces.'

Though the West Riding Squadron can clearly be exonerated, it is a spine-chilling thought that on this day the political convictions of a single French transport driver and/or the absence of starter batteries for nine Merlin engines might well have caused the early elimination of Hitler's arch-opponent, and so perhaps have altered the whole outcome of the war.

Be all that as it may, only one day afterwards 609 was chosen again for the same mission. This time for his final, desperate confrontation with the French government, now withdrawn to Tours, the Prime Minister took with him Lords Halifax and Beaverbrook, plus again General Ismay. It was to be his last visit to France for four years almost to a day.

'The weather was cloudless, and we sailed over in the midst of our Spitfire squadron, making however a rather wider sweep to the southward than before. Arrived over Tours, we found the airport had been heavily bombed the night before, but we and all our escort landed smoothly in spite of the craters.'

Beaumont, Edge and Bisdee now formed part of the team, led it seems by Howell. And if the nine pilots cherished any hopes of relaxing on the sunny banks of the Loire, they were quickly doomed to disappointment. During the four hours they were on the ground, deep in France, they remained at instant notice to take off in defence of both the British and French governments against enemy air, or possibly even ground attack – this time aided by a Hudson full of starter batteries.

'Immediately one sensed the increasing degeneration of affairs,' continued Winston. 'No one came to meet us or seemed to expect us. We borrowed a service car from the station commander and motored into the city, making for the Prefecture, where it was said the French Government had their headquarters. No one of consequence was there . . . It being nearly two o'clock, I insisted upon luncheon . . . We found a café, which was closed, but after explanations we obtained a meal.'

As for the pilots, John Bisdee reports :

'We went into the dispersal hut under an archway painted with the words *BAPTÊME DE L'AIR*. Some baptism! Inside, the atmosphere was that of a flying club, with omelettes all round, and one period telephone to act as ops, radio microphone and for ringing up the members' girl friends. At the end of the day, having been filled up with *"Essence B"* by mechanics with a death wish – they sat on the wings with Gauloises cigarettes dangling from their lips – we took off for home.'

Churchill's negotiations with the French, which included a telegram of appeal to President Roosevelt, finally turned out hopeless, and four days later France sought an armistice with Hitler. Four hundred captured German pilots were liberated, 'and had to be shot down a second time'. And Weygand had actually told Churchill it was wrong to keep *any* squadrons back in England! As he left, Winston says, 'I saw General de Gaulle standing stolid and expressionless at the doorway. Greeting him, I said in a low tone, in French: *"L'homme du destin"* . . . The Spitfires were already in the air, and I slept soundly on our swift and uneventful journey home.'

The Spitfires were indeed in the air, and had been so for half an hour owing, says 'Paul' Edge, to the Prime Minister's car, as they could see, becoming bogged down by refugees on the way to the airport. 'It was touch and go whether our petrol would last as far as the south coast of England, and by the greatest good luck we were not attacked. The Flamingo flew at only 150 m.p.h., and with props at full-coarse pitch and wallowing along at only 1800 revs we felt hopelessly vulnerable.'

But they 'made' it despite the *'Essence B'*. This, Bisdee emphatically maintains, was not designed for Spitfires. 'At full boost our Merlin engines nearly jumped out of their frames – the only thing was to "cruise" off the ground. When we got back we hastily drained the noxious mixture into cans, but it even choked the carburettor of my Ford.'

It is an ill wind, however, that blows *no* good. '100 octane' was not good for car engines either, and its use for road transport heavily punishable by both military and civil authorities. The voice of Gordon Sudworth, which up in Scotland had produced sobs of sympathy and triple the regulation quantity of petrol coupons for his pilot heroes, down here in the 'Inner Austerity Zone' cut no ice at all. Consequently, with no diminution in the number of cars, '*Essence B*' was a godsend that should have kept them running, almost legitimately, for a considerable time.

'We secretly buried two fifty-gallon drums at the back of Dispersal,' G. E. Bradbury, then one of the Squadron's riggers, recalls. 'Method of use : Lift sod and insert stirrup pump. As far as I know the drums may still be there, because we moved away long before they were empty.'

When three weeks later, on 4th July 1940, the West Riding Squadron was ordered west, it is possible that some of its members thought, after the severities of Northolt and the tragic losses sustained, that the immediate future held prospect of comparative ease and comfort. After all, it was in the south-east that the air defence of Britain had always been concentrated, and as expected most of the action so far had involved the squadrons stationed there. At the time of Dunkirk there was no coastal radar chain west of Portsmouth, and in the west there was just one isolated fighter sector, at Filton, designed for the protection of Bristol and the Bristol Aircraft Company. The whole peaceful countryside of Hampshire, Wiltshire, Dorset, Somerset, Devon and Cornwall was relatively untroubled by the sound of aero engines.

In any case (these members may have argued) the Germans, since chasing the B.E.F. home from the Continent, had left England virtually unmolested. Though the British Empire, since 17th June, might have become the only opponent that Germany (and now Italy) had left, it was rumoured that Hitler rather approved of the institution and would like to make peace. If not, why had he not struck at once before Britain's puny aircraft industry could deliver a few more Spitfires and Hurricanes, and the flying schools train a few more pilots to fly them ?

One reason, of course, was that the Luftwaffe itself was not ready. Swift and successful though the campaign in the west had been, it left many of its units badly in need of a rest and refit at home. Furthermore, if full advantage was to be taken of the newly won proximity to English targets, it meant re-deploying the bulk of the German air force over a whole new string of airfields stretching from Holland to Brittany, with all the problems of administration and supply that that entailed.

Till recently such a situation had not been envisaged by Britain's defensive planners, who had provided against air attack from Germany itself, or at worst from parts of the Low Countries. So now the coastal radar chain was hastily extended to cover the rest of the south coast, a new Group (No. 10) was being created, with new Sector operations rooms, and No. 11 Group's most westerly Sector, Middle Wallop, earmarked for transfer to it.

It was to Middle Wallop, situated about half-way between Andover and Salisbury, that 609 was now posted – at first the only day fighter squadron in this vital Sector. If 11 Group was going to be outnumbered, 10 Group, with far less aircraft, would be far more so. The demarcation line in theory separating them would cross the coast somewhere west of the Isle of Wight, and opposite each would be ranged an independent *Luftflotte* or 'air fleet'. From Holland to the Seine would stretch *Luftflotte 2*, from the Seine to Brest *Luftflotte 3*. Between them, by the third week in July, they would comprise some 1,130 long-range bombers, 320 dive-bombers, 800 single-engined fighters, 250 twin-engined fighters, plus long- and short-range reconnaissance aircraft. The operational experience of their two commanders, Kesselring and Sperrle, went back respectively to the Polish campaign and the Spanish civil war.

Yet although Goering had already issued his 'General Directions for the Operation of the Luftwaffe against England' as early as 30th June, the die had still not been finally cast as late as 19th July – ten days after the air battle had in fact commenced. On that day, at a grand celebration in Berlin to mark Germany's victory in the west, and with Goering himself gleaming and glittering in his fantastic white uniform of *Reichsmarschall*, Kesselring and Sperrle, with some army generals, were promoted to the rank of field-marshal. Yet commenting on this after the war, Kesselring wrote : 'I am today perfectly convinced that none of us would have been made field-marshals after the western campaign had Hitler not thought that peace was now probable.' And the *Führer* himself on this occasion said : 'I can see no compulsive reason for continuing the struggle . . . If we do so, it will end with the complete destruction of one of the two combatants. Mr. Churchill may believe that it will be Germany. I know that it will be England.''

Mr. Churchill, of course, saw a *very* compulsive reason for continuing the struggle : the need to rid the world of Hitler himself and all his evil works. For that purpose the priority weapon on which he had for the moment to rely was Fighter Command. On 9th July (and the number was scarcely changed a month later), this weapon comprised nineteen operational Spitfire squadrons and twenty-seven operational Hurricane squadrons, plus six squadrons of Blenheims and two of Defiants. In all they represented some 700 fighter aircraft distributed, however, between Kent and the Orkneys. But in 10 Group (including Middle Wallop, still to be transferred, if excluding a single squadron at Pembrey in Wales), there were just four Hurricane and two Spitfire squadrons. The latter were 609, and 234 at St. Eval in Cornwall.

In the supply of aircraft 609 seems, at this vital instant, to have done rather well. On 4th June the official Fighter Command record could show a total of just 331 serviceable Hurricanes and Spitfires, with thirty-six replacements available to all squadrons from Storage Units. On 5th June 609 received six of these, and on 7th June one more – or 20 per cent of the lot. By the end of June, moreover, all its Spitfires had become far superior aeroplanes. 'Quite unheralded,' states the war diary, 'a crew of De Havilland fitters descended on the Squadron and proceeded to convert the V.P. airscrews to C.S.' With the help of 609's own fitters the whole conversion took eight days,* but 'the improvement in performance is astounding'. V.P.=Variable Pitch; C.S.= Constant Speed. Briefly the advantage was that, instead of depending on a manually operated two-speed 'gearbox', the pilot now had a power system that was at once automatic and more versatile. Operationally it meant that our fighters had in one important respect caught up with the Messerschmitt 109E, which had enjoyed 'C.S.' from the start. Though both our fighters were more manoeuvrable, and the maximum speed of the Spitfire was

---

* According to 'Darkie' Hanson this conversion took place during Dunkirk, he and his colleagues getting only ten hours' sleep during the week, and working with bare feet to stay awake.

similar, the Me 109 still surpassed it in climb – and also dive, when the Rolls Royce Merlin engine, owing to 'g', was prone to cut, unlike the Daimler-Benz direct fuel-injection engine (today a feature of some Mercedes cars).

The pilots of 609 Squadron, to whom these more mettlesome steeds now stood available, were no longer quite the same band of brothers whose laughter, seemingly long ago, had added to the gaiety of nocturnal Edinburgh. One of them who (pursued by the caustic comments of his friends) had gone away from there to undergo an operation on a torn ligament sustained in getting out of bed, recorded his reaction on returning after seven weeks. I quote from *Spitfire Pilot* by David Crook (Faber & Faber, 1942):

'A great change has come over the Squadron . . . The old easy-going outlook on life had vanished, and everybody now seemed to realize that war was not the fairly pleasant affair that it had always seemed hitherto. The general mood now appeared to be one of rather grim determination . . . There were several new pilots to replace the Dunkirk losses.'

Three new pilots – Pilot-Officers Curchin and Miller, and Sergeant Feary – had indeed arrived on 11th June (though with the commentary, 'None are trained'), plus Flying-Officer Goodwin who had come three weeks earlier from another Auxiliary squadron, No. 605. Of the twelve Auxiliary officers who had gone to war, only Barran, Beaumont, Drummond-Hay, Little, Edge, Blayney and Dundas were left – though recently strengthened by the return to the Squadron, after their training with the Central Flying School at Little Rissington, of Mitchell, Appleby and Crook. Of similar age to these last (i.e. about twenty-five), and virtually 'Auxiliaries by association', were the V.R.s Bisdee and Buchanan; while last but by no means least were the young regular Overton and the very experienced Howell. The total – fourteen operational and four non-operational pilots – not only reflected the terrible shortage of trained fighter pilots which prevailed at this time, but was itself two below the average. In the whole of Fighter Command on 15th June there were just 1,094 pilots.

In retrospect it is a little surprising that this crippled squadron, bereft of the leadership of an Ambler in its hour of need, and decimated at Dunkirk, was not, like some other squadrons, sent away to recoup its strength (i.e. allow itself to be rebuilt from scratch) in some quiet part of the country. That it remained in the front line and preserved its corporate entity can only have been due to official awareness of its basic fibre – the crystallization of the spirit that had created it and fused it into something that was more than the sum of its members. Though I have only got to know him now, a whole generation afterwards, it is as clear as a bell that one of the basic props on which 609 at this period rested was its very first pilot and second officer, Stephen Beaumont. By dint of his calm courage, integrity and encyclopaedic knowledge of Squadron history and personnel, he must have been a sort of 'Big Ben' that always went on reliably ticking. The other two props were the flight commanders, Pip Barran and Frankie Howell (who had inherited 'A' flight from Persse-Joynt). Of Howell 'Teeny' Overton writes:

'I often wonder whether there has been a full appreciation of what this quiet and remarkable man meant to 609 in the early days of the "real" war. I believe that, for some time in the summer of 1940, he was the sheet anchor for the flying side of 609.'

It was Howell who, on 29th June, had led Overton and Dundas on a three-man reconnaissance of airfields in northern France, when he surprisingly reported: No aircraft sighted in air or on ground; all landing grounds seen studded with bomb craters – except at Abbeville, where they had seen some Heinkels, and 'A.A. fire was fairly accurate'. Three days later – just before the Squadron's move from Northolt – a repeat recce by the Squadron at full strength was equally negative, and may have given rise to murmurs of 'What are we worried about?' In passing, it is noteworthy that (bar Dunkirk) these were 609's first-ever offensive sorties over enemy territory – and also the last for nearly a year.

For David Crook such a sortie must have been a double strain, it being his first operational sortie of any kind. To increase range they landed to refuel at Hawkinge near Folkestone, 'where we stood around and smoked cigarettes incessantly and made some rather forced conversation, and suffered from that unpleasant empty feeling in the tummy'. Fortunately interception by enemy fighters, expected any time after reaching Rouen from the east, did not materialize. Once or twice, however, the Spitfires were rocked by '*flak*' – an experience so strange that Bernard Little has recently confessed : 'At first I thought the black puffs that kept appearing were balloons . . . but soon realized the true facts and adopted appropriate evasive tactics'.

One other pilot on this day was making his maiden sortie with the Squadron : H. S. ('George') Darley, its brand new commanding officer. His arrival, immediately preceding the move to Middle Wallop, was a good augury for an unknown future. This 'little dynamo', as John Bisdee describes him, was to shake 609 about as much as Dunkirk had done, though this time positively. When, twenty-eight years later, Darley made his speech at the Reunion described in the Prologue, there were loud cries that he should remove his jacket, and he did so. The affectionate allusion was to his first pep talk on taking over the Squadron, when he made the same gesture while challenging any member thereof to fight should he disagree with what he, the new C.O., was about to say.

What this twenty-seven-year-old Regular did, in effect, say, was that 609's pilots were a miserable and ignorant lot, who had yet to benefit from their unhappy war-time experience to date. They were not, however, going to remain that way, if he, their new C.O., had anything to do with it. And he was going to have a lot to do with it.

'Initially we couldn't stand the sight of the man,' says 'Teeny' Overton. 'But this was, I believe, due to the state of the Squadron's morale and the fact that he was determined to alter this, and quickly. It wasn't long before our attitude changed to great respect for what he was doing for all of us'. John Bisdee adds : 'He immediately set up a programme of practice quarter attacks, with himself as the elusive target'. And Beaumont : 'He gave the men and the young pilots hell, but couldn't have been nicer to us older ones.'

At this fateful moment Darley was, in fact, an inspired choice. He could speak with the authority born of having held a commission since 1932, of service in Aden and more recently in France, but perhaps even more so because of his previous experience as flying instructor and/or adjutant of two other Auxiliary squadrons, 602 and 611.

'If there was a reason for choosing me (and I hope there was),' he tells me, 'it was because of my awareness of problems peculiar to such squadrons, which were small communities of personal friends who had probably grown up together, and in which losses were especially keenly felt. Understandably, the general atmosphere in 609 was depressed, which did not help the younger pilots. The basic need was to restore morale by improving the kill/loss ratio.'

It would take Darley all of July and part of August before he fully succeeded, for with 609 Squadron remaining in the front line, 'it became a question of training while we fought'. About the ground staff he adds :

'By this time 609's Auxiliary airmen had become fully integrated with its Regular element, had acquired comparable skills, and as with the pilots I made no distinction between the two. Every man amongst them was as keen as mustard, and I do not recall ever having had to read the "riot act", collectively or individually. In the end the whole Squadron ran on its own momentum, and I only had to use the "control column" now and again !'

The move to the south-west on 4th/5th July required the services of a Harrow transport aircraft and a number of coaches, and was assisted once again by at least one of the two White Horse whisky vehicles requisitioned by Geoffrey Ambler long ago for the move to Drem. It was also complicated, according to the war diary, by 'an incredible number of conflicting instructions issued from H.Q. No. 11 Group'. With various trusted airmen as usual driving their cars, the pilots themselves were directed to fly their Spitfires, not to Middle Wallop, but to the advance coastal base of Warmwell, where the Harrow also landed. This, says Darley, was owing to an S.O.S. from the Navy. Portland had been bombed, 'and a gin factory, it was rumoured, damaged. Our move to Warmwell was to prevent further uncivilized aggression'.

Gin, however, was not the only liquid casualty, for G. E. Bradbury, one of the airmen in the Harrow, recalls seeing 'oil tanks' blazing on Portland Bill – though this may have been Atlantic convoy OA 178, which lost four vessels sunk and nine damaged.

For Bradbury it started a chain of personal misfortunes. First he slipped on descending from the aircraft, which tore his pants to above the knee. This in turn reminded him that his 'best blue' had been left beneath the mattress at Northolt. And finally, after the station commander had indicated that nothing was 'too good' for Auxiliary airmen, they were led to a row of tents.

In the end the Squadron was split up, one servicing flight only being based at Warmwell, from which in general one flight of Spitfires would operate, though based at Middle Wallop. With Warmwell some fifty miles away to the south-west, near Weymouth, it is hardly surprising that Adjutant Gordon Sudworth wrote: 'There may be some good reason for this, but it certainly reduces the efficiency of the Squadron as a whole'. That my own predecessor as I.O., Reginald MacKay, managed to produce reports with pilots landing at both bases, is remarkable.

Middle Wallop itself, though a Sector station, was only just being completed, with 300 workers (says Stan Waterson) still around, and 609 Dispersal (according to R. F. Burgess) centred 'in an old cottage beside the road at the end of the field'. Squadron-Leader and Mrs. Darley inhabited the adjacent house, where (Luftwaffe permitting) tea and cakes were available to pilots each day on the lawn. But in the weeks ahead both air crew and ground crew almost forgot the meaning of the word 'leisure', and for this there were several reasons. One was that the hours of daylight, during which air defence had to be available, at this time of year lasted for twenty out of the twenty-four (03.30 till 23.30). A second was that 609, itself deficient in qualified pilots, was at first virtually the only squadron in the Sector to provide such defence. And of course a third was complete ignorance of what the enemy was about to do. Stephen Beaumont says he can scarcely remember the Officers' Mess: 'We were either flying, at readiness, or asleep'. And for the airmen, Waterson adds:

'We started the routine of sleeping under canvas at Dispersal point every other night, and some mornings were up so early that it was still dark, but had to wait till first light before starting up the engines in case we attracted some Germans returning from a late night raid.'

What the enemy was about to do was not very clearly known

even to himself. Compared with earlier campaigns the planning for the subjugation of Britain was remarkably leisurely – it being hoped, no doubt, that her government would still respond to the *Führer's* peace feelers. Only on 30th June, a fortnight after France had asked for an armistice, did Goering issue his General Directions for the Operation of the Luftwaffe against England. This rather imprecise document was supplemented on 11th July, when he confirmed that Channel convoys were now permissible targets (once the latter had only been warships). Five days later, on 16th July, Hitler at last ordered 'a landing operation against England to be prepared and, if necessary, carried out.' But it was not till 2nd August that Goering's final orders for *Adlertag* – the Luftwaffe's knock-out blow against the British fighter arm – were proclaimed.

Meanwhile the Luftwaffe, using only some ten per cent of its operational strength, was to spend a month probing the British defences by day and night, reconnoitring future targets like airfields, and above all attacking ports and convoys. In the first nine days of July Falmouth, Plymouth, Portland, Weymouth and Dover were all bombed, and seven attacks made on Channel convoys. One of these, as we have seen, was on Atlantic convoy OA 178, which had immediate repercussions not only for 609, but for Fighter Command as a whole. In future, by Churchill's order, convoys would be given a standing patrol of six fighter aircraft – to be reinforced as soon as a German formation was reported approaching. The strain on the defence (some 600 sorties a day) at once became enormous, as did the scope for enemy chicanery. With the initiative entirely his, it was quite a simple matter to lure the reserve British fighters into the air with a few decoy aircraft, then make the attack while they were refuelling; or alternatively to pounce on them from up-sun or out of cloud with unsuspected fighter formations. Whatever the tactics, the British fighters, because they were scattered and had to maintain a standing patrol over every convoy, were almost invariably outnumbered in a ratio of up to 10:1, while their opponents attacked at any chosen moment with virtually any chosen strength. Furthermore, with the target only a short flying time from the German bases, it was essential that the delay between reporting and interception should be reduced to a minimum. Hence the deployment of fighters, in flight or squadron strength, at the advanced coastal bases of Manston, Hawkinge and Warmwell.

It was from Warmwell that 609's first engagement of this phase took place on 9th July – one day before the Battle of Britain, according to most historians, officially began, and a regrettably typical example of what the Squadron was to learn to expect from its adversaries. David Crook recalls that the cloud was so low that when he and Peter Drummond-Hay flew down below it from Wallop early in the morning, they frightened two cyclists into the ditch. 'B' flight then spent eight hours in a tent dripping with rain till 18.30, when Green section – Drummond-Hay, Crook and Appleby – were ordered off to patrol Weymouth. After forty-five minutes Peter, rather fed up, asked permission to land. This was refused, and immediately afterwards Sector Controller reported a formation of Ju 87 dive-bombers. These were sighted amongst the clouds fifteen miles out to sea, and at once the section went to intercept.

'I was flying last in line,' wrote David, 'when to my intense surprise and dismay I saw at least nine Me 110s about 2000 feet above us. They were just starting to dive and overtaking us rapidly. If we were not jolly quick we should all be dead in a few seconds. I immediately shouted desperately, "Look out behind!" But they both continued straight on at the bombers ahead. I have never felt so helpless in my life. At that moment the leading Messerschmitt opened fire at me and I saw his shells and tracer bullets going past just above my head . . . I made a violent turn and dived into a layer of cloud. Emerging at probably over 400 m.p.h. I saw a Ju 87 just ahead.'

He engaged this, then a Me 110, and finally another Ju 87. They were his very first combats, and the second 87 did not get away:

'The flames enveloped the whole machine and he went straight down for about 5000 feet, till he was just a shapeless mass of wreckage. Absolutely fascinated, I saw him hit the sea with a great burst of white foam. Afterwards I was rather surprised to reflect that my only feeling had been one of considerable elation . . .

'A moment later I saw another Spitfire flying home on a very erratic course, obviously keeping a very good look behind. I joined up with it and recognised Michael, and together we bolted for the English coast like a couple of startled rabbits. I made a perfectly bloody landing . . . I got out to talk to Michael and found my hand was quite shaky, and even my voice was unsteady.'

Michael Appleby had left his radio set in the 'transmit' position, and only switched it over in time to hear Crook shout 'Messerschmitt!' Whipping round, he found three Me 110s on his tail, and just managed to fight his way clear at the cost of two spins. About a mile away he saw 'a great flurry of machines, which must have been Peter's last effort against an overwhelming number of Messerschmitts. Knowing Peter,' adds David, 'I bet he put up a hell of a fight.' It seems that Peter too had left his radio set on 'transmit'. Stephen Beaumont recorded in his diary that he and others searched the sea for an hour and a half in vain.

Once again the loss of a friend was even more poignant when that friend had also shared a room. Back at Middle Wallop next day, David went up to it:

'Peter's towel was still in the window, where he had thrown it during our hurried dressing eighteen hours before. Now he was lying in the cockpit of his wrecked Spitfire at the bottom of the English Channel . . . I took my things and went to sleep in Gordon's room next door.'

But the young man's cup was still not full. He and Peter Drummond-Hay had arranged after duty on the fateful day to visit their wives in London, and at lunch time the latter's telephoned to ask why Peter had not rung up to confirm. Their flight commander, Pip Barran, had to tell her, and David went to London alone. When he returned next day, both Pip and Gordon were also dead.

Once more the scene had been some fifteen miles off Portland, and again it was 'B' flight that was involved. After dawn readiness at Warmwell, its five aircraft had been handed over at breakfast time by Stephen Beaumont to Philip Barran, and soon afterwards were called into the air in defence of another convoy. They reached it just as a string of Ju 87 dive-bombers were going down to attack it in line astern. Ordering Green section – just Bernard

Little and young Johnny Curchin – to act as a pathetically small rearguard, Barran straight away led Blue section – himself, Gordon Mitchell and Jarvis Blayney – against the attacking planes. Again it was the No. 3 (Blayney) who in vain called out a warning as he himself broke away on seeing tracer overtake him. Thereafter he intercepted, and at least damaged one of the dive-bombers before again being attacked from the rear, and eventually found himself patrolling in solitude a smoking ship.

'Then,' he recalls, 'Pip came into view, with his aircraft trailing white vapour. The hood was back, and as his airscrew stopped rotating he baled out and I saw him in the sea.'

Like other squadrons, 609 at this time still depended on H.F. radio sets, whose limited range and reliability sometimes had tragic consequences. Now the two pilots of Green section failed to hear the warning from control that a second enemy formation had appeared on the plotting table, and had neither strength nor position to affect the issue as an estimated twenty Me 109s swept down out of the sun.

'I found myself amongst three or four Junkers diving down to sea level,' Bernard Little reported afterwards, 'and fired into the undersurface of one of them. It dropped away on its back with pieces flying off it, but then being attacked by Me 109s I was unable to watch further.'

Curchin fought a similar action (his first), and also circled the bombed ship. All three survivors saw Pip Barran bale out, and did their best to inform control and get a rescue launch sent to the spot. Eventually they saw the Navy pick him up – but, wounded and burned, he had been too long in the water and died on being lifted on board. An air and sea search for Gordon Mitchell was negative, and his body was only found much later off the Isle of Wight.

Referring to such events only a few months afterwards when writing *Spitfire Pilot*, David Crook was still bound by the rules of security that prevented him using people's surnames, and with only nicknames or Christian names as clues, I only identified some of these comrades of long ago by asking the few survivors – of whom the author himself, sad to say, is not one. 'Pip', however, was fairly easy, and this is what Crook wrote about him :

'He never hesitated for a second at rugger or anything else in his life, and did not hesitate now in this last and greatest moment.'

And about Gordon :

'We were at school together, and he, Michael and I had spent the whole (*sic*) war together . . . I just could not get used to the idea that we should not see him again . . . He was a delightful person, a very amusing and charming companion, and one of the most generous people. He was also a brilliant athlete, a Cambridge hockey blue and Scots international. He played any game with natural ease and grace.'

The quotation probably gives an idea of the ties that bound even the younger Auxiliary pilots together. But of the loss to the Squadron of Pip Barran, Crook added : 'He was more than a mere member of the Squadron; you might almost say he was the foundation stone upon which it was built. He was easily the outstanding personality of us all.' Michael Appleby adds : 'He had the gift of making one feel a much better person than one was.'

Philip Barran had in fact been on continuous duty as 'B' flight commander ever since the war began. After his recent Dunkirk experiences he was asked by the new C.O. if he would like a rest. 'He answered that he wished to stay on with the Squadron,' says Darley. 'I was certainly glad to keep him, for he was by far the most competent pilot and leader amongst the Auxiliaries, and his posting would have been a severe blow to the already shaken morale. But when he was shot down, I did ask myself whether it could have been due to tiredness.'

Despite 432 sorties on this 11th of July, Fighter Command's losses were only four. 609's therefore represented half of them, and one wonders whether Philip Barran's life might have been saved had British fighters been equipped at this time with inflatable dinghies, as were the German ones. Unfortunately these and other aids to rescue, including adequate numbers of R.A.F. launches, still lay in the future.

Other things were wrong too. One was the Sector Controller's bitterly resented practice – though perhaps it could not always be helped – of sending up what 'George' Darley called 'penny packets' of fighters against much larger formations. Another was sheer ignorance of proper tactics on the part of both the Sector Controller and the formation leader. 'We were thrown in at the deep end,' says Bernard Little. 'Those of us lucky to live long enough gained experience in combat.' The lesson 'Beware of the Hun in the Sun', later hammered home into every new fighter pilot as standard practice, implied that the Luftwaffe, rich in campaign experience as it was, knew how to exploit the orb long before we did – especially in that summer of 1940 when it shone so much more than usually. Sector operations tables, while plotting the positions of our own and enemy aircraft, only later 'plotted' the position of that governing factor, the sun. Also not fully realized was the advantage of superior altitude, or the fact that it took the Mark I Spitfire thirteen minutes to climb up to 20,000 feet.

Then there were the traditional, numbered, modes of attack which, like other squadrons, 609 under Ambler had practised in the early part of the war. The fighters would form up in line astern and attack the bomber (it was always a 'bomber') in succession, each breaking away in standard fashion and offering a target to the enemy rear gunner as he did so. The possibility of enemy *fighter* intervention featured in the scheme as little as did the possibility of enemy occupation of the opposite Channel coast.

All these deficiencies Squadron-Leader Darley, after first-hand study of enemy methods, began to put right as swiftly as was possible under the circumstances. 'Each combat,' he says, 'produced its own lessons, the fault in the past having been the inability to draw the correct conclusions.' In particular, the conception of what constituted a fighter formation was due for fundamental change. 'There had to be a flexible pattern, with a protective section weaving up-sun and higher than the main body.' Like the Luftwaffe pattern, in fact.

Most important of all, he insisted on team-work – the need, whatever the size of the formation involved, to fight it out together:

'I pointed out that if eight of our aircraft were engaged by sixteen of the enemy, the odds would be 2 : 1 (in actual practice an unusually low ratio). If however four of our aircraft, willingly or unwillingly, left the formation, the odds would be 4 : 1 – a ratio that might spell *finito* for the remaining four.' And to drive home the lesson : 'I made it abundantly clear that I would not welcome personal "aces". As far as I was concerned, the only figures that counted were Squadron ones, and an immediate and lasting improvement in the kill/loss ratio.'

It would be achieved, quite astoundingly, but not quite yet. In the process Squadron-Leader 'George' Darley went through the phases of being hated, held in awe, and finally loved. Of the second phase Michael Appleby recalls : 'As C.O. his authority was enormous; yet when I met him again after the war, I was surprised that he seemed to be younger than I was.'

609 improved the kill/loss ratio slightly during the two days following the loss of Barran and Mitchell. On 12th July Howell, Edge and Curchin attacked and damaged a lone Heinkel 111 in foggy weather; on the 13th Dundas and Miller, while searching for a convoy not (as was frequently the case) in the position reported, got involved together with Hurricanes of 238 Squadron in a battle with Dornier 17s and Messerschmitt 110s, claiming one of the latter destroyed and one of the former probably destroyed. But on the 18th both Howell and Edge were, incredibly, shot down by a single remarkable Junkers 88, which they attacked in a dive down to sea level. Its diving speed, Edge reported, was about 350 m.p.h., and to catch up he had to use emergency boost, bringing his own speed up to 400. He also reported his belief that he had been hit by fixed guns firing back from the enemy's engine nacelles. Be that as it may, he was obliged to make a forced landing on Studland beach, where his Spitfire came to a skidding halt in a few inches of water.

'Before I could get out,' he recalls, 'the Army appeared higher up the beach, yelling that I should stay where I was, as the beach was mined. Eventually I was conducted along an approved route and given the hospitality of their Mess in a seaside bungalow. They were extremely helpful and got hold of a local farmer who brought a pair of cart horses and made a valiant attempt to drag my kite out of the water. Not surprisingly they failed even to move it. It was engulfed by the incoming tide.'

Meanwhile Frankie Howell had baled out into the sea, whence he was picked up, none the worse, by a naval vessel, and only the third member of the section, Sergeant Feary, landed normally. Though the Ju 88 was itself reported down in the sea by search-light and gun positions and the Fareham gunnery control officer, it seems that 'one Ju 88 probably destroyed' was all that could be set against two Spitfires definitely destroyed. If their two pilots returned to base a little sheepishly, attention by that time had probably been distracted by a very similar combat involving Over-ton and Bisdee. It was the latter's first, and they claimed a 'dam-aged'.

Three days later the indefatigable Flight-Sergeant Cloves re-corded that 'Pilot-Officer Bisdee in Spitfire N3024 got left some-what behind the formation due to his aircraft not being fitted with a constant-speed airscrew. Someone in the convoy thought he was hostile and put a shot through his elevator.' And five days after that Cloves actually expressed his approval when a Spitfire was written off without any help from the enemy:

'F/O Newbery in K9815, on a trip to Warmwell, found his engine doing all kinds of queer things and decided to force land. He did, and made a good job of it, the aircraft catching fire. Which was just what we wanted, as the aircraft was an old patched-up crock forced on to us to replace one of our losses.'

About the same time he records the following conversation piece between himself and his flight commander, Frankie Howell, on the latter's return from an operation conducted from Warm-well:

Flight-Sergeant: 'Bags of joy, Sir?'
Flight Commander (from cockpit): 'Yes, we shot down . . .'
F/Sgt.: 'With no losses?'
F/Com.: 'No, but "A" has a U/S compressor, "B" has various bullet holes, "D"'s engine cuts out, "E" wants . . .,' etc.
F/Sgt. (sotto voce): 'Hell's bells . . .'
F/Com.: 'And my own aeroplane . . .'
F/Sgt. resignedly): 'Yes, Sir?'
F/Com.: 'It goes like a ding-bat!'

On 8th July the Squadron had received its first intake from one of the newly created Operational Training Units, known hence-forth as 'O.T.U.s', and one almost hears a sigh of relief behind the words of the war diary : 'Having all done a few hours on Spit-fires, these pilots should be operational very shortly.' Their names were J. C. Newbery, M. E. Staples and N. le C. Agazarian – the second two V.R.s. John Bisdee remembers Mike Staples for his 'inborn wit and enormous fund of stories, especially of the shaggy-dog variety', and that 'he was walking out at the time with some posh well-known actress whose name I can't remember' Noël Agazarian – who has already been referred to in the Introduction – he remembers for his 'beautiful soft enunciation'. Like Richard Hillary, whose great friend and rival he was, 'Aggie' had begun his flying with the Oxford University Air Squadron, and the two together had been through flying school, flown Lysanders and Hectors during a brief assignment to Army Co-operation before Dunkirk, and only parted on leaving O.T.U., when Noël went to 609 and Richard to 603. In his classic, *The Last Enemy*, first published in 1942 by Macmillan, the latter wrote :

'Noël had been sent down from Oxford over a slight matter of breaking up his college and intended reading for the Bar. With an Armenian father and a French mother he was by nature cosmopolitan, intelligent and a brilliant linguist, but an English education had discovered that he was an athlete, and his University triumphs had been of brawn rather than brain . . . Noël's flying was typical of the man : rough, slapdash, and with touches of brilliance.'

Darley, his operational C.O., adds : 'His confidence was always greater than his competence!' He survived the Battle of Britain, though neither he nor Hillary survived the war.

In fact, the turn-round at O.T.U.s at this time was necessarily so swift – four weeks later reduced to two – that few pilots on reaching a squadron had much chance of survival unless they could be taken in hand by those with experience. Now the war diary, parsimonious of words though it is at this period, twice carries the sentence : 'Flight-Lieutenant Beaumont and Flying Officer Little instructing new pilots' . . . despite all the operational commitments. Stephen had again taken over 'B' flight on Barran's death, and on one occasion while airborne with his pupils had to excuse himself from them on perceiving (despite his poor eyesight) unidentified smoke trails high up in the sky above. Having the only machine equipped with oxygen he climbed right up to 27,000 feet, only to find a light blue Junkers 88 reconnaissance plane 3,000 feet higher still and beyond reach. (On another occasion – so Flight-Sergeant Fitzgerald recalls – Beaumont's was the only serviceable Spitfire one day at Warmwell when his attention was called to enemy aircraft attacking Portland Bill. 'I can see them,' he said with a Nelson touch. Handing Fitz his revolver, he added : 'Please look after this till I get back.')

Patrol convoy – patrol base – patrol Weymouth – patrol convoy – patrol base – patrol Portland – patrol Christchurch – patrol convoy : such reiterations appear again and again in the Form 541, the summary kept by the N.C.O.s in charge of Flights of each aircraft's time in the air, together with the name of its pilot. Usually at this period they were section patrols, occasionally flight patrols, often patrols by just one or two aircraft. Often, too, they went on all day, and as if this were not enough, there were even sometimes night patrols for those pilots deemed to be 'night-operational'. Automatically these included, once again, Stephen Beaumont.

'I remember his glasses,' says Bisdee – 'they were *reading* glasses. How on earth he managed to see anything, I just don't know.'

On one such patrol the Bish himself made an 'involuntary' landing at Andover (a training station), while Michael Appleby recalls how John Dundas, David Crook and himself landed during some 'night trials' :

'John landed first, hitting a Bofors gun and damaging that and his Spit; David landed second and wrote off all the paraffin flares, and I was left stooging about in the dark, my petrol getting lower and lower, till they were re-lit.' Then the flare-path indicator misled him by showing the wrong colours. 'Suddenly I noticed that my altimeter was reading 100 feet – and that had been the height at which I had made my long approach over the fields, woods and houses, with a hill of 200 feet just to my left ! I throttled back completely, where-upon great flames licked out from the exhaust stubs, making it im-possible to see anything below me, and I landed more by feel than judgement.'

Exhaust flare was in fact one reason why Spitfires were virtually useless as night-fighters, though 609 persisted in flying them by night at Drem, Middle Wallop and later Biggin Hill.

On 27th July Air Chief Marshal Dowding ruled that henceforth his tired pilots must have a minimum of eight hours off duty in every twenty-four, and a continuous twenty-four hours off each week. On the same day, in the course of another convoy battle also involving Hurricanes of 238 Squadron, with Ju 87s and Me 109s, 609 lost Pilot-Officer James Buchanan without any compensating score. Whilst leading Crook and Curchin he simply vanished, and though they both took off again and searched far out to sea, almost to the French coast, no trace of him was ever found. Its second R.A.F.V.R. officer, 'Buck' had joined the Squadron on the same day in December 1939 that Geoffrey Ambler relinquished his command, and while still in Scotland shared with Desmond Ayre 609's first 'kill' of the war. 'Potentially he was one of the best pilots we had,' says Stephen Beaumont, who had befriended him – 'of the quiet, efficient, Dawson type.' And automatically Beaumont took over the correspondence with the young man's bereaved but terribly courageous mother.

His death marked the end of a phase in Luftwaffe strategy, and also in the history and fortunes of the West Riding Squadron. In nine weeks since the start of Dunkirk it had lost nine pilots, including seven of the twelve Auxiliary officers who had gone to war station on 27th August 1939. In the first phase of the Battle of Britain, between 10th July and 7th August, 1940, the fifty-odd squadrons of Fighter Command had flown some 15,000 sorties and lost seventy-three pilots and double that number of planes. 609's effort, with about 670 sorties, had been twice the average, and its pilot losses more than twice. During the same period the Command claimed to have destroyed 188 enemy aircraft, and though most subsequent claims of both sides were found after the war to have been grossly exaggerated, this one was actually four too few. With its own claim for July of only two or three 'confirmed', 609 itself had probably been too modest.

3

THE WEAPON STRIKES

'So far as 609 was concerned, the Nazi blitz began on 8th August
... Four pilots engaged and accounted for five Huns.'

So wrote Flying Officer John Dundas, journalist, on assuming
responsibility for the Squadron's war diary. In 1938 he had written
an eye-witness account of the German occupation of Czechoslovakia for *The Yorkshire Post* and 1939 met Mussolini in Rome, and
it is strange to think that he was already then an officer of 609
Squadron. His light-hearted but penetrating comments on things
terrestrial, as well as celestial, made the diary a living document
and set an example that later scribes like myself tried hard to
follow.

Since the loss of Buchanan on 27th July there had been an
eleven-day lull – caused largely by a sharp decline in Channel
shipping – during which activity by 609 was mainly confined to
training and (according to Crook) chasing enemy reconnaissance
machines 'over most of south-western England', only to find they
were too high and fast. 'We had a private and somewhat jocular
theory that this unnatural peace was due to Goering having given
the whole German Air Force a week's leave to get them fit for
"things to come".' In fact the time was spent by the G.A.F. con-
solidating itself on occupied airfields and getting ready for
Adlertag.

When the storm broke, 609 had already seen many changes. On
1st August the telephone had rung at the home of the Beaumonts
in Wakefield – their home since 1936 (and still their home in
1970). It was Mrs. Little on the line : 'Betty? I've got wonderful
news ! Bernard's in hospital with appendicitis.'

Four days previously Jarvis Blayney had suddenly blacked out at 12,000 feet, had come round at only 1,000 feet and force-landed at Boscombe Down – after which the M.O. banned him from operational flying. And on the last day of July Beaumont himself flew for the last time with the Squadron.

'Darley had taken me aside and asked if, at thirty, I didn't feel I was getting a bit too old for fighters.' And Beaumont – who already two years before had suggested to Ambler that he should go into reserve because of increasing legal practice and responsibility for a wife and two children – was bound to confess that perhaps he did.

Of the four older Auxiliary officers still alive only Edge (at nearly thirty-two the oldest of all) stayed on for another three weeks. Constant service since war's outbreak, with night readiness added to the interminable daylight duty of high summer, had exhausted them, and for their sake as well as the Squadron's, it was Darley's duty to replace them as soon as he could with younger men. Blayney and Edge went to Training Command (where both won A.F.C.s), Beaumont and Little to O.T.U., after which Little was six months in hospital with frozen joints, while Beaumont ended the war as a Group-Captain in 84 Group. In his own words, 'We had all of us seen the bad days, but did not remain to see the good ones.' They left Dundas, Goodwin, Appleby and Crook 'as sole champions of the Auxiliary attitude' (as Dundas wrote).

On 1st August 'B' flight was taken over by Flight-Lieutenant J. H. G. ('Butch') MacArthur, whom I have mentioned in the Introduction. He was a Regular who had helped form 238 Squadron, now also in the Middle Wallop Sector, and had previously been a test pilot. 'B' flight replacements for Yorkshiremen Little and Blayney were two Poles (Flying Officers Nowierski and Ostaszewski), and hard on their heels came a new intake of three Americans ('Red' Tobin, 'Shorty' Keough and 'Andy' Mamedoff).

'Neither of the Poles,' wrote Dundas, 'could speak much English at the time, but both rapidly acquired efficiency on Spitfires,' while their C.O., Darley, well aware of the dangers that could arise from inability to receive or transmit messages on the R/T, warned them : 'If I overhear you speaking in Polish, I will stop you flying!'

Their proficiency in English, he tells me, thereafter progressed with remarkable speed. And they had beautiful manners.

They were both seasoned pilots who, despite inferior planes had already fought the Germans first over their own country, then in the *Armée de l'Air* over France and whose escape to Britain was now, like that of many others of their countrymen, of immeasurable benefit to the Allied cause. Having seen their homeland ravaged, they displayed the same courage and hatred of the enemy that had become a tradition of exiled Polish warriors over 200 years. To a British squadron the intensity of their hatred was a little new.

Also well liked and admired, though for the opposite reason, were the Americans, who had come along to fight long before their own country was even in the war. Apart from Billy Fiske of 601 Squadron, and 'Hack' Russell, they were perhaps the first Americans to join the R.A.F. Two of them, Tobin (called 'Red' because of his hair) and Mamedoff (of Russian extraction), had originally signed on for the war in Finland, despite the fact that the former's previous flying was limited to 200 hours in light aircraft, and the latter's to barnstorming in his own plane. Missing that war, they had come to Europe, with Keough, to join the French *Armée de l'Air* – but too late again, only got away on the last ship leaving France. Since then, they had had just four weeks at O.T.U.

They were a colourful wise-cracking trio, 'Red' being notable for a delightfully casual outlook and manner, 'Andy' for his gambling, and 'Shorty' for the fact that, at 4ft. 10in., he was the shortest pilot in the R.A.F. The reason for this was that he had been a professional parachute jumper and (according to Michael Appleby) had had two vertebrae removed after something once went wrong. Consequently he needed cushions to enable him to see out of his Spitfire's windscreen. Soon after they arrived, the Squadron was honoured by a visit from Air Commodore the Duke of Kent ('whose shoes,' Bisdee recalls, 'were so shiny I thought they were patent leather'). Said 'Shorty', 'Say, what do we call this guy – Dook?'. He was told that 'Sir' would do, and later had quite a chat with the 'Dook'.

Full of courage as they were, they were also very green, and their British C.O., Darley, wisely did not let them join in the *mêlée* that was about to start 'until I was certain that they could look after themselves. From time to time I had to tick each of them off for his own good, and it was not till they had all had some narrow shaves that they admitted I was right.' Thus to say, as does Richard Collier in *Eagle Day*, that already 'in a space of months they'd seen more action than any other squadron member' is sheer nonsense. Excellent though the book is, it in fact gives more space to the three Americans than the rest of 609 Squadron put together.* The two Poles alone proved more lethal to the enemy. During the Battle of Britain they and their countrymen in Polish squadrons accounted for 20 per cent of all the enemy aircraft destroyed.

If, in intensity, the 'Nazi blitz' of 8th August marked the beginning of the second phase of the Battle of Britain, it belonged strategically to the first. It was sparked off when the *Freya* radar station on Cap Gris Nez reported a convoy of twenty-five balloon-flying merchant ships escorted by several destroyers sailing westwards through the Channel, after no ships had braved it for the previous nine days. First it was attacked by E-boats, then by fighter-escorted Ju 87 dive-bombers with orders from General von Richthofen, commander of VIII Air Corps (and cousin of the first-war German fighter ace) that it should be wiped out. By the time it reached the part of the Channel defended by 609 Squadron – today operating for the first time under 10 Group control – much of it had been.

'It was the sort of day the Germans love,' wrote David Crook, 'because they come out at a big height and dive down to attack out of the sun, rendering themselves invisible.' A small layer of cloud, twelve miles south of Bournemouth, seems however to have

*H. S. Darley adds: 'In about 1965 I was invited to lunch by an American film company and was closely quizzed by the script writer and chief camera man till it became evident that they wished to portray how the Americans won the "B. of B." Despite my admiration for the 609 trio and the fact that they were all later killed (in the American "Eagle" Squadron), I could not go along with this idea, particularly as the three did not become operational for some time. I heard afterwards that the project had been abandoned. Eventually another backer was found, a new script written and the film will be released in September 1969.' (It has been, of course.)

been enough to cause the five operating Spitfires of 'B' flight to lose each other. Despite this, and the fact that Crook himself was deprived of victory over an enemy fighter by an interloping Hurricane, his new flight commander MacArthur claimed two of the attacking Stukas, and his C.O., Appleby and Curchin one each of the escorting Me 110s. With Appleby's Spitfire 'slightly peppered' as the only debit score, it was easily the biggest success the Squadron had claimed to date, and very encouraging for the future. Some other squadrons were not so lucky – notably 238, 609's partner at Middle Wallop, which lost two pilots and four aircraft, including that of its commander, Squadron Leader Fenton, who was picked up wounded by a naval launch that already had a German pilot on board. It is said that this Hurricane squadron had been formed so quickly that they had never done a training flight together, and with previous losses including two flight commanders, it was sent to Cornwall a few days later to recuperate. Though Fighter Command's total claims for the day were twice the actual score, and the Luftwaffe's two-and-a-half times, the real figures on both side were the highest since the Battle started on 10th July. If the Germans lost thirty-one aircraft, the British also lost nineteen – a figure that caused Dowding much anxiety, for it was just two days before the second phase of the Battle, the attack on his fighters' airfields and radar stations – the *Adlerangriff* – was scheduled to begin.

Before proceeding with the Battle, it might be well to have a look at the forward base from which 609 fought much of it. There were now three day-fighter squadrons in the sector, and at the beginning of August these comprised 609 and 238 (Hurricanes) based at Middle Wallop, and 152 (Spitfires) at Warmwell. On the authority of John Dundas 609's routine was :

'A day on fifteen minutes' availability at Wallop.
A day of release off camp.
A day of readiness at Warmwell, where we kept a servicing party of thirty-eight airmen under Flight-Sergeant Agar and Sergeant Fitzgerald.
'At this time,' Dundas continues, 'Warmwell possessed, though in rather irregular proportions, the two chief characteristics of a forward station – action and discomfort. Every third day at mid-day the

pilots would set off from Wallop in squadron formation, their cock-pits bulging optimistically with sponge-bags, pyjamas, and other articles of toilet which they got very little opportunity of using. Sleep-ing accommodation was provided for visiting squadrons in the sergeants' quarters, but after some experience of this pilots preferred to accommodate themselves as best they could in the dispersal tent, which was furnished with beds, dirty blankets, and an assortment of unreliable telephones. As it had not rained for a very long time, the surrounding terrain came to consist of dust and stones which blew into the tent whenever an aeroplane was "run-up" in the vicinity.'

There was no water or, at first, sanitation, and the proximity of a public road presented a dilemma (says Darley) whenever it was necessary to answer the calls of nature. 'One risked either prose-cution for indecent exposure or returning too late for a scramble.'

But the worst aspect of Warmwell was meals (or lack of). The station commander (a Group-Captain with a first-war D.F.C.) 'failed to see' why the intruding fighter pilots could not take them at regular hours like the officers of the Central Gunnery School, and at other hours ordered the door of the dining room to be locked. Dundas commented: 'All our efforts to get the Luftwaffe to respect the C.G.S. meal times having failed, deadlock occurred.'

The final straw was breakfast, which the civilian cooks at the Officers' Mess refused to serve at the uncivilized hour the Squadron had to be on duty. Darley reports:

'One morning I got up at about three, got the kitchen going and personally supplied all the chaps with eggs and bacon and tea. At nine-thirty the station commander was on the 'phone ordering me to his office. I said I couldn't leave Dispersal. He insisted, saying he would accept full responsibility. When I presented myself he said the civilian cooks had complained that I had not cleaned up their kitchen, and I was never to use it again. In turn I told him what I thought of his cooks etc., and then rang up the A.O.C. 10 Group. Although the latter came down straight away, he said that as he did not control Warmwell as a station he could only *ask* its commander to be a little more understanding. As a concession some latrines were erected and we were presented with an assortment of primus stoves and crockery to use at Dispersal' – where, the diary adds, 'Sergeant

Fitzgerald and Corporal Walker did a first class job with the bacon and eggs.' *

And Darley had a most satisfactory last laugh. The very same day he and his squadron intercepted a formation of escorted Ju 87s over Swanage as they were making for Warmwell itself.

'We soon sorted them out, and only one or two managed to lob their bombs on to the sacred airfield, with damage, as I could see, restricted to its surface. On landing at Wallop I could not resist the temptation to ring up the Warmwell station commander and say that I did not expect any thanks for saving the hangars, personnel and planes, not to mention the officers' mess and kitchen.'

We return to 10th August – the day the *Luftflotten* of Kesselring and Sperrle declared themselves ready to launch their great assault to wrench command of the English air from the R.A.F., given three consecutive days of fine weather. In the event the German met. men made a mess of things: with lousy weather on the 10th, *Adlertag* ('Eagle Day') was postponed till the 13th, and meanwhile the sun unexpectedly shone on the 11th and 12th. The Germans promptly changed the programme and exploited them.

On the 11th, despite feints designed to concentrate R.A.F. fighters over Kent, there was a major strike – estimated by the radar stations to comprise some 150 bombers and fighters – against docks, oil-tanks, barracks and gas works in Weymouth and Portland, and 609, scrambled from Warmwell, was one of several squadrons ordered to intercept. While 152 Squadron dealt with the bombers, 609 was vectored towards the enemy fighters. Dundas recorded:

* In his own account Irishman Bill Fitzgerald gives credit to 'the two volunteers, Geoff Walker and Sammy Barran.' He himself, approaching the station cook house after the first successful service to see what was going on 'and maybe scrounge a cup of tea', found that such a mountain of eggs, tea, sugar, tins of Nestles milk and packets of Kelloggs corn flakes had been issued that he asked the two, who needed three journeys in the Dundas Lagonda to transport it, how long they expected the war to continue. 'Nothing to do with us,' was the reply. 'It's just that those people up there think we are bloody marvellous. Why don't you go on up? They've got barrels of beer too!'

'Squadron-Leader Darley led "B" flight in an attack against a large offensive circle of Me 110s, with Me 109s around and above, at about 23,000 feet. He attacked by flying straight across the circle, taking full deflection shots.'

One section of 'A' flight joined in later, and MacArthur, Dundas, Bisdee and Agazarian were all credited with a Messerschmitt 110 destroyed. 'Everyone came streaming back in ones and twos,' wrote Crook, 'and to my surprise nobody was missing. After such a fierce scrap it seemed too good to be true.'

There had in fact been some close shaves. He himself had narrowly missed a collision, Dundas returned with his Spitfire streaming glycol coolant, and added that 'Flight-Lieutenant MacArthur got a new record for evasive action by spinning for 15,000 feet, after which he admitted to feeling rather unwell.' According to Crook, Mac's success on the 8th had made him 'rather over-confident', the writer adding a little patronizingly: 'From now on he was a very wise and successful flight commander.'

Though 152 Squadron registered its first claim of the war against the bombers, the day's engagements had been mainly fighter against fighter, which with Fighter Command's limited resources was contrary to policy. Of the day's score of thirty-eight enemy planes destroyed, thirteen had been Me 109s, and ten Me 110s, and the Command's own losses had been thirty-two. It was not then known that every German fighter had been ordered to stay and fight for twenty-five minutes.

The eve of *Adlertag*, 12th August, was also its prelude, with attacks on radar stations and coastal airfields. But there was also a sharp raid on Portsmouth docks and city, and Ventnor radar station near by on the Isle of Wight was the only one knocked out. For Fighter Command, the Luftwaffe and 609 Squadron – who now for the first of many times went to the help of No. 11 Group – the day brought the biggest effort yet. According to one pilot, 'There was the whole German air force bar Goering.'

At noon 'Butch' MacArthur, Noël Agazarian and David Crook were about to drive to London on twenty-four hours leave when they were called to readiness and immediately afterwards scrambled. Crook was first caught shaving, then left behind when he found his radio dead. Eventually he reached the Isle of Wight, quite alone, to find 'circling and sweeping all over the sky, at least 200 Huns. "My God," I said to myself, "what a party!" '

It was. 609 again encountered an orbiting circle of Me 110s, this time estimated at eighty in number. 'A' flight 'flew straight into the circle, taking full beam shots and breaking away downwards, while 'B' flight got rather scattered and attacked individually.' Crook, arriving a bit later on the scene, attacked even more individually and pulled out of his dive so violently that he bent both wings of his Spitfire. Again without loss, five Me 110s, plus three Me 109s were claimed destroyed, Dundas, Overton, Agazarian and Crook adding to their scores, and Flying-Officer Goodwin, Pilot-Officer Staples and the Squadron's lone N.C.O. pilot, Sergeant Feary, starting theirs. David Crook recalled that 'Teeny' Overton, landing at a nearby airfield to rearm and refuel, borrowed a bicycle and pedalled purposefully towards the Mess. While doing so he saw another Spitfire land, whose pilot also seized a bike. It turned out to be John Dundas, and they met over pints of iced Pimms. David himself, with his two companions, eventually set off for London five hours late, and found his wife waiting anxiously at the Trocadero with Michael Appleby. They were back next day at noon in time for *Adlertag* ... or, rather, *Adler 'nachmittag'*, the Luftwaffe's morning programme having been largely cancelled once again owing to a meteorological bomb.

Once more the south received more than its fair share of attention, with mass attacks on Portland and Southampton (whose docks and warehouses took a 'pasting' from Ju 88s), and airfields as additional targets. With formations of twenty-plus, fifty-plus, thirty-plus and thirty-plus appearing on its plotting table No. 10 Group sent up 152, 238 and 609 squadrons from the Middle Wallop sector and 213 squadron from Exeter, while 601 from the 11 Group Tangmere sector covered the Isle of Wight. All were heavily engaged, and about the doings of his own squadron Flying-Officer Dundas wrote in its diary :

'Thirteen Spitfires left Warmwell for a memorable Tea-time party over Lyme Bay, and an unlucky day for the species Ju 87, of which no less than fourteen suffered destruction or damage in a record Squadron "bag", which also included five of the escorting Me's. The enemy formation, consisting of about forty dive-bombers in four vic formations, with about as many Me 110s and 109s stepped-up above them was surprised by 609's down-sun attack.'

Seldom has a four-minute action by one squadron received so much contemporary and subsequent publicity :

'All the nine Junkers were brought down . . . by a single Spitfire squadron, as well as four of the Me 109s. This same squadron had brought down seven enemy aircraft the previous day.' – *The Times*, 14.8.40.

'No. 609 Squadron found a golden opportunity and took it . . . Attacked out of the sun, the Stukas made a perfect target. On the way the Spitfires dived through five Me 109s, breaking them up, Pilot-Officer D. M. Crook sending one spinning down into a field on fire . . . For once the Spitfires had altitude, position and surprise and they used it to deadly effect.' – *The Narrow Margin*, by Derek Wood and Derek Dempster, Hutchinson, 1961.

'Unbeknownst to 609 Squadron, VIPs had watched their battle royal. From the cliffs above Portland, Winston Churchill, along with Lieutenant-General Alan Brooke, C.-in-C. Home Forces, Claude Auchinleck, GOC.-in-C. Southern Command, and the 5th Corps' Major-General Bernard Montgomery, had broken off a survey of coastal defences from Exmouth to Weymouth to marvel at the spectacle.' – *Eagle Day*, by Richard Collier, Hodder & Stoughton, 1966.

'One pilot saw five German dive-bombers going down in flames, still more or less in formation.' *Spitfire Pilot*, by David Crook, Faber & Faber, 1942.

And the German view :

'First off was a long-range fighter *Gruppe* of twenty-three Me 110s, from Caen, its leader briefed only to make landfall near Portland . . . Had the British ground control officers known that the approaching force consisted merely of twin-engined fighters, they would have taken no defensive action. As it was they 'scrambled' three Spitfire and Hurricane squadrons based at Exeter, Warmwell and Tangmere . . . This was just what the Germans wanted them to do. The Me 110s were to draw the British fighter squadrons into combat. When bomber formations then followed after a well-judged interval, these squadrons would have reached the end of their fuel, and would be helpless . . . just the right moment to bomb them and their bases. So, at least, was the plan . . . But it was 17.00 hours before fifty-two Ju 87s of Major Graf Schönborn's StG 77, escorted by Me 109s of

Lieutenant-Colonel Ibel's JG 27, crossed the Channel . . . British ground control guided seventy fighters towards the force from different directions. While the Messerschmitts became locked in dog-fights with the Hurricanes, the fifteen (*sic*) Spitfires of 609 Squadron dived steeply on the Stukas and shot five of them down . . . It was the second bitter lesson of *Adlertag* – the day that had been designed to demonstrate the superiority of the German Luftwaffe over its British opponents. August 13th seemed indeed to be an unlucky day.' *The Luftwaffe War Diaries*, by Cajus Bekker, MacDonald, 1967.

The desperate cry, '*Achtung, Spitfeuer!*' had indeed been heard, strangely on their own wave-length, by 609's pilots, one of whom remarked that though this year he had rather missed the 'glorious twelfth', the 'glorious thirteenth' was the best day's shooting he had ever had. Claims : *

F/O P. Ostaszewski :	2 Ju 87s probable
P/O M. J. Appleby :	1 Me 109 and 1 Ju 87 damaged
F/Lt. J. MacArthur :	1 Me 109 damaged
F/O T. Nowierski :	1 Me 109 destroyed, 1 Me 109 damaged
P/O D. M. Crook :	1 Me 109 destroyed
F/Lt F. J. Howell :	2 Ju 87s destroyed
F/O H. M. Goodwin :	2 Ju 87s destroyed
Sgt. A. N. Feary :	1 Ju 87 destroyed, 1 Me 110 damaged
F/O J. C. Dundas :	1 Ju 87 destroyed, 1 Ju 87 damaged
P/O C. M. Overton :	2 Ju 87s destroyed
P/O R. G. Miller :	1 Ju 87 destroyed, 1 Ju 87 probable
P/O M. E. Staples :	1 Ju 87 destroyed, 1 Ju 87 damaged

This made 609 and 601 (who also claimed thirteen destroyed) Fighter Command's star *Adlertag* performers. If the number of dive-bombers destroyed had to be reduced after the war from nine to five, the exaggeration was nothing compared with the Luftwaffe's whose own was 700 per cent. Actual losses for the day : R.A.F. thirteen, Luftwaffe forty-five. But if, once more, all 609's pilots had come home, this was thanks in part to the enemy's fighter

* Darley alone made no claim, but he was the victory's architect. 'I managed to slip the Squadron through the fighters then went right through the Ju 87 formation, taking pot-shots without throttling back. This enabled the chaps behind to position themselves without having to avoid me.'

escort having been also engaged by 238. Again this squadron, on the eve of its departure, was not so lucky.

As night fell on this opening day of the Luftwaffe's offensive to destroy the R.A.F., the West Riding Squadron looked at itself and liked what it saw. In four days' hard fighting on the 8th, 11th, 12th and 13th, it had been credited with the destruction of thirty of the enemy without any loss to itself. Suddenly, after a period of decimation, sorrow and failure lasting nearly three months, everything seemed to be going right. Thanks above all to Squadron Leader Darley and Flight-Lieutenant Howell it had emerged from the slough of despond as a highly trained, skilful and confident fighting team. In the words of David Crook: 'Whenever in future the Squadron went into action, I think the only question in everybody's mind was not, "Shall we get any Huns today?", but rather, "How many?"'

The recent success also proved a tonic for the airmen on the ground, who were in somewhat the same position as grooms who like to see their own horses, and jockeys, win. Wrote Crook:

'Their loyalty to the Squadron and their keenness and energy knew no bounds, and as a result we always had the very comforting feeling that our Spitfires were maintained as perfectly as was humanly possible ... Frequently in those hectic days they would work all through the night in order to have a machine ready for dawn.'

So the 13th was their day too. During the action overhead those at Warmwell had stood in frustrated excitement listening to aeroplanes zooming and machine-guns crackling above the clouds, but with nothing to look at except some German aircraft dropping down through the clouds in flames. Little did these airmen and those at Middle Wallop know that they themselves were part of the intended target. Thanks however to their pilots, and the clouds, the bombs were scattered over three counties, and though a few fell at Wallop village just behind 238 Squadron's dispersal point, the only airfield damaged was that at Andover, which was not fighter but Army Co-op. Unfortunately the same would not be true on the morrow.

On this day, 14th August, the weather was so bad that although the Luftwaffe's sorties were only one third of the previous day's, it was possible for small formations of bombers to fly over England unescorted. So it was that a Ju 88 of the elite unit LG 1 (or three of them, according to some published accounts) found Middle Wallop despite the cloud and made the most lethal airfield attack of the day.

Crook: 'At about 1500 feet he let go four bombs – we could see them very distinctly as they plunged down – and a second later there was an earth-shaking "whoom" and four great clouds of dust arose' – one just beside the billet where 609's airmen were quartered.

Airman R. F. Burgess: 'We were standing at the door of the billet watching a Blenheim of 604 Squadron diving on the airfield, when we noticed at the last moment that it was a Ju 88 instead.'

Airman S. Waterson: 'Having had tea I thought, good, I'll have time to go to the toilet, and have a crafty shave as well if I'm lucky – but I was caught with my pants down.'

Undramatic? Then try this:

Death, for the first time, seemed to lay its hand upon Red Tobin. He was within eighty yards of Hangar Five when fear charged him like an electric current: a blue-bellied Junkers 88 dive-bomber, its twin Jumo engines bulking enormously, was 1,500 feet above the hangar, gliding like a giant bat. As the first stick burst from its bomb bay, Red, moving faster than he'd ever done, dived headlong for the earth. . . .

The last quotation is from Richard Collier's *Eagle Day*. Somewhat typically it makes no mention of Tobin's English companion at the time, 'Paul' Edge, who simply says:

'We had rather foolishly elected to walk back to the Mess from Dispersal across the aerodrome, and had reached almost the exact centre when the bomber appeared out of low cloud. I started to run wildly away from it, but Red yelled for me to follow him, and we ran directly underneath it. The bombs landed near enough, but we were unharmed thanks to Red's better understanding of ballistics. The row of craters lay right across my original line of escape.'

They both turned quite white – with chalk dust.

And without any drama three of 609 Squadron's airmen went to their deaths bravely trying to save its aircraft:

'When the alarm sounded,' Edge continues, 'a maintenance party under Corporal Bob Smith (whom I had known well in civilian life) was ordered to close the huge steel-plated doors of one of the hangars. They were desperately winding on the big hand cranks when the bomb entered through the roof. The blast blew the doors off the upper guide rails.'

Besides Smith, the victims were Leading Aircraftmen Harry Thorley and Ken Wilson. Corporal F. H. Appleby was injured, as were ten airmen at station headquarters, which became a shambles. 'On being discharged from hospital minus an eye,' says Appleby's colleague Bradbury, 'he dislocated his shoulder crashing the famous whisky waggon – dead unlucky, he was.'

The dead were not unavenged. Sergeant Feary, already airborne, was close behind the bomber and thirty seconds later shot it down. It crashed five miles away and Crook, who flew over the wreckage, reported all the crew killed. He himself later damaged two Heinkels in amongst the clouds, one of which Dundas subsequently finished off. This Heinkel contained two senior Luftwaffe officers, presumably taking advantage of the weather to take a first-hand look at how things were going.

But when the pilots landed that evening, Harry Goodwin was missing, despite the absence of enemy fighters and the fact that all the known individual actions had taken place near base. Some ten days later, however, his body was washed up on the Isle of Wight. It was presumed he had chased one of the bombers out to sea, and been intercepted by German fighters there.

Despite the bombs, it is clear that Middle Wallop (rechristened by the three Americans 'Centre Punch') was much preferred as a station to Warmwell, even though the staple diet, says R. Burgess, was meat roll and tinned tomatoes (relieved in his own case by late-night 'fry-ups' thanks to his being billeted with the cooks in the married-quarters block). It is hard to credit that, at the height of the Battle of Britain, the West Riding Squadron still occasionally fielded its peace-time rugger fifteen, most of them members of senior Yorkshire Rugby Union teams. C. R. Crowther remembers :

'Soon after our arrival the Station Warrant Officer, whose own team was his pride and joy, enquired rather condescendingly if we had one or two players good enough to join it. When our captain, Johnny Payne, suggested a trial match between Squadron and Station, he was told in effect to "get lost". However, the match took place, and after 609 had run a "cricket score" without conceding a try, the selection of a new Station side proved a matter of some embarrassment.'

The victory may have impressed a Squadron intake of newly trained airmen mechanics who arrived about this time and included, according to one of them, Messrs. Cooper, Fovargue, David, Cottriall, Jagger and Moles. 'We were the first batch of "foreigners",' says Hubert Fovargue, 'and were called "juffs" by the Yorkshire "natives", who, however, soon made us feel very much at home.' Leslie Cooper adds about another of them (whom it is kinder not to identify) :

'Despite a good training record, he was just hopeless with the tools. After dropping a plug between two banks of cylinders on a Merlin, and at his second attempt getting the plug cross-threaded and ruining the block, he ended up sweeping the hangar. From that point he gradually effaced himself until "Flights" thought he was "Maintenance" and "Maintenance" thought he was "Flights" – though in fact he was neither. In the end he just turned up for pay parades.'

With the whole Squadron now on duty at Warmwell one day in three, the servicing crews at Wallop had more free time. 'As soon as the Spits were airborne,' Stan Waterson recalls, 'we had the afternoon off, and certain of us had permission from the pilots to use their cars while they were away.' Evidently this was part of a tacit bargain, for : 'During the following morning, while waiting for them to return, the cars were cleaned, oil and petrol topped up, ready for handing back.'

The emphasis, of course, was on petrol, and the art of diverting aviation spirit to their own or their officers' private transport seems to have been an obsession, with certain airmen, only second to that of keeping the Spitfires in fighting trim. In their letters thirty years afterwards it remains one of their most abiding memories. Examples :

'Pool petrol was rationed, therefore aviation petrol was used, as the ration soon ran out. Many ingenious devices were made to fit in tanks, so if samples were taken, the sample was always "pool".' (R. Chadwick).

'The amazing Ron Carlton, probably the finest mechanic any squadron could have, had his own Brough Superior. Caught running on 100-octane R.A.F. fuel, without current road fund licence and with leave pass expired. Awarded one month's detention but took his camera concealed in respirator to prison and emerged with quite a wealth of interesting shots.' (H. Fovargue).

'As it was not always "convenient" to get petrol out of the bowser, I kept a reserve of two 5-gallon drums in a locker shared by two pilots. Organising three keys, I gave each of them one and kept the third, thus ensuring that no other "bod" could win them.' (S. Waterson).

One day Waterson was driving Flying Officer Goodwin's car when the police stopped him because its licence had expired. To serve a summons on its owner, 'a copper took to dropping in at odd times at the "flights", always to find this pilot was either flying, on day off or at Warmwell. Came the day when I waited in vain for his return from a scramble. We weren't troubled by that policeman after that.'

On 15th August the Luftwaffe flew 1,786 sorties, its biggest effort during the whole Battle of Britain. Not only did *Luftflotten* 2 and 3 send wave after wave of raiders across the English Channel against the south and south-east, but for the first and only time other forces were despatched by *Luftflotte 5* across the North Sea from Norway and Denmark against targets in the east and north – only to find, to its cost, that Dowding also had fighter squadrons there.

Though it was not till five in the afternoon that 10 Group became involved, during the next twenty minutes it plotted no less than seven formations totalling some 200–300 aircraft approaching the coasts of Hampshire and Dorset, and in the course of the attack 150 Spitfires and Hurricanes from 10 Group and the adjoining sectors of 11 Group were airborne – the largest force yet dispatched against one assault. In the words of the R.A.F. official historian :

Fierce battles developed near Portsmouth and Portland, where many of the Germans were beaten back before they could cross the coast, and long struggling encounters took place all over the southern counties. Yet such was the ascendancy of our pilots, and so small was the proportion of the enemy's bombers to his fighters, that once again the damage on the ground was insignificant. Only at Middle Wallop airfield did the German crews reap the slightest reward.

Unlike the day before, the weather was fine and the attacking force comprised a dozen Ju 88s (again from LG 1) escorted by twin-engined Me 110 fighters – Middle Wallop being a bit far for single-engined Me 109s. Till now 609 had been held in reserve, and as they took off bombs were exploding behind them.

Squadron-Leader Darley: 'I saw two formations of Ju 88s approaching the aerodrome and jumped into an a/c which was u/s owing to R.T. trouble.'

Flight-Lieutenant Howell: 'I found one a/c serviceable after "B" flight had taken off. As I took off, salvos of bombs dropped on the hangars . . . I easily caught up one Ju 88 doing 320 m.p.h. which dived for cloud . . . R.T. talking in German was very loud indeed.'

Airman Waterson: 'Not liking the claustrophobia-like atmosphere in the shelter I said to another airman, "Let's go down to Dispersal on my motor-bike." We were going past the hangars like the clappers when I looked up and saw these Ju 88s. I steered for the hedge and we rolled off unharmed and watched the bombs come tumbling down . . . When I got back to the billet, there was a huge crater just where my motor-bike had stood.'

The bombing cost the enemy dear, for they were harried all the way to the coast and out to sea. The C.O., both flight commanders, Edge (his last combat), Newbery and Ostaszewski all making claims that totalled one Ju 88 and four Me 110s destroyed, and three Ju 88s probably destroyed. Most dramatic was the victory of Polish 'Osta', who clung to his Me 110 opponent like a leech as in an effort to escape it dived to ground level, circled a church spire, then tore straight through the Southampton balloon barrage. After a final burst from 100 yards it crashed on to a concrete road on the Isle of Wight.

In this assault in the south-west the Luftwaffe lost one third of its day's total of seventy-five aircraft destroyed, and Fighter Command sixteen of its own total loss of thirty-four. In addition, David Crook shot down a Blenheim of 604 – Middle Wallop's night-fighter squadron. At the time of the bombing this aircraft had been on a practice flight, and was therefore the first fighter in position to 'have a go' at the retreating enemy – a temptation its pilot was unable to resist. By the time 609 caught up, it appeared to be one of the formation of Ju 88s – to which aircraft the Blenheim bore a notorious resemblance. Though Crook hit both engines, its pilot managed to crash-land safely at base, and the only sore subject was the rear-gunner's bottom, punctured by one of David's bullets.

Despite the much greater number of attackers, the damage sustained by Middle Wallop airfield was a good deal less than on the previous day. This was due to a two-second misjudgement by the enemy formation leader, *Hauptmann* Wilhelm Kern, whose followers were trained to let go their bombs at the same instant as himself, with the result that of twelve 2,000-lb. bombs the majority fell safely wide of target. Two hangars were hit, one aircraft was destroyed and five damaged (plus another near miss on 609's billet). Yet on return Kern reported that he had bombed Andover. Evidently the Germans were still unaware that Middle Wallop was a far more important station.

At the end of this crucial day in the Battle of Britain Winston Churchill drove away from the operations room at Fighter Command deeply moved, and to General Ismay in the car beside him he first uttered the now famous words: 'Never in the field of human conflict was so much owed by so many to so few.' To which Michael Appleby, thinking of his pay as a Pilot-Officer, added cynically '. . . and for so little.' When I met Michael recently, he said: 'Some of us had been pilot officers for so long that the thin little stripe on our sleeves had eroded almost clean away.'

Next day German Intelligence calculated that Fighter Command could by now have a mere 300 serviceable fighters left (the figure in fact was over 700). Yet the Luftwaffe itself could not have felt exactly happy. Its 1,786 sorties of 15th August included only 520 by bombers, and despite the increased fighter escort Goering on the same day decreed that in future no bomber crew should contain more than one officer. On this 16th August, though the enemy effort was nearly comparable, it was directed almost entirely against airfields in 11 Group, and Tangmere, nearest fighter station to the Isle of Wight and home of 601, lost 'all its hangars, workshops, stores, sick quarters, pumping station and officers mess', with multiple casualties to personnel and aircraft. Though 609 was scrambled several times, its pilots this day earned no glory.

But on the 17th its ground staff did. With the Luftwaffe virtually taking the day off, it was time to clear the unexploded bombs that had accumulated at Middle Wallop over three successive days. Next to the largest lay the obviously vital oxygen-filling plant, and it is recorded :

'Flight-Sergeant Roberts called for volunteers to obtain this equipment, and 75 per cent volunteered, so lots were drawn. The following party did the job : Corporal Walling, Leading Aircraftmen Routledge, Dyson and Fletcher, Aircraftmen Jackson, Picton and Tobin. Sergeant Albrecht was in charge.'

Two days previously there had taken place the following exchange of letters, which as a spontaneous expression of mutual loyalty between officers and other ranks in wartime must surely be rare, and which to morale were worth even more than the messages of congratulation received the same day from the Secretary of State for Air, Sir Archibald Sinclair, and the Chief of the Air Staff, Sir Cyril Newall.

From : N.C.O.s and Men of No. 609 Squadron.
To : Squadron-Leader Darley and all Pilots of No. 609 Squadron.
In view of the recent successes achieved by the R.A.F. and No. 609 Squadron in particular, we wish to offer all Pilots our sincerest congratulations, and 'good Hunting' for the future.
We feel honoured to have such excellent Pilots in the Aircraft we service.
For and on behalf of N.C.O.s and Men of 'A' and 'B' Flights,
Flight-Sergeant Cloves, C.W.   Flight-Sergeant Roberts, H. J.

From : Officer Commanding, No. 609 Squadron.
To : All N.C.O.s and Airmen in Flights and Sections.
Date : 15th August 1940.
On behalf of the pilots of this Squadron, I thank you for your appreciation of our efforts.
Our results can only be achieved by confidence in our aircraft, and it is due to your hard work and skill that the engines have kept going, that the bullets have found their mark, and that the air is filled with Sorbo war whoops.

Keep going hard, with all your skill and might, for I shall have to ask you to keep up and increase this pace before this show is over.

(Sgd.) H. S. Darley,
Squadron-Leader, Commanding
No. 609 Squadron, Warmwell.

On 18th August the till now famous (or infamous) Ju 87 (Stuka) dive-bomber was sent over Britain in force for the last time. On that day 609's fellow Spitfire squadron No. 152 and 11 Group's No. 43 (Hurricane) squadron demonstrated its vulnerability by together destroying twelve out of a force of twenty-five. Altogether thirty were lost or severely damaged, after which most of the rest were 'put in moth balls' to await their role against the Royal Navy on invasion day. In most accounts 18th August is also regarded as marking the end of the second phase of the Battle of Britain – the week inside which Goering had reckoned he could destroy the Royal Air Force – while 24th August, following five days of bad weather and little action, represents the beginning of phase three. Inasmuch, however, as 24th and 25th August saw the last big-scale daylight raids by *Luftflotte 3* for several weeks, for 609 – geographically at least – they marked the end of phase two.

It was 'geographically' only, for following another conference between Goering and his commanders at his country estate in eastern Germany on the 18th, new Luftwaffe tactics were adopted. One of these was to fly constant patrols up and down the Channel, with feint attacks, in order to confuse British radar and mask the genuine ones. So it was that, on 24th August, a force of a hundred bombers and fighters had already reached the threshold of Portsmouth and Southampton before either their strength or intentions were known, and in the former a hundred civilians were killed in the Luftwaffe's most destructive day of the whole Battle of Britain. Though 10 and 11 Groups between them had four squadrons ready, 609 alone got near enough to intercept, but failed to fire a single round. Still climbing, they found themselves 5,000 feet below both enemy bombers and fighters, right in the middle of anti-aircraft fire from ground batteries and all the ships in Portsmouth harbour, and down-sun as well.

To the enemy fighters they should have been sitting ducks, and it can be confidently said that only a fully experienced squadron, such as 609 now was, could have again got away without a single pilot casualty. One Spitfire was damaged and another a write-off – the latter that of the American, Andy Mamedoff, whose first action it seems to have been. He himself somewhat incredibly got away with only a slightly bruised back despite the fact that, as Flight-Sergeant Cloves recorded, 'a shell entered the tail of his aircraft, went straight up the fuselage, through to the wireless set, just pierced the rear armour plating' and presumably dented the pilot's uniform.

It is interesting to note that this was the last flight of 609's very first Spitfire, L1082, which Squadron-Leader Ambler had flown to Yeadon from the Supermarine works at Woolston, Southampton, just over a year before. Damaged in several early accidents, it seems to have been allocated first to Edge, then Overton. The former had flown it in the Squadron's first successful action on 29th January, 1940, but was unable to keep up in what Cloves already termed 'the old warrior', while the latter fought with it victoriously over Dunkirk and last flew it on 16th August. Before then and since it had been the old workhorse on which a succession of new pilots had won their spurs. In the words of its chief groom, 'Our old crock was game to the last, being nursed back to base, where the tail end collapsed on landing.' After over a year of operational service, L1082 had earned its rest.

Next day, while *Luftflotte 2* and 11 Group rested, it was *Luftflotte 3's* turn to have its own biggest daylight 'bash'. Around tea-time various formations appearing round Cherbourg and St. Malo on the radar screens coalesced into a gigantic raid, and all serviceable fighters from Tangmere to Exeter were put into the air to obviate the risk of their destruction on the ground. 609 was one of two squadrons sent out as a reception committee – appropriately, for the main target was their own forward base, Warmwell. And this time the enemy revealed another new tactic : a mighty increase in the proportion of fighters to bombers. Forty-five Ju 88s were surrounded by such an impermeable screen of Me 110s and Me 109s that only one bomber became a casualty either of fighters or guns. But this time 609 had at least the height advantage of the German fighters as Darley led them down in line astern. Wrote Crook, who was at the end of the procession :

'I shall never forget seeing the long line of Spitfires ahead, sweeping round and curling round at terrific speed to strike right into the middle of the German formation. It was superb! . . . The onslaught split up the Huns immediately and they scattered all over the place, with Spitfires chasing them right and left.'

Darley himself bagged a fighter of each species, the two flight commanders a Me 110 each, and other 'kills' were by Johnny Curchin (Me 109), Sergeant Feary (Me 110), Red Tobin (Me 110), and Noël Agazarian and Geoffrey Gaunt (shared Me 110). In addition, 'probables' and damaged were claimed by 'Red' Tobin, John Dundas and John Bisdee.

It was Red's first combat, fought at 19,000 feet without oxygen. Not surprisingly, as he said afterwards, 'I blacked out colder than a clam'— and only regained consciousness at 1,000 feet over the sea. The only casualties were Crook's and Polish Ostaszewski, who after being hit by cannon fire had to land without flaps and crashed through the periphery hedge. He was 'nastily battered on the head by his windscreen', had a wound in the arm, but soon recovered. His Spitfire didn't.

In this action *Luftflotte 3* recorded the loss of eleven of its fighters (plus the single bomber), while Fighter Command lost eleven aircraft and eight pilots killed or wounded. And, hardly surprisingly, Warmwell did not go unscathed. Two hangars were damaged, station sick quarters burnt out, and communications disrupted for eighteen hours. There were also the usual unexploded bombs – and thereby hangs a tale to illustrate the initiative and spirit of Auxiliary mechanics. It is told by the West Riding Squadron's most long-standing member, 'Darkie' Hanson, then a corporal :

'Flying Officer Harvey, 609 Squadron's Engineer Officer, sent for me and said that a pilot of "B" Flight had landed at Warmwell with a badly damaged engine. He instructed me to take two fitters and a replacement engine down there, so that this Spitfire could be ready for combat again as soon as possible, as we were short of aircraft. I chose Leading Aircraftmen George Ellis and Stanley Fletcher to go with me, and on arrival at Warmwell, which was about sixty miles away, I reported to the Station Engineer Officer. To my dismay he didn't seem very interested in my problem, and calmly informed me that in any case I would not be allowed to carry out the engine change as there was an unexploded 500-lb. bomb two feet from the tail-plane. I asked him when the bomb had been dropped and he said the previous afternoon along with four others that were in the hangar, where there were other Spitfires. When I asked him rather indignantly why our Spitfire had not been pushed away from the bomb, he said it was too dangerous, and the same applied to the kites in the hangar. I then asked him for the loan of a tractor to tow my Spit away to safety so that we could get on with the engine change. His reaction was startling. First he forbade me to go anywhere near 609's Spit, and secondly if I was not very careful I would be on a charge for insolence.

'At this stage I thought I had better retire and hold a quiet council of war with my two mates. We decided that, lacking official permission to carry on, we would do it the "Auxiliary" way – namely move the aircraft and argue the rights and wrongs afterwards. I put it to George and Stanley that if they were prepared to take a chance for about three minutes I would borrow a Fordson tractor when no one was looking, hook it up to our aircraft and tow it away from the nasty German bomb. Needless to say my two friends were flat out for this idea, and it worked like a dream. George drove the tractor while Stan and I steered the Spit to a safe position about half a mile away.

'Next day, whilst changing the engine, I happened to glance across at the hangar and noticed that it seemed to be swelling. Immediately there was a hell of a bang, and up it went complete with the Spitfires inside – a case of when a little guts could have saved them, and a totally different result to when 609 had aircraft and unexploded bombs in the hangar at Middle Wallop, when there was no lack of volunteers and the kites were repaired and flew again.

'But now we had another snag. One of the parts to be changed from the damaged engine to the new one was the B.T.H. compressor, and we found someone had "liberated" it to make another aircraft serviceable. This meant I had to face my arch-enemy again, and ask him for a replacement – convinced that he would promptly charge me with disobeying his order to keep away from our Spit. To my amazement he didn't even mention the matter. But he was still not very keen to help me to get our kite back to the Squadron, and as for a compressor the only suggestion he could make was to dig one from the wreckage of a Hurricane which had crashed about six miles away. We found it without great difficulty, but the snag was that it appeared to have hit the ground at full power from about 20,000 feet, so that all we could see was a huge crater with some pieces of metal sticking out of the ground. Whilst deciding what to do next, and all being in full agreement that the Station E.O.'s parents had never been joined together in wedlock, we heard a noise like an angry wasp and a bullet went past us at a high rate of knots, followed by the crack of a rifle. We immediately took cover, and then found out that we had got mixed up in a private war between two gentlemen of the Luftwaffe, who had taken to the silk, and some Army bods who were trying to capture them.

'In the end I had to send back to Middle Wallop for a compressor, and we at last completed our task. But it was worth all our trials and tribulations, for the next time this Spitfire flew it delighted us by shooting down an Me 109.'

Amongst the combatants of 25th August the attentive reader may have noticed with surprise the name of Geoffrey Gaunt – last mentioned as the last Auxiliary officer to join the Squadron before the war, and too late to complete even initial flying training at its hands. Now, a year later, and to the joy of his remaining peacetime friends, he had returned to the fold fully qualified and full of promise. At No 7 O.T.U., Hawarden, he had fittingly enough been one of the initial pupils of 609's very *first* Auxiliary pilot, Stephen Beaumont, who had left it only a fortnight or so before. And before his first combat his life-long friend David Crook had completed his operational training by dog-fighting him all over the sky.

Altogether, there is something terribly poignant about this young man – so popular, so handsome, and so tragic. Just recently I happened to meet a lady with whom, thirty years ago, he would lightly propose marriage on their daily walk to a Huddersfield bus stop. 'His eyes were so blue,' she told me, 'that they matched his uniform.' And she is still unmarried. More poignant still, I have before me as I write two 'R.A.F. Large Note Books, Form 407'. One bears the name 'S. G. Beaumont'. On the cover of the other the name 'G. M. Gaunt' has been deleted and that of 'A. K. Ogilvie' substituted. In it is recorded that at Middle Wallop they shared a room, and it is clear that Gaunt never had a chance even to begin his diary. But Ogilvie did, and when he was posted missing in 1941 it was forwarded to an address in Ottawa written on the fly-leaf. Thirty years later it has been sent to me by its Canadian owner – who after all survived.

'It will be seen,' wrote Dundas, in concluding 609's official diary for August, 'that the Squadron was becoming cosmopolitan. One might think that this heterogeneity would interfere with team-work or morale, but this was not so. Under Squadron-Leader Darley's quietly firm and competent leadership the Squadron gained steadily in skill and confidence, and remained a veritable "Band of Brothers".'

The 'Band', twenty-one strong of whom just one-third are alive today – consisted at this moment of four Auxiliaries, six Regulars, four or five Volunteer Reservists, one Dominion, three United States and two Polish pilots. Here are their names:

S/Ldr H. S. Darley	P/O C. N. Overton	F/O P. Ostaszewski
F/Lt F. J. Howell	P/O J. D. Bisdee	F/O J. C. Newbery
F/Lt J. H. G. MacArthur	P/O J. Curchin	P/O E. G. Tobin
F/O J. C. Dundas	P/O R. G. Miller	P/O A. Mamedoff
P/O D. M. Crook	P/O N. le C. Agazarian	P/O V. G. Keough
P/O M. J. Appleby	P/O M. E. Staples	P/O A. K. Ogilvie
P/O G. M. Gaunt	F/O T. Nowierski	Sgt A. Feary

Between 8th and 18th August alone – the Phase Two period during which Fighter Command destroyed 367 enemy aircraft at a cost of 154 of its own pilots killed, missing or severely wounded – this 'Band' had been credited with thirty-six confirmed victories plus ten 'probables' for the loss of a single pilot. Even if the actual score was only half, such a performance may well have been unique. Had not Darley said something about improving the kill/loss ratio?

2

It is now generally conceded that a few night bombers of the Luftwaffe, followed by a single action of Winston Churchill's taken in defiance of his air advisers, together altered the whole course of the Battle of Britain, and enabled victory to be plucked from defeat.

Hoping that the British government would still come to terms without the necessity of an invasion, Hitler had expressly ordered that London itself was not to be bombed. When, therefore, during the night of 24th/25th August this happened owing to a navigational error by a few Luftwaffe crews, the German leaders were even more shocked than the British, and Goering promptly demanded to know the names of the guilty aircraft commanders in order to remuster them to the infantry. And the very next night Bomber Command, at Churchill's insistence, despatched eighty-one twin-engined Whitleys, Hampdens and Wellingtons on a 600-mile each-way flight to Berlin, the city that Hermann Goering had guaranteed would never see an enemy plane. It matters not that few of them reached it, or that even fewer dropped their bombs through cloud in the target area – it was, militarily, one of the master strokes in Winston's long career. For after four such raids within ten days the *Führer*, driven into a frenzy, proclaimed : 'Since they attack our cities, we shall wipe out theirs!' Almost in one breath London became the target, and the fighter airfields and organization round about them were able to recover at the eleventh hour.

Phase Three of the Battle of Britain, lasting from 24th August till 6th September, had indeed seen the Luftwaffe's concentrated assault on the inner ring of London's protective airfields, in the Kenley, Biggin Hill, Hornchurch, North Weald, Debden and Northolt sectors, in a final and all-but successsful attempt to deliver the final knock-out blow to Britain's air defence that was orginally planned to happen within three days of *Adlertag*. Now there was no question of the bombers not reaching their targets : unbeknowst to Fighter Command most of *Luftflotte's 3's* single-engined fighters, after 26th August, had also been crowded into the Pas de Calais area, enabling the previous scale of fighter escort to be doubled or trebled. On 31st August, when Fighter Command suffered its worst loss of the whole Battle, the ratio was actually 150 bombers to 1,300 fighters. If the British fighters didn't want to be destroyed on the ground, they were forced – contrary to Dowding's policy, but in accordance with Goering's – to fight their opposite numbers in the air. During this desperate fortnight 11 Group's twenty-two squadrons lost 466 aircraft destroyed or severely damaged, 103 pilots killed and 128 severely wounded. Some squadrons had been almost wiped out. No. 603 (City of

Edinburgh), whose members included Richard Hillary and 'Sheep' Gilroy (a future commander of 609) lost sixteen Spitfires and twelve pilots between its arrival from Scotland, on 28th August, and 6th September; No. 253 at Kenley lost thirteen Hurricanes and nine pilots in seven days, and 616 (the squadron of John Dundas' younger brother Hugh) twelve aircraft and five pilots in eight. Experienced pilots, in the words of one account, were 'like gold dust', and those that remained were exhausted. Fighter pilots of any sort were so scarce that Bomber, Coastal, Army Co-op Commands and the Navy were all canvassed for volunteers, and those that came went through a conversion course lasting a futile six days.

And during this whole fortnight (bar 24th and 25th August) one of the most experienced 'A' class squadrons,* No. 609, failed to intervene, though itself almost undented and still as fresh as paint. True, during the second week – when it at last became clear that the day-time Luftwaffe was now concentrating on the 11 Group area only – the Squadron had been on almost daily factory-protection patrol at about 10,000 feet over Guildford, Brooklands, Windsor, and sometimes western 11 Group airfields, mainly against low-level attack. Unfortunately it was not then known that Goering had stopped low-level attacks on airfields, and it also happened that on the one day the Vickers works at Brooklands did suffer severely, 609 had been detailed to patrol Northolt. Though it was logical that squadrons arriving from the furthest distance should man the lowest patrol line, it seems in the event to have been too low – whereas some 11 Group squadrons, determined to have the advantage, were in fact too high.

But on 7th September, the day the Luftwaffe switched to London as its main target, things were different. This was the beginning of Phase Four, which lasted till the end of the month. And

* 'A' class squadrons comprised those in No. 11 Group and the adjoining Middle Wallop and Duxford sectors. 'B' class squadrons in Nos. 10 and 12 Groups were intended to replace 'A' squadrons, when needed, as whole units. 'C' class squadrons, with a maximum allowance of six experienced pilots, existed mainly as training units. The worst fate that could befall an 'A' class squadron was to be demoted, owing to losses, to grade 'C'. When this happened, temporarily, to 601, the author of that squadron's story reported that it 'almost lost its soul'.

however wrong the German decision, there was in fact a tactical argument in its favour as well as Hitler's political one. On 3rd September, at The Hague, the two *Luftflotten* chiefs, Field-Marshals Kesselring and Sperrle, pressed their conflicting views on Goering, rather as the commanders of Nos. 11 and 12 Groups, Air Vice-Marshals Park and Leigh-Mallory, respectively argued the advantages for interception purposes of squadron or wing formations before their own top brass. While Sperrle (correctly) wanted the offensive against the British fighter bases to continue, Kesselring argued that these were expendable : if too badly damaged. their squadrons could be withdrawn to other bases behind London and beyond the range of German fighter escort. 'We have no chance,' he said, 'of destroying the British fighters on the ground. We must force their last reserve of Spitfires and Hurricanes into combat in the air.' Only an attack on the nerve centre of the British Empire would accomplish this.

So on 7th September Goering stood with Kesselring on the coast near Calais and watched as over 300 bombers and 600 fighters formed the first two waves of the first major attack on London. He had, he announced, taken over 'personal command' of the Luftwaffe. On the same day, incidentally, Air Ministry informed Fighter Command : 'Invasion regarded imminent.'

Invasion or no invasion, Fighter Command was in fact having some difficulty in coping with the present raids. Obsessed by defence of its own bases and the usual tactics and routes used by the enemy to reach them, it was taken by surprise when the two main waves headed respectively straight for the Thames Estuary and central London, with the bombers themselves between 16,000 and 20,000 feet – too high for accurate Observer Corps reporting. 'The 11 Group controller,' write the authors of *The Narrow Margin*, 'got everything he could vector on to the advancing phalanx, but it was in penny numbers compared with the solid masses of the Luftwaffe.'

One of the 'penny numbers' was 609, diverted from its usual factory-protection patrol between Brooklands and Windsor at a mere 10,000 feet as the enemy began to withdraw. Leading the Squadron on this occasion was Flight-Lieutenant MacArthur, who reported : 'We saw about 200 enemy aircraft over London surrounded with A.A. fire. We climbed towards them.' Sergeant Feary, after attacking a Me 110 and subsequently damaging one of a pair of Me 109s, continued his combat report:

'As I climbed again and came up the Thames Estuary, I saw a large formation going south and another (Me 110s) approaching from the north at 8,000–10,000 feet. I was in the way of the latter formation, some of which accelerated to intercept me, but I dived out of their path. I climbed again to 16,000 feet and saw a formation of Ju 88s over Redhill going south, and I picked out one that was behind the rest.'

F/Lieut. Howell (after attacking two Me 110s in a dive and nearly colliding with one of them): 'I looked above me and saw a Me 110 spinning down with one wing completely broken away, and another exploded in mid-air, engine cowling and pieces of aircraft flying in every direction.' After which he attacked two Ju 88s.

P/O Agazarian: 'Three of us attacked the last Do 17s . . . As I broke away beneath I could see fire coming down at me at an angle of 80 degrees.' He went on to attack some Heinkels, 'but a bullet had gone through my oil sump and I force-landed at White Waltham.'

Considering that 609 had to climb to intercept, it was lucky to emerge yet again unscathed (except for 'Aggie's' engine) in its claim of two Me 110s, two Me 109's and two Do 17s destroyed, plus four enemy aircraft probably destroyed and another damaged. Claimants: MacArthur, Howell, Nowierski, Curchin, Feary, Staples, Ogilvie and Bisdee. Eleven pilots fired their guns, and afterwards the whole Squadron adjourned to a cocktail party given by actor Gordon Harker in aid of the Spitfire Fund. The party was no idle gesture, for on this day twenty-eight Spitfires and Hurricanes were lost by Fighter Command, with nineteen of their pilots. Forty German aircraft were destroyed but most of them were fighters and many bombers had attacked without opposition, for the first time using 3,600-lb. bombs. During the following night 247 more of them stoked the fires and added to the destruction, leaving 306 civilians killed and 1,337 severely injured. One of my own indelible memories is the awful glow and pall of smoke in the east. The damage was so great that this day the Luftwaffe really thought it was winning.

To fight over London a Spitfire squadron based in Wiltshire

had a distance to fly comparable with that of a Messerschmitt 109 squadron based behind Calais. The combat effectiveness of each was limited by fuel; but whereas 609 used up a good deal of this in manning a patrol line before engagement and the Me 109s could fly direct to the target, the penalty for over-indulgence in combat might for the latter be ditching in the Channel, while the former had only to seek the hospitality of an 11 Group airfield.

If, during the following week, 8th–14th September, some poor weather, plus the swift readjustment of Fighter Command to the new threat and some considerable Luftwaffe squabbling about the methods of fighter protection for bombers, caused a varying pattern in the London battle by day, the destruction, killing and maiming in darkness went on almost every night until late in the autumn, while the crash of bombs and the roar of the anti-aircraft barrage made sleep often impossible even for those off-duty. These attacks were carried out largely by bomber units of 10 Group's opposite number, *Luftflotte 3*, who, deprived of most of their single-engined fighters, were set their new night role with little time to train, and with Liverpool as an additional target.

But if effective defence against night attack was still lacking, it was only by day that important targets could be attacked with any precision, or Fighter Command brought to battle and destroyed. Yet during the next big encounter, on 9th September, not only was the capital much better defended, but Fighter Command destroyed much more of the Luftwaffe than *vice versa*. Though the Brooklands group of factories was again one of the three main targets, and 609 was there below cloud to act as a reception committee, the Luftwaffe never kept the appointment. On the 11th, when Brooklands was once more on the list, it is recorded that 609 was kept at home patrolling its own base, ready to intervene against new raids that took place on Portsmouth and Southampton. And although Hitler on this day postponed for three more days his decision about the invasion date (and on the 14th for another three), Bomber Command's successful attacks on the barges in the Channel ports, and its previous blocking of the Dortmund-Ems canal (their route from the Rhineland), probably had something to do with it.

Moreover, with the air fighting today favouring the Luftwaffe, who shot down twenty-nine British fighters (and claimed many more) against their own loss of only twenty-five, the German High Command decided that air supremacy was still on the cards, and the *Führer* himself that Britain might still be brought to her knees by air attack alone. The great test was to come on the 15th, which saw the most decisive battle since 15th August, exactly a month before. By the author of *Eagle Day* it is dubbed 'the greatest air battle of all time', and the 15th September has become known ever since as Battle of Britain Day.

At 11 a.m. on this Sunday morning great masses of German aircraft were plotted assembling over the French coast, and this time they flew straight for London without any of the usual feint attacks. So on this occasion Fighter Command was ready. Opposite page 244 of Basil Collier's great work, *The Defence of the United Kingdom*, is a map showing the disposition of the squadrons involved, as at 11.30 : eleven squadrons of 11 Group, mostly operating in their now standard teamed-up pairs (Hurricanes v. bombers, Spitfires v. fighters); Bader's 'big wing' of five squadrons coming in from 12 Group in the north, and a long thin arrow marked '609' to indicate the single squadron from 10 Group in the west.

This last had reached the Brooklands-Windsor line at 15,000 feet, with MacArthur of 'B' Flight leading the Squadron, when Howell's 'A' flight was detached to investigate what the London A.A. guns were shooting at. It turned out to be twenty-five–thirty Dorniers in two formations flying west at 17,000 feet over the centre of the city, escorted by many Me 109 fighters on both sides and above. MacArthur led 'B' flight in line astern up to 20,000 feet and turned in to attack 'from ahead of beam. I overshot a bit and finished up ahead of the bombers, encountering very heavy forward fire.'

When the enemy fighters intervened as well, it evidently became for 'B' Flight a case of *sauve qui peut*. Appleby, leading Green Section, reported : 'I attempted to turn sharply to starboard to meet the approaching fighters head-on, but my aircraft started to spin and I had to half-loop out, losing height.' And one pilot was lost.

'A' flight, though eventually more successful, also had a close call because four Hurricanes above them did not attack. Complained Howell: 'We waited for them, and waiting became dangerous as the 109s were starting to come down, so I broke away left and swung round in front and underneath' before attacking. Dundas, leader of Yellow Section, takes up the story. As befitting the master warrior he had by now become, he evidently treated the enemy fighters with calm disdain:

'Having received no orders on the R.T., and thinking it unwise to wait around under the Messerschmitts for too long, I turned in and attacked a bomber in the centre of the formation from below and the beam, and saw one of its motors stop. On breaking away I was attacked by a 109 from above and astern. After evading this I made a second attack on the Dorniers, this time from almost vertically below. I was then attacked by three Me 109s which peeled off from 2,000 feet above but gave themselves away by opening fire at excessive range. They did not stay to fight. . . .'

Early that morning Dundas had awakened 'Red' Tobin, and when the latter protestingly asked why, is said to have replied: 'I'm not quite sure, old boy. They say there's an invasion on or something.' (*Eagle Day*)

And today it was the American, 'Red' Tobin, and the new Canadian, Keith Ogilvie, both of 'A' flight, who achieved the greatest distinction. For a thrilling account of the former's battle, presumably based on his diary, see *Eagle Day*. In his combat report he stated merely that he was about to attack a Dornier when he noticed three yellow-nosed 109s coming down behind. He throttled back, made a 360-degree turn, then attacked one of his erstwhile pursuers in a dive that for Tobin ended when his adversary was absorbed by clouds at 8,000 feet. Climbing up again to 10,000 feet, he saw a lone Dornier making for the same clouds, and with a feeling of 'now or never' attacked it before it got there, pulverizing its port aileron and producing a satisfactory stream of white smoke – glycol coolant – from its port engine. This time 'I followed it down through clouds and saw a Dornier 17 make a crash-landing two or three miles east of Biggin Hill. Three of the crew got out and sat on the wing.' Though he honestly admitted to some uncertainty that it was the same aircraft, he was in fact deservedly recognized as its conqueror.

Ogilvie's proof was photographic. Though he too modestly admitted that he was not the only attacker – and in fact Sergeant Holmes of 504 Squadron (who ended up by rolling off a Chelsea roof into a dustbin after baling out) also made a claim – Keith's attack (his own third) must have been the decisive one, for his 16-mm cine-camera, mounted in the wings like the eight Browning .303 guns and synchronized with them, recorded a film showing an almost wingless Dornier fuselage in one part of the sky and its tail-unit in another. He wrote : 'I could see fire in the Dornier's cockpit. As I went beneath it I saw two men jump and their para-chutes open' – the whole disintegration being 'a most amazing and terrifying sight.' The two German aviators landed on the Oval (fortunately without disturbing any cricket), whereas the main part of their aeroplane arrived in the forecourt of Victoria Station, and the tail-unit (as is recorded in the Squadron's war diary) 'just outside a Pimlico public house, to the great comfort and joy of the patrons'. Their joy was shared by royalty :

> Dienst Van H. M. de Koningin,
> Der Nederland,
> 82, Eaton Square,
> London S.W.1.
> 17 September, 1940.

I am commanded by Her Majesty Queen Wilhelmina of the Netherlands, to convey to you Her Majesty was most gratified to see from Her London House a german bomber shot down by an eight gun fighter during the air battle in the morning of 15th September.

Her Majesty would be very pleased if Her congratulations should be conveyed to the Squadron concerned in this battle and to the pilot who shot down the german aircraft.

> (Signed Major General de Jonge Van Ellemeet
> Aide de Comp on service.
>
> To :—The Air Ministry,
> London.

The above message, together with one addressed to No. 609 Squadron from Headquarters, Fighter Command, ordering that no publicity was to be given to it, is in front of me as I write, pasted on an early page of the notebook that Keith Ogilvie in-herited the same day from his mate, Geoffrey Gaunt. For at last the Squadron's long run of luck had ended, and one of only a dozen pilots lost during the whole of this great day was Geoffrey Gaunt, who like Gordon Mitchell was an only son. They and David Crook, who introduced Geoffrey to the Squadron, had all been together at The Leys School. By the luck of the draw David was on leave at home in Yorkshire when Mrs. Gaunt telephoned Mrs. Crook to say her son was missing. Though greatly upset, in his book David wrote :

'I don't think his death was altogether a surprise to me, because for some time past I had the feeling that he would not survive this war. I had the same feeling about some other friends . . . and two months before Gordon's death I told Dorothy I was sure he would be killed. . . . On the other hand, I am firmly convinced that some other people, Michael for instance, will not be killed. I cannot explain this feeling; it is not based on their qualities as pilots, because they were all good pilots. . . .'

He was right again about Michael Appleby, who I can testify is very much alive today. Happily David appears to have had no premonition about himself.

As Big Ben, on this memorable Sunday, boomed out the hour of one p.m., Germany lost the chance of winning not only the Battle of Britain, but probably the whole war. About an hour earlier Churchill, grimly watching the progress of the battle in the 11 Group operations room fifty feet underground, and noting that all available squadrons were engaged, had asked his famous question, 'What other reserves have we?' – only to be told by the A.O.C., Park, 'There are none.' Had the Luftwaffe been commanded by a military genius the strokes of Big Ben would have sounded the death-knell of Britain as the seventeen squadrons which had just been engaged were destroyed on the ground as they refuelled and rearmed. According to the author of *The Luftwaffe War Diaries*, the Germans were unable to provide a fresh fighter escort in time, but (in my humble opinion) genius would have recognized that at this moment no escort was necessary. As it was, when the second, and heavier, attack on London was made, the defence was again ready, and despite a shorter warning period, was stronger.

Statistically, one of the few fighter aircraft airborne during the vital interval was, strangely, that of 'Red' Tobin, who is recorded as having taken off at 13.15 from Biggin Hill (where he evidently landed and refuelled after his combat), and as having regained his base at Middle Wallop twenty-five minutes later. *Eagle Day* has it that he landed, straight from his combat, with only seven gallons left, only to write off his Spitfire on hitting the Middle Wallop crash-waggon that suddenly shot from behind a hangar, and consequently missing the following operation, in which both his American colleagues were engaged. Strangely, that arch-recorder of accidents, Flight-Sergeant Cloves, makes no mention of this one.

In the afternoon 609 was ordered off only at 14.30 – ten minutes after the enemy had crossed the Kentish coast – and so was employed to harry him long after he had done his bombing and was on the way out. From the Brooklands-Kenley patrol line Darley led his squadron south-east in a climb, thereby placing it in what he for once reported as 'a very advantageous position'. Two formations of Dorniers were sighted near the coast, but they were in a flat-out dive for home from high altitude, and only two unfortunate stragglers were caught. Assailed by a swarm of thirteen Spitfires, they were overwhelmed. With few German fighters left to protect them (for only MacArthur was attacked by one), it was so easy that Michael Appleby reverted to old-time training jargon and ordered, 'Green Section, No. 1 Attack, Go!' – only to find that his followers were already attacking in less classical fashion. One Dornier turned back and force-landed ten miles north of Hastings ('I saw two Germans climb out and waited till I saw them captured,' reported Mike Staples), the other spun into the sea without any wings, two of the crew baling out after the ever-observant Howell had seen them ejecting packets of marker dye. Keith Ogilvie followed one of the Germans down to the sea and later wrote, 'He waved wildly, figuring I was going to machine-gun him'. Though Dundas had been hit by return fire, he and Howell obligingly took different bearings to enable the German to be rescued.

While 609 and another Middle Wallop squadron were away assisting 11 Group, the enemy took advantage of their absence by staging a simultaneous raid on Portland in their own home Sector, with only the third Middle Wallop squadron left to oppose him. And at 17.40 609 took off for the third time to help deal with the final raid of the day, on Southampton, in which there seem to have been few positive results for either side. When the day ended, Air Ministry made its biggest and most exaggerated claim of the whole Battle of Britain : 185 enemy aircraft destroyed. Nothing like that number of wrecked German planes could be found, and in fact the score was only fifty-six, including twenty-four Dorniers, for four of which 609 could supply pretty concrete evidence. But many other enemy aircraft limped home in a very unserviceable state, and for the Germans the day was a serious defeat. To quote *The Defence of the United Kingdom* :

'If 15th August showed the German High Command that air supremacy was not to be won within a brief space, 15th September went far to convince them that it would not be won at all.'

Though the invasion of England went on being talked about for some weeks more, it was in fact no longer possible, and perhaps it is not surprising that two days later Hitler said to Sperrle's chief of staff : 'The world would have been much better off if the aeroplane had never been invented.'

During the week that followed Luftwaffe activity by day was much reduced owing to some bad weather and no doubt the need for repairs, and London was let off relatively lightly. Though 609 was several times again on patrol over the 11 Group area, activity was now increasing again in its own, with *Luftflotte 3* evidently once more in possession of its single-engined fighters. On the 21st a new and ineffectual raid by two aircraft on Middle Wallop itself ('One appeared with a Hurricane on his tail and hurriedly dropped some heavy stuff behind the officers' mess, but only made some nice holes in the ground,' wrote Cloves), coincided with the start of a fresh wave of attacks on aircraft factories. On the 24th the target was the Supermarine works at Woolston near Southampton, and though there was little damage, about a hundred of the staff were killed or wounded in a shelter. But about the nature of the enemy force and how it fared there is a strange conflict of evidence. The only published account that I can find describes the raiders as Me 109 fighter-bombers, who afterwards 'for twenty minutes trailed their coats. Not a British fighter was to be seen, but the A.A. guns blazed away and shot down one German aircraft.' (*Narrow Margin*.)

Yet at least half a dozen combatant eye-witnesses from No. 609 Squadron, including a trained journalist (Dundas), not only testified that the raiders consisted of Dorniers escorted by both Me 110s and Me 109s, but shot several of them down :

Yellow 1 (*Dundas*): 'Fired dead astern at starboard Dornier . . . heavy return fire . . . Broke away and saw a number of Me 110s coming down. One shot past my tail. They started to form a circle but soon gave up and made off for France . . . A lone straggler went into a steep climbing turn. We circled round each other for some time, but I could easily hold his climb and turn inside him. I fired . . . he went into a spin, the tail came off and he dived straight into the sea.'

Yellow 3 (*Miller*): 'Attacked a Dornier with Red 2 (Feary), which crashed south of the Isle of Wight.'

Red 3 (*Staples*): 'Attacked two Dorniers, second from astern. Fire started in cabin. Spun into sea.'

Green 1 (*Curchin*): 'Dogfighted with a single-engined fighter which eventually went into sea. Looked different to a Me 109 – probably a (French) Morane.'

Yellow 4 (*Ogilvie*) *in his diary:* 'My wireless packed up at a most inopportune time and I had to guess what was going on. "Dogs" Dundas was leading Yellow section and I stuck to him like a brother . . . I attacked a Do 17 and had his port engine on fire. From about 20,000 feet he dove for the sea – I waited for the splash, and was my face red when he levelled off and went like a ding-bat for home ! I dove after him and caught him about thirty miles out to sea. But flying Betsy at "the gate" had poured oil over my perspex and I couldn't see . . . Nearly rammed him on one attack. Emptied my guns . . . but I'm afraid he got home alright.' *

Next morning, 25th September, there was a much more formidable attack on the Bristol Aeroplane Works at Filton—target for a mixed force of He 111 and Do 17 bombers, Me 110s and (it seems) some Me 109s, presumably sweeping independently. Though Filton itself was a fighter Sector, no squadron was based there at this moment,

*The actual 'bag for 24th September 1940 is at Appendix D-Ed.

and though 10 Group put up three and a quarter squadrons, the enemy concealed his intentions by making a diversionary attack on Portland and also flying over Yeovil, causing Control to think that the Westland aircraft works there was the intended target. 609, after successive instructions to patrol first Portland, then Swanage, then Yeovil, only caught up with the main raid thirty-five minutes after becoming airborne, just as it was reaching Bristol. Acting swiftly, Darley made an initial down-sun interception before the bombing, but though this doubtless helped, his men were too few, and the enemy too many, to prevent an attack that curtailed bomber production for many weeks and killed or wounded over 250 people. Darley recalls:

'There were three large arrow-head formations of about sixty aircraft each, and above this lot about 30 Me 110s. As we were the only squadron on the scene, the odds were about 20 to 1. Being the first in, I had a most uneasy feeling that at least 200 rear gunners were firing at me! After our first attack, the A.A. opened up, so the amount of lead whistling about the sky was prodigious. The next thing was a realisation that three Me 110s were on my tail, and I had quite a tussle with them until I ran out of ammo. As far as I can recall, we all got back safely, but how on earth we all escaped being shot down is still a mystery!'

There were indeed some narrow shaves. Dundas reported that the enemy were so tightly packed together that not only was it unnecessary and impossible to aim at a separate aircraft, but that he was nearly hit by bombs falling from aircraft above him. Sergeant Hughes-Rees, a Welshman who had recently joined the Squadron (and was destined to remain with it for a long time) made a wheels-up landing in a field near Glastonbury, and both Newbery and Ostaszewski pulled out of a power-dive with such violence that they bent their Spitfires' wings and shattered the perspex hoods. In addition Newbery's seat was torn clean off its fastenings, and the pilot was taken to hospital with severe internal injuries. But probably the narrowest escape was Keith Ogilvie's:

'I was giving a Dornier hell and both engines were streaming glycol when there was a gigantic "pow" and a nice hole appeared in my right wing. Immediately saw a 109 quite close behind, and it was evident he didn't want to be my valentine. I only shook him off after he had sent another through my tail, one up my fuselage exploding in my wireless, and one in my port wing puncturing that tyre. Certainly my closest call yet.'

And after all that this modest, courageous little Canadian from Ottawa still went on fighting:

'Caught a chap close to the water, but could only get one engine smoking before my ammo gave out ... Nearly turned over on landing, but got away with it.'

Perhaps more astonishing still is that he still had some fuel, for despite several combats he had been airborne from 11.10 till 12.25 – longer than anyone else.

609 went on harrying the armada all the way back to the English Channel and the final action – involving Miller, Agazarian, Curchin and Nowierski – was against a straggling trio of Heinkel 111s over Bournemouth. One crashed into a house near Poole harbour after three of the crew had baled out; the second made a successful landing in a field near Swanage, and the third had the effrontery to machine-gun a flying boat in Poole harbour. Altogether 609 claimed six destroyed. The Secretary of State for Air again congratulated the Squadron, which had landed with scarcely a round of ammunition or a gallon of fuel left between them.

On the following day, about tea-time, fifty bombers and fighter-bombers, with escort, made another attack on the Supermarine works at Woolston. Evidently misleading the defence about their intentions, they got there unopposed except by anti-aircraft fire, and did some effective bombing. For a short time no further Spitfires could be produced, a Southampton warehouse full of grain was gutted, and thirty more people were killed. Four 10 and 11 Group squadrons were scrambled, but it is not certain whether all eventually engaged. Darley's report states that 609, ordered to patrol base, then Bournemouth at 20,000 feet, first sighted the enemy force south of the Needles, when it turned north-east towards Southampton, and evidently it was then too late to intercept it before it got there. When he did, Darley appointed 'A' flight as top guard to deal with the fighters, and himself led 'B' flight against the bombers, only to have his starboard aileron struck from astern by a fighter cannon shell. And once again Ogilvie was giving and getting into trouble. After 'playing ring-around-a-rosy with a 109', he was soon on the tail of 'a huge Heinkel. I could see yellow flashes as my bullets hit, but he soaked it up. His rear gunner was no sissy and threw plenty back, bouncing a couple off my wings and putting one through the main spar.'

From this encounter Dundas and Agazarian each claimed a Me 109 destroyed, and Curchin a He 111 – with other enemy planes damaged or 'probable'. Whether the other squadrons made claims I do not know, but the Luftwaffe's loss was in fact three aircraft, the R.A.F.'s six aircraft and two pilots.

Next day, 27th September, it was Bristol again, and London – though this time with a difference, inasmuch as in both cases the main raiders were bomb-carrying Me 110s escorted by Me 109s. The era of massed daylight raids by 'real' bombers – Dornier 17s, Heinkel 111s and Junkers 88s – was nearly over, and the twin-engined Messerschmitt 110, which to Goering's bitter disappointment had failed dismally as a day fighter, now assumed the first of its many future roles (of which the most bizarre was to be the transport of Rudolf Hess to Scotland in the belief that his pre-war 'friend', the Duke of Hamilton, possessed the authority to stop the war). Even a third of the Me 109s, to the disgust of their pilots, became earmarked as fighter-bombers. Such raids not only came in higher and faster, making them more difficult both to detect and intercept, but – since radar could not determine whether an approaching formation carried bombs or not – greatly increased the scope for deception.

This day, however, represented one of the early experiments, and to judge from messages sent to the relevant squadrons by the Secretary of State for Air (Sir Archibald Sinclair), the C.-in-C. (Air Chief Marshal Dowding), and Sir Stanley White of the Bristol Aeroplane Company (via Lord Beaverbrook), 10 Group this time managed to prevent all but ten fighter-bombers and some fighters (out of a force of eighty) from reaching the target, while the scrambling of 504 Squadron (now based at Filton itself) compelled even these to jettison their bombs indiscriminately over the Bristol suburbs. Sir Stanley signalled that the fighter squadrons 'undoubtedly saved the factory from serious damage and heartened and encouraged all the factory employees'. He wished 'thanks and appreciation to be conveyed to all concerned'.

Yet 609 was critical. In the words of its diary, 'For the second time in three days No. 10 Group Control positioned the Squadron so badly that they had little or no chance of catching any of the bombers over the coast'. These had been seen, already to the north, far above at 18,000 feet, and the next thing that happened was that 609 Squadron was itself nearly broken up by a squadron of Hurricanes that dived on them out of the sun. And to make things still more difficult the radio sets both of Darley, commanding the Squadron and leading 'B' flight, and of Dundas, leading 'A' flight, packed up, leaving Pilot-Officer Miller, in command of Yellow section, to lead the attack on some fifteen Me 110s which were circling Warmwell at 23,000 feet, presumably as additional fighter escort.

'We climbed around them,' Dundas reported, 'then dived into the middle of the circle. I saw Yellow 1 collide with a 110 while executing a beam attack.'

Right behind Miller in Yellow section was Ogilvie, who confided to his diary:

'The 110 turned out to get his cannon working on Mick, and they hit head-on. There was a terrific explosion, a sheet of flame and a column of black smoke. I glimpsed a Spitfire wing fluttering out and the white of a parachute with something on the end. It was ghastly. Somehow I shot straight up, half-rolled, and coming down saw a 110 float under me. I pressed the button and kept it pressed and he went straight down in a sheet of flame. The whole vicious action lasted only a few moments.'

The circle was now disintegrating, with the enemy planes streaming out to sea, hotly pursued. With no single-engined fighters above to help them, it was murder. Two plunged into the sea, shot down by Dundas and Agazarian. Crook hit another, and when to his disgust his ammunition ran out, he heard a voice on the R.T. saying, 'O.K., O.K., help coming!' and Bisdee overtook him, to pursue and finish off the job sixty miles out from the coast. Two more were apparently hit in the first beam encounter by Staples and Forshaw – though the latter involuntarily taught a lesson in deflection shooting by admitting the one that was hit was not the one he was aiming at. It spun down in flames, its pilot landing by parachute on *terra firma* ('I circled till he was captured by some local farmers'), while Staples last saw his limping only fifty feet over the water towards Poole harbour, with both engines seemingly done for.

Altogether, seven of the enemy were claimed destroyed – including of course the one rammed by Miller – and on this occasion the evidence for at least five seems completely authentic. 609's contribution had evidently been to deprive the raiders of one whole escort formation. The total enemy loss for the day, including the London raid, was fifty-five, while Fighter Command lost twenty-eight aircraft.

Miller, 'whose loss was deplored by his associates', the diary records, had joined the Squadron at Northolt on the 26th of June.

The last day of September saw the last big daylight raids by twin-engined German bombers, both against London and the west, as well as others by the new fighter-bombers. 'The weather was brilliantly clear,' wrote David Crook, 'and when we got up we shook our heads dismally, as we knew there would be a lot of trouble. As Mac used to remark, "we should have a job to keep the Grim Reaper at bay".'

609's first scramble was at ten-thirty, when once again it was sent to defend London. Inside half an hour, however, it was recalled and five minutes later, without time to refuel, sent towards the south coast. They were still climbing when the Middle Wallop controller called on the R.T.: 'Hello, Sorbo leader, more than 100 bandits approaching Swanage, angels twenty' – and got the answer from Frankie Howell, 'Your message received and understood.'

This enemy force consisted of Me 110 fighter-bombers escorted by Me 109 fighters, but on this occasion 609 only encountered the latter. As soon as they were spotted in the distance, Howell led the Squadron out over Weymouth Bay and made the approach to landward and down-sun at a height of some 27,000 feet. 'A' and 'B' flights then split to intercept different enemy formations. Yellow section were attacked by six Me 109s 200 feet above them, but were saved from the enemy fire when their leader, Bisdee, promptly ordered them to break to port. He himself hit one of the assailants before being attacked and himself hit by more of them, and Ogilvie recorded: 'We tangled with a 109 circus and I found myself a playmate. He had too much staff for Junior, and though he got a deflection shot which floated across in front of me, I never got a shot at him.'

'B' flight was led by Michael Appleby, at the head of Blue Section, with his friend and fellow Auxiliary David Crook leading Green. When six other Me 109s inadvertently flew across their bows, it became their day. David wrote in his book:

'We all went down after them in one glorious rush and I saw Michael, about a hundred yards ahead, open fire on the last Messerschmitt in the enemy line. A few seconds later this machine more or less fell to pieces in mid-air – some very nice shooting on Michael's part. I distinctly remember him saying on the R.T., "That's got you, you bastard."

'What a dive it was! I came down on full throttle from 27,000 feet to 1,000 feet in a few seconds, and the speed rose with incredible swiftness to 600 m.p.h. I never reached this speed before and probably never shall again . . .I pulled out as gently as I could, but there was a sort of black mist in front of my eyes.'

Right down on the water he proceeded to shoot two Me 109s into the sea, the second after a long chase that took him to a few miles off the Cherbourg peninsula. And when this German pilot was finally at his mercy, Crook admitted that pity nearly made him desist – though in fact this fight, unlike that of yesterday, was equally matched in quality of aircraft, and in numbers evidently favoured the enemy.

In the afternoon forty Heinkel 111 bombers, escorted by both Me 109s and Me 110s, were sent to attack the Westland aircraft works at Yeovil. Harried by British fighters both ways, they even had to bomb blind – thanks to a layer of cloud – when they arrived, and it was near-by Sherborne that suffered. For 609, to quote its diary, 'the now customary tea-time scramble led to a second engagement over Swanage with a 100-plus mixed raid. The Squadron was outnumbered and out-manoeuvred and only three pilots were able to get to grips with the enemy.'

Two of these were Crook again and Nowierski, both of Green section, which was sent by Howell to investigate six aircraft to port and below, which Crook first thought were Hurricanes. They turned out to be Me 109s, one of which Crook in all probability destroyed after a protracted dogfight in and out of cloud, and another of which was definitely accounted for by 'Novo', for its pilot baled out. (It is indicative of Polish feeling about the Germans that the former is said to have rejoiced when the parachute failed to open.)

The third pilot to be engaged was Noël Agazarian of Blue section, who was weaving at the back of the Squadron when five Me 109s came up behind. On turning to confront them, they dived away and he lost the Squadron as well. He then decided to make a solo attack on the rearmost of the returning Heinkels, but though he hit its starboard engine and produced a lot of black smoke, he was worse hit himself, and reported wryly that the return fire from the enemy bombers was 'highly concentrated'. Evidently it was, for the Heinkels also accounted for no less than four Hurricanes, and a Me 110 for a fifth.

Altogether, in this last flare-up of the great daylight battles, Fighter Command destroyed forty-seven of the Luftwaffe, and itself lost twenty aircraft and eight pilots killed or wounded. Assessing the work that the Luftwaffe had provided for himself and his men, Flight-Sergeant Cloves recorded in his factual way:

'N3113 (Pilot-Officer Bisdee) shot through main planes, air-screw, fuselage and tail unit, but got back safely. Few minor holes in R6961 (Flying-Officer Novo) fixed with patching technique. Pilot-Officer Agazarian in R6915 * had his glycol system shot away and force-landed at Warmwell.'

* This was the second time this Spitfire and pilot had force-landed, and it was also damaged by enemy action on two other occasions, the second of them 7th October, when Dundas was wounded. Altogether it was flown on operations by thirteen different pilots, including Darley. It now hangs in the Imperial War Museum, credited with a score of five enemy aircraft destroyed and three damaged.

3

The fifth and final phase of the Battle of Britain is generally considered to have lasted for the month of October, 1940, and then to have ended. For 609, with a few subsequent defensive engagements, it went on, in effect, till the end of the year – and under different leadership.

Squadron-Leader H. S. ('George') Darley had led his squadron in the air for the last time on 26th September, when he was taken ill. Eleven days earlier Flight-Lieutenant 'Butch' MacArthur had ruined his ears during the afternoon engagement of the memorable 15th. Finding his oxygen had failed, he had put 'B' flight in Appleby's charge and then, all alone, been attacked by a Me 109. Without oxygen a dogfight at 25,000 feet could have but one result: he became unconscious, fell about five miles in a few seconds, and only recovered at 2,000 feet. He was succeeded by Dundas, and on 9th October both of them, as well as Frankie Howell, who had led 'A' flight since Dunkirk, were awarded the D.F.C. – the first such awards since the posthumous one of 'Hack' Russell. Darley won the D.S.O., and in response to the Squadron's letter of congratulation (for he had departed five days before), wrote in characteristic fashion:

'I thank you all for your extremely kind letter, but hasten to assure you that your congratulations are entirely misdirected. That award is due to the whole Squadron – pilots, N.C.O.s and airmen – who all backed me up whatever I asked them to do. Please convey my gratitude to them all.'

He wrote from Exeter, to which he had been posted as station commander, with the rank of Wing-Commander. As he was leaving, John Bisdee recalls, 'We all stood in rows with tears streaming down our cheeks'. Far more than the chants of 'For he's a jolly good fellow,' with which officers and men tried to disguise them, the tears betrayed the depth of gratitude and affection they all felt towards the leader who had first saved them from disaster, then fashioned them into a squadron second to none, full of exuberance and self-confidence. Yet now this same man, who during three long months had demanded such effort and high standards from all ranks, simply (in the words of David Crook) 'stood there, looking exactly like a rather sheepish schoolboy, while we all sang at the top of our voices'.

His successor, Michael Lister Robinson, was probably already known by sight, for he had just spent precisely one week as a flight-commander (like MacArthur before him) in 238 Squadron, now back in the Middle Wallop sector. Immediately before that he had been training the raw recruits who now formed two-thirds of 601 Squadron during its unhappy and temporary eclipse as a 'C'-class squadron at Exeter. Though he too was destined to leave his own indelible mark on 609 Squadron, it is hardly strange that at first he was regarded with suspicion, and by a few with dislike. Blue-blooded, (he was the son of Sir Roy, later Lord Robinson, chairman of the Forestry Commission), exquisitely handsome and immaculately clad, he looked like some pilot of romantic musical comedy who had somehow strayed across the footlights. As yet undecorated, he was doubtless considered by some as a fop and a dandy, ill-equipped to lead a squadron of veteran pilots.

For veterans they were. No less than six of them – the three remaining Auxiliaries Dundas, Appleby and Crook, plus Howell, Overton and Bisdee – had flown and fought together since the far-off days of Dunkirk. Others, like Curchin, Feary, Agazarian, Staples and the two Poles, Nowierski and Ostaszewski, were not far behind in experience, and even the 'baby' of the Squadron, Keith Ogilvie, apart from impressing the Queen of the Netherlands on 15th September, had flown on every one of the subsequent ten missions, been in combat during four out of five successive days, knocked down or damaged Luftwaffe planes on three of them, and twice managed to land his own damaged aircraft successfully. Not surprisingly he confided to his diary :

'I find that slowly I'm learning a few tricks of dog-fighting and of the value of conserving ammunition. Live and learn, I suppose. The two certainly go hand in hand in this racket.'

As far as New World wit and humour were concerned, this lone little Canadian took over the tradition founded by the three Americans, and especially 'Red' Tobin, who much to their own and their comrades' regret had departed to help form the first all-American Eagle Squadron, with which they and many others all tragically perished in 1941. That Keith Ogilvie joined 609 at all seems to have been partly fluke, partly skilful manoeuvre. After failing in his application to join the R.C.A.F. before the war, he approached the R.A.F., heard nothing for months, but at the eleventh hour was granted a short-service commission in the summer of 1939. After completing his service training on twin-engined aircraft together with a group of Oxford University graduates that included Leonard (later Group-Captain) Cheshire, his 'dreams of fame and fortune via the shot-and-shell route were abruptly dashed' when he was posted to Central Flying School as an instructor. There, however, it turned out that the 'wonderful elderly gentleman' who was his flying partner was a buddy of no less an officer than 'Boom' Trenchard, and when the latter appeared on one of his ubiquitous visits, 'an impassioned plea on behalf of the young fella from Canada who had come all the way, etc.' was successfully made, and the next step was to the first O.T.U., formed from the survivors of No. 1 Squadron after the Battle of France, which had also been attended by Richard Hillary and Noël Agazarian.

'They never asked what I had been flying before (namely twin-engines), and checked me out on a Harvard, a Master and (day of days) a Spitfire. I applied for the all-Canadian Squadron, Doug Bader's, but was advised that there were no vacancies. Instead they would send me to a good Spitfire Squadron, No. 609.'

So far as the West Riding Squadron was concerned, it was Canada's best-ever contribution. After thirty years Darley still remembers him as 'very pleasant, most courteous and well-spoken', as well as a 'keen and capable pilot'.

On the same day as the new C.O. there arrived two more Polish pilots, from 234 Squadron in Cornwall – J. Zurakowski and Z. Olenski. (The 'Z' stood for 'Zbigniev', but as such a name was much too difficult for English-speaking tongues, it was promptly changed by Ogilvie to 'Big Enough'.)

The last phase of the Battle of Britain was for the British fighters perhaps the most dangerous, inasmuch as the enemy, using fighter-bombers escorted by fighters, or sometimes fighters alone, was able to concentrate the latter at altitudes beyond the effective reach of the Spitfire or Hurricane Mk. I. Above 25,000 feet the Me 109, with its two-stage supercharger, could outmatch even the Mk. II versions of these aircraft. Exploiting this advantage, the enemy evidently planned his patrols, in the words of David Crook, 'with the sole intention of annoying us and killing as many of us as possible'.

For 609 such a situation occurred on 7th October – a day so bright and clear that even from 15,000 feet, Crook recorded, South Wales, Cornwall and the Channel Islands were clearly visible at the same time. Together with 238 Squadron on their flank they had been sent to Weymouth to intercept a raid of 'fifty plus' consisting of Me 109s, Me 110s and even some Ju 88s, which is said this time to have succeeded in dropping eighty-six bombs on or near the Westland aircraft works at Yeovil. 609 had nearly reached Weymouth at 19,000 feet when an enemy formation (evidently the Ju 88s) was sighted some miles out to sea, but with Me 110s between the Squadron and them. Simultaneously there was a babel of voices on the R.T. as various people drew attention to a lot of Me 109s right overhead. Michael Robinson, in his first 609 personal combat report, wrote :

'238 suddenly appeared to break up . . . It was extremely bright, and as we were heading into the sun extremely difficult to pick out enemy aircraft ahead – also we were rather embarrassed by the Me 109s above us. I ordered the Squadron into sections line astern and turned beneath the 109s, then saw a circle of Me 110s just ahead and proceeded to attack.'

In the *mêlée* that followed the Squadron became split up and there were a number of individual actions. The C.O., after disposing of one Me 110, climbed up again and asked whether control could give him the position of any more. He was told they had one plotted over Lyme Regis. Proceeding in that direction he found the same or another Me 110 circle ten miles north-west of Portland, and again brought down one of them. Frankie Howell set a third 110 on fire but his own engine seized up on being hit by the rear gunner and he had to force-land, wheels up, in a field near Shaftesbury. His No. 2, John Bisdee, attacked a fourth which came down in another field near Cerne Abbas. Sergeant Hughes-Rees seems to have picked a fight with the Me 109s, and severed the wing of one of them before being attacked by another. Mike Staples, shot in the thigh, baled out of his flaming cockpit at 21,000 feet and landed by parachute near Blandford Forum. John Dundas, after putting both engines of yet another Me 110 out of action, was hit from astern by an explosive cannon shell and landed at Warmwell with many bits of shrapnel in his leg; and Sergeant Feary was killed after baling out too low.

Though five of the enemy were claimed as 'definite', it had been an expensive action in aircraft and pilots, for apart from Feary, Staples never flew with 609 again. He had lost much blood on his slow descent, and was in Blandford Hospital for some time. John Bisdee remembers that when he went to visit him there, he was reading a pile of letters from the local school children, who had been set the topical task of writing 'to our pilot in the hospital'. When he did return to flying, it was with 604, John Cunningham's night-fighter squadron, and he tragically lost his life when in the dark he hit a hill almost in the Middle Wallop circuit.

About Alan Feary it is recorded in 609 Squadron's diary:

'He seemed to regard his Spitfire with the kind of jealous care and affection that some others bestow upon animals, and the notion has been advanced by those who knew him well that this trait in his character may have contributed to the loss of his life, causing reluctance to bale out from a spin which he was unable to control.'

For months the Squadron's only N.C.O. pilot, he must at times have felt dreadfully lonely, yet he had fought right through the summer with distinction that should have earned him a decoration. 'He was most reliable at all times. I never found a single fault in him.' The words, again thirty years afterwards, are those of his commanding officer.

Dundas, after dismounting, made his way unaided to the Warmwell sick quarters and typically enough was flying again the very next day. Howell was unhurt, but returned somewhat inebriated after being forcibly entertained for some hours by the Shaftesbury police and local inhabitants. His aircraft, conceded Cloves, was 'not badly damaged'.

Two days previously 609 had suffered the total loss of a Spitfire when Nowierski was unable to lower more than one wheel. Crook, flying beside him, told him on the R.T. that he must bale out. This he did over Salisbury Plain, 'and a few minutes later dropped into the middle of a hen run, to the consternation of the poultry' – and, apparently, of Crook, who seeing the local population rush towards him, feared that Novo, with his broken English, might be mistaken for a German parachutist. And the day after that many pilots of 609 were nearly written off in the officers' mess, to which they had retired to drink beer and play billiards because the weather precluded all flight, when a sharp whistle of descending bombs caused much spilling of beer as officers hurled themselves to the floor, and two terrific explosions rocked the building to its foundations. No one denied that it was a piece of marvellous navigation on the part of the German raider, and it so surprised Johnny Curchin, himself about to navigate the red into a cloudless pocket, that he reacted by flinging his billiards cue through the window and breaking it. He and the others probably regarded this effort to knock them out on the ground as a Luftwaffe compliment.

Michael Robinson's claim of two Me 110s destroyed in the course of his very first operational sortie on a Spitfire did much to convince the team he had taken over that, though they might not yet be accustomed to him, as a pilot he was as good as any of them. Just a week before he had made exactly the same claim while flying a Hurricane. No doubts were raised on either occasion, and having later interrogated him many times myself, I know that, whatever the bewildering and even contradictory facets of this unusual man, he never boasted of anything that he had not achieved.

On 15th October – a day when German fighter-bombers also blocked all but two of the lines at London's Waterloo Station – 609 had one of its luckiest escapes yet. Ordered to intercept a raid of fighters and fighter-bombers stepped up from 16,000 to 30,000 feet near Southampton, and arriving on the scene at a mere 10,000 feet, sun, altitude and numbers were all against them. Crook wrote:

'We were in a hopeless position, a long way below and outlined against the white cloud underneath us. However, we continued to climb and all the time watched the Messerschmitts like cats, as sooner or later they would obviously drop down on us. Suddenly I saw two Me 109s just behind John's Spitfire. I never saw them come down and they must have dived very fast ... I immediately shouted on the R.T., "Look out, Messerschmitts!" and never saw the Squadron break up so quickly.'

And somehow the tables were turned. The same John (Dundas) wrote in his personal combat report:

'Their aim must have been very poor, and only Blue 2 was hit ... I tried to reform "B" flight in vain and my transmittor began to fade, so climbed up alone and executed two beam attacks on a circus of fifteen to twenty Me 110s at 18,000 feet over Christchurch. Had to break away after each attack to avoid the Me 109s above, and after the second was chased for some time by two of them.'

The pilot who was hit was Noël Agazarian, one bullet piercing his cockpit hood just above his head. Despite this, it seems that when the Squadron broke and dived away, he and Nowierski boldly stayed aloft and immediately delivered a successful counter-attack on two of the enemy. Noël's was a 'flamer', Novo's disappeared into cloud, but was followed by his fellow-countryman Olenski, who saw it crash after the pilot had baled out.

This brought the West Riding Squadron's tally of victories credited to it by Fighter Command to ninety-nine—as shown on the pad of numbers on the wall of its dispersal hut, one sheet of which was gleefully torn off, like a day from a calendar, each time the Squadron shot down one of the Luftwaffe. And now, as five whole days went by without a chance to reach the century, the tension was so great that one pilot remarked despondently:

'We shall still be here this time next year, with grey hairs, long beards and the score on the wall still reading ninety-nine.'

But on the morning of 21st October it happened, and 609

became, it is said, the first Spitfire* squadron to be credited with one hundred victories. In weather much too bad for formation flying by either side, a patrol of two Spitfires—Frankie Howell and a newcomer to the Squadron, Sidney Hill—was told by Control of a single aircraft posing as a Blenheim, but machine-gunning the R.A.F. airfield at Old Sarum from an altitude of fifty feet. Down went the two Spits† to 200 feet, and patrolled between Salisbury and the coast, hoping to catch the raider on his way out. And with excellent help from the Controller, Flight-Lieutenant Fieldsend (much praised in Howell's report), they did so, Hill spotting the 'Blenheim' first, directly below them. Though black crosses on the wings were now clearly visible, the rear gunner of the Ju 88 (for that is what it was) even now tried to put them off by firing smoke signals. It didn't work, and after a chase which, in Howell's words, 'was never more than ten feet above the tree-tops', they fired in turn and the aircraft crashed near Lymington. Part of its tail fin, suitably inscribed, held pride of place on the walls of successive Squadron dispersal huts till 1944.

As darkness began to fall and duty ended on this autumn day of 1940, Airman Bradbury, G. E., recalls the new C.O. arriving at Dispersal with his 'brake crammed with bottles provided by the blue bloods'. That was the first party, shared by all ranks. The second was a little later in the Officers' Mess, where, according to Crook, 'We trooped into the writing room and found a couple of waiters almost hidden by the large stock of champagne and brandy that had been installed for the occasion . . . We toasted practically everyone we could think of in round after round of champagne cocktails'. If the new C.O. was one of those with a hangover next day, it did not deter him from saving the pilot of a Battle from a nasty crash. This aircraft, Cloves records, came in to land with only one wheel down. After it had been temporarily warned off

---

* No. 1 (Hurricane) Squadron had already achieved this distinction, four months earlier in the Battle of France.

† The one flown by Hill, X4590, still exists. By a strange coincidence 'Paul' Edge was in Grantham in October 1970 when he saw it on display during the showing of the film *Battle of Britain*, and recognised his squadron's letters PR.

with red Very lights, 'Squadron-Leader Robinson took off in a Spit-fire which had the instruction, 'Land with wheels UP' chalked on its side. He formated on the Battle, the pilot of which took this advice and made a successful landing.'

The third party was the official 'Century' Celebration Dinner, which took place on 29th October and included the following guests:

Air Chief Marshal Sir Arthur Barratt, KCB, CMG, MC

Air Vice-Marshal Sir Quintin Brand, KBE, DSO, MC, DFC (A.O.C. No. 10 Group)

Air Commodore Harald Peake (Director of Public Relations, Air Ministry)

Group-Captain C. V. Howard, DFC (O.C. R.A.F. Station, Warm-well)

Wing-Commander D. N. Roberts, AFC (O.C. R.A.F. Station, Middle Wallop)

Wing-Commander H. S. Darley, DSO

Major W. L. Steele and other officers of the Coldstream Guards

Representatives of Nos. 238 and 604 Squadrons.

To quote the author of 609 Squadron's war diary:

'This symposium (in the literal meaning of the word) will long be remembered by members of the Squadron who took part, and not least by the additions to the Mess Bills to which it gave rise. There were several speeches which led to controversy, and the A.O.C. was given a rare opportunity of hearing pilots' views on the methods and practices of No. 10 Group's operational control.'

At this point the informed reader, knowing how claims had to be revised after the war in the light of German statistics, will be prone to comment that 609's claim to have shot down one hundred enemy aircraft was a pipe-dream. Almost certainly the actual figure was less, though not by so very much. The following table compares the claims of both sides, between 10th July and 31st October, 1940, with the actual number of aircraft lost:

	Claims	Actual Loss Inflicted	Exaggeration
British	2,698	1,733	55 per cent
German	3,058	915	330 per cent

On that basis 609's score on 21st October should be reduced to about seventy-two, and – on the principle that devaluation affects all – those of other squadrons accordingly. It might even be argued that having, in the main, fought as a single squadron, its claims were less subject to duplication than those of other squadrons who in the later stages of the Battle operated in larger formations. Be that as it may, the fact that the first Spitfire squadron believed to have been credited with one hundred victories was based in 10 Group, and not 11 Group, requires some explanation, part of which is supplied by the following quotation from Wood's and Dempster's *The Narrow Margin*:

'Normally a fighter squadron remained in the line for a month or six weeks, but the intensity of the fighting and resultant losses had required some units to be replaced after a week or ten days.'

609 had been 'in the line' since May. Unscathed during the grim fortnight when the Sector airfields near London, with their whole communications system, were nearly knocked out and their squadrons decimated, it was afterwards all the more potent and valuable. During September, to quote Darley, 'our bailiwick stretched over the whole of southern England, from London to Bristol, so we had plenty of opportunity to raise our score'. Which they did, by thirty-five.

There was, however, something more important than 'centuries', and Darley adds: 'I would be much happier to be credited with the best kill/loss ratio of the Battle of Britain.'

The evidence suggests that he certainly should be. During the three months of his command the Squadron lost just eight pilots, four of them in July. After he had left, three more of his pilots were awarded the D.F.C. – Crook, Curchin and Nowierski. So was his successor, Michael Robinson, though in his case mainly for service in other squadrons. To qualify for such an award there was, at this time, a rigid yardstick of six confirmed victories. With a bag of something like five and three-quarters, it was generally considered that the dashing and fearless Noël Agazarian was unlucky not to get one too. Perhaps eight D.F.C.s for one squadron might have looked too many.

As autumn yielded to winter the enemy assault slowly petered out like the dying notes of an alarm clock, and with shorter days this 'almost all-star squadron' – as Ogilvie described it in his diary – could spend more time at its two nocturnal retreats, the Square Club at Andover and the Black Swan (re-christened the Mucky Duck) at Monxton. I sometimes wonder whether, if one revisited either at dead of night, one would hear ghostly voices still arguing the odds of these air battles of long ago, and reminiscing about Pip and Stephen, Mick and Geoff, Buck and Gordon, and others they had known or heard of from a past that even then seemed aeons away. As always happened during periods of less activity, changes were made in personnel. The Squadron Adjutant, Flying-Officer R. M. D. Anderson, gave way to Pilot-Officer E. W. Tidswell; the Squadron Engineer Officer, Flying-Officer C. Harvey, to Flying-Officer H. Wilson, late of the Fleet Air Arm aboard the ill-fated *H.M.S. Glorious*. And though the Auxiliary ground staff remained basically intact, two of the three remaining Auxiliary pilots, David Crook and his friend Michael Appleby, were successively posted as instructors at Central Flying School, Upavon. 'And then' – to quote that poignant nursery rhyme, *The Twelve Little Nigger Boys* – there was one.'

This one surviving Auxiliary officer, now commander of 'B' flight, is described by his commanding officer during all but the last phase of the Battle of Britain as 'An excellent pilot, if a little over-confident, and had to be watched'. John Bisdee, who as a fellow scholar from the other university shared a room with him, adds: 'He got everything he could out of a Spitfire'. On 27th November, long after Darley had ceased to command, and when 'the Bish' was on leave, John Dundas justified both their remarks when it was learnt from Operations that a Ju 88 was flying down the coast on its way home after a raid. Eager as ever, John immediately asked permission to pursue it, but was refused, presumably because it was now considered out of range. O.K., in that case he would like to take up a section for practice flying. Any objection? No.

Whether the Controller suspected anything is not known, but of course as soon as he was airborne Dundas detached himself and, directionally aided by anti-aircraft fire from Southampton, tore out to sea at full boost in pursuit of the quarry. By the time he caught up both aircraft were over the Cherbourg peninsula. A swift attack, and the enemy plane was going down with its fuselage and one engine on fire. No time to confirm the crash : all alone over enemy territory, a hundred miles across the Channel, he was almost directly above a fighter airfield 'well stocked with Me 109s'.

It was the last of his many narrow escapes. The sands of fortune had run out, and next day he lost his life. Yet as befitted the most successful warrior 609 Squadron ever had, the manner of his going was epic, like that of a hero of Hellenic legend. There was even a 'Greek Chorus' in the shape of staff officers and 150 cadets from Sandhurst, who at the invitation of Michael Lister Robinson had come to tour Middle Wallop station and 609 Dispersal, with rugger, soccer and hockey matches laid on as side-shows. At the same time 609 Squadron itself was in the throes of packing up in preparation for a total move, notified only the evening before, to Warmwell on the morrow.

To the visitors it must have seemed like part of the entertainment when 609 was 'scrambled' twice. On the second occasion some fifty smoke trails were seen approaching in line abreast over the Isle of Wight, only to break up into the usual game of hide and seek. But afterwards Keith Ogilvie recorded in his diary :

'I was Yellow 3 and was weaving merrily behind, keeping an eagle eye above, when I caught a glimpse of three "yellow noses" in my mirror. They were obviously crack pilots by their tight formation and strategy. I gave the warning and dove as the centre Johnny opened fire on me, and was speeded on my way by a cannon shot up the fuselage and a second through my prop.'

And the Squadron diary records :

'Flight-Lieutenant Dundas was heard by the Controller (Flight-Lieutenant Fieldsend) and by his C.O. to say over the R.T. "Whoopee! I've got a 109," to which Robinson was heard to reply, "Good show, John" – after which nothing more was seen or heard of Dundas although Robinson tried persistently to speak to him.'

His No. 2, Pilot-Officer P. A. Baillon, a solicitor and married man, who had successfully baled out just a month before on being hit by return fire from an enemy bomber near Upavon, was also lost. Ogilvie, following his parachute down to the sea, saw no sign of life.

That evening the Luftwaffe High Command is said to have broadcast an appeal to the Air Ministry asking for information about the fate of one of their three top fighter commanders, Major Helmut Wick, and it soon became established that his was the Me 109 that Dundas claimed with his last words, only to be shot down himself, with Baillon, by the German leader's Nos. 2 and 3. Though only one parachute was seen by 609, according to German records Wick baled out too, and in a vain effort to rescue their respective pilots naval gunboats from both sides clashed in a battle of their own.

Helmut Wick, *Kommodore* of Jagdgeschwader 2 'Richthofen' was credited with no less than fifty-six victories, one less than Major Adolf Galland, one more than Major Werner Mölders, his former chief, and was idolized by the German public. Keith Ogilvie, who only just got back after one of his magnetos packed up as he circled Baillon's parachute was nearly Wick's fifty-seventh victory, while for John Dundas, himself one of Fighter Command's ten top-scoring pilots, with a bar to his D.F.C. awarded after his death, Wick was his victory number thirteen.

Both were posthumously eulogized by the press and radio of their respective countries, and the *News Chronicle* published comparative pictures, one showing Wick 'line-shooting' before an admiring group of his followers, the other Dundas apparently trying to suppress a smile. Indeed, had they ever met other than in the way they did, they would probably have disliked each other on sight. While they might have admired each other's prowess as fighters, each in fact was fighting against what the other stood for. To Wick, the pro, with militarism a way of life, Dundas, the amateur who only fought because it was necessary, would have seemed like one of Hillary's decadent 'long-haired boys', whose casual attitude to life and resistance to discipline in German eyes reflected the effete liberalism of Britain and her Empire. To Dundas, on the other hand, Wick would have seemed as humourless, rigid and dangerously patriotic as Wagner's Siegfried. He would have been recognized as one of the instruments by which the three freedoms were to be rooted out all over the world and replaced by the dictatorial rule of the *Herrenvolk*, whom John had personally witnessed tramping and trampling into Czechoslovakia.

Aristocrat, intellectual and athlete, but at the same time 'carefree, gregarious and amusing, John succeeded in doing things nearly always better than other people, but apparently without trying, which of course irritated them'. So I was recently told by his brother and fellow Auxiliary, Group-Captain Hugh 'Cocky' Dundas, D.S.O., D.F.C., who went on, 'In fact he tried very hard and worked like stink, but infuriated his teachers because he also managed to have a frightfully good time.'

Bisdee adds : 'I believe he was one of the chaps whose loss was almost a national one. His presence after the war would have helped to make the world a better place.'

Provided he was not thought to be trying.

On the day following his death, 29th November, 609 Squadron was scrambled fifteen minutes after reaching Warmwell, now to be its permanent base for three long winter months. Once again it operated under canvas, but instead of being blasted by the dust and stones to which Dundas had referred in August, Dispersal was now situated in a swamp. Cloves wrote :

'Another gale hit us and once again the operations marquee and other tentage were flattened, while a downpour of rain added to the fun. The operations blokes and three pilots extricated themselves from the wreckage, and moved en bloc to the airmen's marquee. The G.P.O. were summoned to move the telephones rescued from the mud, and life went on as usual. We fight the Jerries – and the elements.'

And that, it will be remembered, was the insalubrious spot where the author first encountered the West Riding Squadron.

4

MICHAEL

If 'George' Darley had made 609 a great squadron, with a record to be proud of, Michael Robinson taught it how to wear the trappings of greatness.

'You're good,' John Bisdee remembers him telling his pilots soon after assuming command, 'so bloody well let people *know* you're good!'

His own total commitment to his job, though by no means obvious to those who only saw him in a social setting, was (in the words of another of his pilots, 'Joe' Atkinson) 'the same as, in earlier days, was expected of a crack cavalry commander.' Before long he had communicated some of his own self-assurance and glitter to the Squadron he took such pride in commanding.

It could not have had a better showman. In no time at all, all the Battle of Britain survivors had been immortalized in portraits by the well-known war-artist, Captain Cuthbert Orde; a flagpole had shot up beside Dispersal, and from the top of it a probably quite unauthorized pennant proclaimed to the world that down below was the H.Q. of no ordinary squadron, but of No. 609.

To airman Waterson this last seemed a little unfair. Not long before, under the Darley regime, he and another airman out for a jaunt on the Velocette had expressed their appreciation of an excellent meal at a tea-house by writing in the visitors' book and signing themselves 'Two 609 boys'. Ten days later they were paraded in front of their C.O. Didn't they know 609 was a mobile squadron, moving about to confuse the enemy, and that by their carelessness they had made its location quite obvious? Punishment: seven days confined to camp. And now here was this flag, with the number 609 writ large upon it, fluttering right beside the public highway!

Certainly the last thing that Michael Robinson wanted was to *hide* his squadron. 'I *want* the Luftwaffe to know we're here,' he might have said. 'Let them come and fight us!'

Yet on 22nd February, 1941, 609 was not quite such a good squadron as the one he had inherited four and a half months before. Dundas was dead; MacArthur, Crook, Appleby and Agazarian had been posted away, and their replacements were still relatively untried. Worse, after three months with hardly a combat, the Weapon had begun to rust in its scabbard. Consequently, when its C.O. that evening announced that Frankie Howell, its tower of strength since 1939 and 'A' flight commander right through the Battle of Britain, had been promoted to take over the new 118 Squadron at Filton, that the four Poles were leaving, and that in this shorn state the West Riding Squadron was to proceed forthwith to Biggin Hill in 11 Group, there was a stunned silence. For of all Fighter Command stations Biggin Hill was the most famous. A few months earlier, though bombed and blitzed day after day, it had still managed to carry on, with craters filled up again and again, Operations Room transferred to a grocer's shop, Officers' Mess to the N.A.A.F.I. More recently, after a slight turn of the tide, pilots had read in Intelligence summaries of how Biggin Hill Spitfires had set off over France on the first offensive sweeps.

'It's not the sort of place any of us would be advised to start shooting lines in,' Michael added. 'When you get there, wait to speak until you are spoken to.'

Meanwhile a few beers were all that was necessary to convert the stunned mood into one of exhilaration. All suddenly decided that after eight months in the Middle Wallop sector, the summons to Biggin was a great honour.

'At least there'll be no more hanging about,' their C.O. continued. 'And though we may be in the forefront of the battle, and the London balloons are bloody close, don't forget that Piccadilly itself is only about fifteen miles away by road. By the way, Zieg' – I had rejoined the Squadron just a week before – 'you might draw up a map showing just where these balloon areas are.'

In the end, Michael being a man of influence in high places, the

Poles were recalled and rejoined us at Biggin until the newer pilots could be trained. But not Frankie. I had discovered that this disciplinarian flight commander with the military moustache and nine victories was, underneath, an artist and a romantic. On the wall of his room was a caricature of the station commander inspecting 609's waterlogged Dispersal, with the caption, 'Tent blown down? Ha! Wet and miserable? Ha! Now, in the last war . . .' There was also a picture of a beautiful girl.

'Do you want to marry her?' I asked.

'She's going to marry someone else,' he replied without bitterness, adding philosophically, 'You see, though by some miracle I survived last year, there's very little chance of my surviving this one.'

I never saw him again. Some time later he was posted to Singapore as a Wing-Commander, was on the battleship *Prince of Wales* when it was sunk, and was captured by the Japanese trying to reach Sumatra. And after all that he died, tragically and unnecessarily, when the war was over. Given command of a Vampire squadron, he was making a ciné film as the aircraft taxied when the wing of one of them decapitated him. 'I gave up believing in God after that,' says Darley. For the record, Frankie's Battle of Britain combat films remain some of the best and most convincing that were taken.

The departure of a squadron from a station whose fame had depended on its presence invoked a traditional ceremonial. The leader would take it out of sight in the wrong direction; then after some abuse having got his pilots into decent formation, he would lead them back in a final salute in the hope that those left behind would say, 'There goes a jolly good squadron.' On this occasion, there was more abuse than usual simply because 609 had not flown as a whole squadron since the previous November. Finally, just as it was approaching in pageant formation, the urgent voice of Sidney Hill was heard complaining that his engine was on fire, and could he land?

'Not on your life!' came Michael's savage reply. 'Not until we have finished this beat-up.' And somehow Sidney managed to stay there, and honour was saved, particularly as those Spitfires surplus to the Twelve –and known as the 'gaggle' – were flown away without parading by new pilots under the charge of the Bish and Keith Ogilvie. They all landed safely at Biggin Hill with one exception. One of the sergeant pilots – who were now on the increase – turned over at the end of an unaccustomed concrete runway and wrote off not only his Spitfire but a civilian worker's bicycle. Cloves commented : 'Civvy very peeved and wanted a new one . . . we should have offered him the Spitfire remains in lieu.'

I had left the evening before by car, staying the night at an uncle's house in the New Forest which held many peacetime memories. In those unchanged surroundings the R.A.F. and the war momentarily took on the semblance of a dream, and my uniform that of fancy dress. Next day, after driving through Reigate along the foot of the North Downs and turning left at Westerham, I mounted the Biggin escarpment and arrived soon after the Spitfires. Driving through the barrier, I felt like a prisoner returning from a brief outing on parole; for though airfields were set in the country, the monotony of uniforms, the drab ugliness of camouflaged buildings and the constant roar of engines somehow insulated them from it.

At Biggin there landed for the last time a squadron equipped with the old Mk. I Battle of Britain Spitfires. An hour or two later, No. 66 Squadron (to their disgust) flew away in them, leaving their own more advanced Spit IIs for 609 to inherit (though it was not till the following afternoon that the Squadron's technical staff discovered how to operate the new 'Coffman starters'). The Officers' Mess, this first evening, presented a gloomy sight as pilots of 609, whose baggage had not yet arrived, straggled in, shy and tired and dirty, to be confronted by those of 92 Squadron, straight from their baths and resplendent with D.F.C.s. The last time this squadron and 609 had met had been during the Dunkirk operation nine months previously. In the interim, it had been Stanford Tuck's squadron, and 'was now commanded by a Scot, Jamie Rankin. Yet with no other squadron, except perhaps No. 198 much later, was 609 ever to have such a strong bond of friendship. Such names as Brian Kingcombe, R. H. Holland, T. S. Wade, Tony

Bartley and Don Kingaby (all of them decorated) will still be familiar to their few surviving contemporaries in 609.

The other squadron in the Biggin Wing was No. 74, at present dispersed at the satellite airfield of Gravesend. Till recently, this had been commanded by the most famous of all Battle of Britain pilots, the South African A. G. ('Sailor') Malan, now Biggin Hill's 'Wing-Commander Flying' – a recently created appointment at fifteen Sector stations throughout the land. Now he said nothing as the Station Commander, Group-Captain Soden, suggested that on the morrow 609, whose last operational sortie as a complete squadron had taken place in November, 1940, should join his wing on an offensive operation over France – a suggestion to which Michael's reply, in his own words, was 'keenly doubtful'. As yet, none of his pilots had even tried their new aircraft.

They did so the following afternoon, by which time lorries had disgorged cases of equipment, and the cold and bleak Dispersal huts had taken on a semblance of order and comfort as stoves were lighted and quarters allotted to the Flights, the Orderly Room, the Armoury and Signals section. Meanwhile Johnny Curchin, borrowing a hat here and a pair of gloves there, disappeared in the direction of Buckingham Palace for his D.F.C. investiture. At eleven o'clock that night, Michael came into the bar and said, 'Zieg, it appears we cannot operate without a special R.T. code. Will you go and get it?' So in the pitch dark I set off to find the Operations Room secreted in one of a row of similar houses three miles away.

The following morning saw 609's first operational sortie from Biggin Hill as top cover to the Wing – one of several wings protecting a dozen Blenheim bombers whose mission was to bomb Calais harbour. Pale but determined the pilots set out, while an apprehensive I.O. awaited their return. No one need have worried : though they 'stooged' over Calais at 28,000 feet and for the first time (in most cases) were shot at by *flak* – inaccurate enough at this height – the only hostile aircraft seen were three Me 109s 10,000 feet higher still. In fact the only incident was when 'Teeny' Overton, Dunkirk veteran, had oxygen trouble and fell 10,000 feet before regaining consciousness. He and Bisdee were the only pilots left from the time 609 had last crossed the enemy's coastline eight months previously, and for the rest it was a tonic to morale just to have done so.

Such early offensive operations reflected the decision of the Air Staff (which coincided with the appointment of Air Marshal Sir Sholto Douglas as C.-in-C. Fighter Command and that of Air Vice-Marshal Leigh-Mallory as A.O.C. No. 11 Group) that when possible the fighter force should 'lean forward into France'. At the moment, however, such operations were 'luxuries' owing to the Command, after so many losses, being short both in numbers and experience, and also to the continued need for day defence both against sweeps by enemy fighters and (once again) of Channel shipping. Keith Ogilvie recorded that in March, 1941, he actually flew more hours than in September, 1940. But though in 1941 609 lost three of its first four pilots over England, such defensive patrols, and the long periods of Readiness that preceded them, were generally just a bore. The following excerpts from a contemporary radio conversation between ANTEATER (Biggin Controller), BEAUTY LEADER (Michael Robinson) and one or two other 609 pilots are indicative :

0916.	BL to A :	Understand patrol MICA Angels 11.
		Is this correct?
	A to BL :	Correct.
0920.	BL to K :	Come on, Q, get up there !
	K to BL :	Q is weaver.
	BL to K :	What the hell is he doing on my left then ?
0926.	BL :	Turning to right, go !
0958.	BL to A :	Have you any information for me ?
	A to BL :	No, nothing at all. Just cruise around.
	BL to K :	O.K. This is rather boring.
	A to BL :	Your message received rather sympathetically .
1006.	BL to G :	Why have you left the formation ?
	G to BL :	I lost you in the sun.
	BL to G :	You are very stupid. Come up again.
	BL to Y2 :	Stop b . . g . . g about and join formation.
1019.	BL to A :	Have you any information for me ?
	A to BL :	Yes, you will be relieved very shortly now.
	BL to A :	Thank heavens for that !

Michael always seemed to like his call-sign BEAUTY LEADER,

and somehow it seemed very appropriate. MICA was code for Maidstone, the usual patrol line. As he flew over it now, he must have contrasted this patrol with the events of 31st August, 1940, when he was a flight-commander in 601. After damaging two Me 109s, he had pursued a third low over the Maidstone roof-tops, only to find he had no more ammunition. In his combat report, he wrote about the enemy pilot:

'He never rose above 100 feet until well south of Maidstone and then throttled back. I overtook him and formated on him, pointing downwards for him to land. He turned away so I carried out a dummy quarter attack, breaking very close to him. After this he landed his Me in a field ... I threw him a packet of twenty Players and returned to base.'

So much of the story has already been published – and was evidently all that Michael thought it politic for higher authority to know. In fact he did *not* return to base – not for some time. Instead, so he confessed to me much later, he landed his Hurricane in an adjacent field, got out and walked over towards the pilot of the Me 109:

'It was a scorching hot day and I was only wearing a shirt. He was sunbathing, but as I came up he put his hand in his pocket and I thought, "Good Lord, he's got a gun!" Instead, he took out a comb, combed his hair and addressed me in perfect English (I think he had been at Oxford): "Why didn't you shoot me down?" I explained why, but he wouldn't believe me, so I took him over to my Hurricane, sat him in the cockpit and told him to press the firing button. At that moment, the Home Guard came up, removed his footgear and marched him off.'

It is a pity fate decreed that the two could never meet again after the war.

Though the three squadrons took it in turns to be at Readiness, Available or Released, the Release period, weather permitting, was used for bringing new pilots up to the necessary standard of operational training – a thing that 'Sailor' Malan was rightly most insistent about. If there were experienced pilots over, they flew for fun in the non-operational aircraft, in which 609 was unusually

rich. Besides the Miles Magister, the Squadron's appointed communications aircraft for picking up marooned pilots (or taking
them on leave), Michael owned (or had been lent for the duration)
a Puss Moth – much more comfortable in that it had an enclosed
cockpit in which pilot and passenger sat side by side. But he also
owned one of the most bizarre aircraft ever seen, called the 'Drone'.
It was a sort of glider powered by a Ford 10 engine, with the pilot
sitting in the extreme prow. Michael had brought two of these
with him to the Squadron and (its identification letters being PR)
they were promptly painted PR! and PR? The former, in a bashed
condition, never left a Middle Wallop hangar, and it may have
been this one (powered only by a motor-cycle engine) that airman
Hubert Fovargue recalls being so indifferently landed by Keith
Ogilvie that 'his feet finished through the floor of the cockpit on
the runway' – perhaps the only occasion on which an aeroplane has
been taxied in with the help of human legs.

The top speed of PR? was about 40 m.p.h., its maximum altitude about the same figure in feet. At one time (Michael told me)
he used to try to hand the evening paper to the driver of a certain
train, but the latter was nearly always too fast; and the Bish tells
me that when sent to fetch this machine to Biggin he experienced
the utmost difficulty in clearing the Hill. Yet the 'Drone' won a
personal victory for me. At Biggin was a station I.O. called Honey-
sett, who having previously been a member of the Royal Observer
Corps impressed all his colleagues (and particularly me) with his
infallibility in aircraft recognition. One day, hearing a sound like
the buzzing of a million bees, he left the office to investigate, and saw
the C.O. of my squadron drifting slowly past station headquarters
smoking a cigarette. 'What aircraft is THAT?' I asked triumphantly, and for the first time he did not know. Alas! Soon afterwards Sidney Hill landed the Drone in a cabbage patch and his
great friend Johnny Curchin, trying to recover it, flew it through
a hedge. Thereafter, for years to come, beside the piece of the
Ju 88 that had constituted the Squadron's hundredth victory, was
another piece of aircraft labelled 'PR? The only Drone destroyed
by 609 Squadron.'

Even 'Sailor' Malan was human. Occasionally, fed up with his responsibilities, he would take himself and the commanders of 92 and 609 Squadrons on a private tour of the French coast hoping to show what one Wing-Commander and two Squadron-Leaders could do if their opposite numbers would like to meet them.

And the responsibilities of the three did not always end with daylight. In the early spring the enemy resumed his intensive night attacks on London, and the magic tocsin *Fighter Night* was rung again, despite the dearth of night-operational pilots and the not ill-founded conviction that as night-fighters Spitfires were useless. On a night when some five hundred enemy aircraft attacked the capital Michael, Johnny Curchin, Keith Ogilvie and John Bisdee were all ready to take off when bombs cut radio communications and power, and they waited all night in the dark at Dispersal, occasionally diving to the ground as bombs whistled down near by. I was on duty at the Operations Room, and the building shook and trembled as the W.A.A.F.s calmly plotted '100-plus' just overhead, and the Controller, working in his shirt-sleeves, tried hard to make his orders heard through the noise. Going out, I saw we were ringed with fires. One of them was the laundry, in which we nearly all lost some items of apparel that night.

Once or twice a pair of 609 aircraft did patrol. Bisdee recalls: 'The sight of the burning city was an extraordinary experience, with all the searchlights, bags of ack-ack and the odd balloon silhouetted against the fire ... but I'm afraid I never saw an enemy aeroplane.'

The real answer was to be the Beaufighter, and later the Mosquito, carrying airborne radar. Meanwhile, the regular night-fighters were supplemented by the two squadrons of Boulton-Paul Defiants, long since withdrawn from the daylight battle. One of these, No. 264, was based at Biggin, and my only personal experience of flying in a fighter was when Flight-Sergeant Thorn, of Dunkirk fame, took me on a hedge-hopping expedition in the gun turret of his aircraft. After the 'Maggie' it seemed fast indeed, though from an altitude of some fifteen feet the landscape was just a blur. At least from the 'Maggie' one could see something – notably the hundreds of bomb craters with which the whole airfield and the surrounding country were saturated. They were, of course, filled in, yet Cloves' diary in its finishing pages is a chronicle of Spitfires tipping up into still-soft craters and the resulting need for airscrew changes.

On 25th April, 1941, this intelligent, humorous and often avuncular Regular Flight-Sergeant was, alas, posted away as an instructor, and though he nominated a successor to carry on as scribe, the ink in the latter's pen apparently never flowed. The penultimate entry is typical :

'Pilot-Officer Van Lierde P8094 found he was trying to fly on air so decided to force-land. He chose a nice big field and made a good landing but unfortunately got mixed up with the trip wires planted for the sole use of the Luftwaffe. Too bad, but it showed the trip wires were effective.'

Pilot-Officer W. Van Lierde was one of the first batch of Belgian pilots to join No. 609 (West Riding) Squadron early in April, 1941, soon after the Poles had finally departed. They arrived on Budget Day, and while the Chancellor of the Exchequer was making his speech 609 actually received the instructions to 'patrol Westminster'. On being interpreted, this meant that 'A' flight was to patrol Biggin-Hornchurch below cloud, and 'B' flight Biggin-Gravesend above. As, however, cloud base was at 3,000 feet, and the London balloons were flying in cloud at 4,500 feet, Michael not unnaturally declined to lead the former into such danger – to the relief of the I.O., who twenty minutes before take-off had been instructed by the Controller to brief the pilots on a route *through* the balloons. In the end both flights patrolled above cloud, and this time their C.O. relieved his boredom by making up nursery rhymes. Recited on the radio, they may well have discouraged the enemy from interfering with the Budget.

Three days later, the Squadron was again airborne when two more Belgian officers arrived at its Dispersal hut with all their baggage, saluted the I.O. and called him 'Sir'. Was this 609 Squadron headquarters and were they really expected? – because they had spent a week reporting to one station after another, including the Orkneys, and were determined not to unload their baggage again unless . . . I said others of their countrymen had already arrived, and directed them to Southwood Manor about five miles distant, where 609's pilots were quartered in dispersed safety.

One of the two, I remember, was Pilot-Officer le Comte du Monceau de Bergendael (soon to be known as 'Duke'). At the time he was the least experienced Belgian pilot, but as he is now Major-General, C.V.O., D.F.C., in command of the Belgian Tactical Air Force, he recently seemed the right person for me to ask how it was that Belgians came to constitute half the pilot strength of the West Riding Squadron from spring 1941 till the end of the war. This is what he wrote to me :

'In mid-July, 1940, five officers of the Belgian Air Force, who had just arrived in England after escaping from Belgium via Casablanca and Gibraltar, were travelling by train from Liverpool to the Belgian depot at Tenby when an R.A.F. officer boarded the train. He had his arm in a sling, spoke very fractured French, but seemed particularly pleased to meet Belgians – a welcome novelty for the latter – and even talked about getting together in a squadron, etc.

'Having been one of the five Belgians, imagine my surprise, on reaching Biggin Hill, to find the commander of 609 Squadron was the same R.A.F. officer we had met on the train nine months earlier.'

Michael Lister Robinson, while serving as a flight-commander with No. 87 Squadron in France, had been injured in a flying accident near the front about thirty-six hours before the Germans launched their Western offensive on 10th May, 1940. Helped by the local population, Michael evacuated himself from hospital to hospital just ahead of the German advance until finally he reached the house of an aunt in Pau, near the Pyrenees. So much of his story Michael once told me himself, but now the 'Duke' adds : 'As he was still in hospital clothes, a Belgian air force detachment which had been evacuated to Pau equipped him with air force blue and drove him to Bordeaux, where he managed to hop a plane to England.' Shortly afterwards a Belgian government was set up in London, and it seems that soon after Michael took over command of 609 he repaid his debt to Belgium by applying to the Air Ministry for Belgian pilots.

'And so,' says today's Belgian Air Force general, 'the Belgian Flight of 609 was born. It never existed as a Flight except on paper, for neither the British nor the Belgians desired such discrimination,' and today the numerals *Six-Cent-Neuf* still mean almost as much in Belgium as 6-0-9 mean in the West Riding of Yorkshire. Though two wholly Belgian fighter squadrons were later formed, to have fought under the emblem of the White Rose was always the greater distinction.

So returning this April evening from London, Michael Robinson became aware that the seeds he had once sown had suddenly sprouted into about eight Belgian pilots, all of them a bit lost. Characteristically, he faced up to his new social responsibility by arranging a dinner party at which each Belgian sat next to an Anglo-Saxon. At first they all ate in silence, till under the influence of the wine their C.O. had ordered, the stiffness began to thaw.

'Well, what is *your* name?' asked Sidney Hill, turning to his neighbour with his involuntary wink.

The Belgian addressed was a sensitive, good-looking young man, with much social sense, called Malengreau. 'I am Roger,' he said with a smile. 'That is my *prénom*. And you wish the names of the others? There is François, that is Vicki, here are Bob, Strop and Van; and at the other end of the table, next to the C.O., is Le Duc.'

Wanting to be known by their Christian names was rather appealing, and by the time the port came round they were speaking freely, if with varying degrees of fluency. All had escaped from Belgium at about the time of Dunkirk, and many, after re-training on Hurricanes, had been in time to fight at least the last phase of the Battle of Britain – three of them with Michael's former squadron, No. 87. Some, like Bob Wilmet, 'Strop' Segers and Van Lierde* seemed to be professional soldiers of fortune who had worn some kind of uniform almost since childhood (Van, I recall, was actually thirty-seven). 'Strop' was a Fleming and round like a barrel – his nickname, Flemish for 'strap', being common to any citizen of Ghent, some of whose burghers were once due for hanging. Instead of being hanged, this 'Strop' had some months before been shot down into the 'drink', where he had floated like a cork.

Different from all of them was François de Spirlet, an enter-

* Not to be confused with 'Mony' Van Lierde, who joined 609 in 1942.

prising individualist who did not give a damn for anyone, yet who progressively evinced a curiously English sense of humour. Wildest, most dashing and most irresponsible was Vicki Ortmans, who arrived already credited with three Battle of Britain victories from 229 Squadron. Theoretically he spoke hardly any English at all, yet his square face would break into a slow self-accusing grin whenever he understood more than was expected of him. At Biggin, his first 'black' was when 609 Squadron was observed crossing the airfield in perfect formation, except that one Spitfire was upside down. 'Who the hell is that?' I was asked by 'Sailor' Malan. 'Doesn't he know he's ruining his engine?' (I knew perfectly well who it was, but I left Michael to deal with the matter.)

After the brandy it was found that Bob Wilmet could play the piano, and that Vicki could tap-dance on top of it. For the first time the West Riding Squadron became indoctrinated with foreign songs that later became standard, such as:

> *Alouetta! Gentille Alouetta!*
> *Alouetta! Je te plumerai ...*

and:

> *Au Chevalier de la Table Ronde*
> *Allons voir si le vin est bon ...*

which goes on for ever. If the British pilots failed to understand the words, they at least joined lustily in the singing, and I remember the evening culminating in a war dance round a bonfire in mid-dining room. When a table laden with glass and crockery also began to dance, and Sidney Hill was found beneath it, Michael decided it was time to stop, and at his orders his international squadron's first operation was sweeping and tidying everything up. To cement the new alliance, a landmine that night blew in the windows of Southwood Manor.

Sidney's inseparable companion, since he had joined the Squadron over half a year before, was Johnny Curchin, himself a veteran from pre-Battle of Britain days. On the ground they were playful to a degree, and delighted in 'taking the micky' out of anyone verging on the pompous. One, only semi-endearing, habit in the bar was for one of them to engage such an officer in the most unexpectedly friendly conversation. Just as the latter began to reciprocate in surprise and delight he would receive a push in the chest and topple ignominiously and painfully backwards over the body of his other antagonist lying prone against his legs. (It happened to me once or twice, till I felt obliged to call on my early judo training.)

But in the air they were different, and Johnny, being calm and deadly as well as extremely experienced, was now given the command of 'B' flight in succession to Forshaw. At about the same time 'Teeny' Overton, now the doyen of the Squadron, having joined in November, 1939, and who had taken over 'A' flight from Frankie Howell, was posted to O.T.U. as an instructor, having, I believe, been on the sick list since he had fallen unconscious for 10,000 feet.

His successor, Paul Richey, took over as a result of sheer, if legitimate, nepotism. Not only was Paul married to Michael's beautiful sister, Teresa, but the two had known each other since Michael had been head of Downside, and Paul head of one of the houses – at which time they both decided to join the R.A.F. Michael applied for a short-service commission first, and by 1937, when Paul did likewise, was already a member of No. 111 Squadron's formation aerobatic team (in 1938 he flew 200 miles from Middlesex to Lancashire in thirty-three minutes, at an average speed of 380 m.p.h.). At war's outset Paul went to France, Michael following with 87 Squadron in April 1940. It was while flying over to join Paul for a joint birthday celebration (they had even been born on successive days) that Michael suffered the injury that prevented him taking part in the succeeding battle. Paul, with No. 1 Squadron, had gone on to win one of the first D.F.C.s of the war, and was so badly wounded that he was off flying for a year. During that year he wrote his best-seller, *Fighter Pilot*, and in the Battle of Britain contributed to 609's success as one of the Middle Wallop Controllers. And now, before his period of convalescence was officially over, Michael had managed to get him posted in as commander of 'A' flight. On the morning after his arrival, he put on his white overalls, inspected his allotted Spitfire, organized his Flight and smiled his gay and humorous smile. For, like his C.O. and brother-in-law, he possessed abundant charm, was a fellow Catholic, and likewise something of a patrician. The only thing he had to learn, as a Regular, was that Auxiliary N.C.O.s such as Darkie Hanson and Eric Ingall did not expect to be called to attention when reporting about a good job of aircraft maintenance.

On the morning of 8th May, 1941, 609 (to anyone but its members) was just a fighter squadron that had done well in the past. At Biggin it had been in action only a few times and lost two pilots: Sergeant MacSherry (its latest N.C.O. pilot) and Flight Sergeant Bennett (its very first, who along with his fellow V.R.s Bisdee and Buchanan had joined in December, 1939). It was this same Flight Sergeant Bennett who, during the Dunkirk evacuation, had been shot down and rescued badly wounded from the 'drink'. Many months and two C.O.s later, he had unobtrusively returned to the fold, only to be shot down, ironically enough, on another operation off Dunkirk—this time without being rescued. Against these losses all the Squadron could show was a 'damaged' scored by Keith Ogilvie, who typically enough had been in action twice on two separate days—being rewarded in the evening of the second with a dance, at a Mess party, with Vivien Leigh.

Yet by the evening of 8th May (Michael's birthday), 609 had achieved perhaps the biggest single success any squadron had achieved since 1940. Later the engagement became known as The Battle of the Dinghy and was immortalized in an oil painting which, till long after the war, hung over the fire-place in the Biggin Officers' Mess, and now hangs in the Mess at Church Fenton, together with a framed copy of the combat report I wrote at the time. At 16.49 hours 609, being the squadron at Readiness, took off with the usual 'stooge' instructions to patrol Maidstone at 15,000 feet. Then they were told of a dinghy containing a German aviator (evidently a very important one) in mid-Channel. On reaching the spot they found a British air-sea rescue launch with Messerschmitt 109s circling over it. The Squadron was flying in three sections, each of four aircraft. Leaving one of them as top cover, Michael dived with the other two to the rescue. He was too late: the rescue launch was on fire; the top section was attacked, and Sergeant Mercer hit. The Squadron reformed and found a second launch attended by more Me 109s. This time Michael appointed Paul's section as cover and went down again. No one knew how many of the enemy there were, but it was to be no skirmish. Michael quickly shot down the nearest; Johnny Curchin sent a second into the sea and hit another, which David Hughes-Rees the Welshman finished off. Two more were claimed in swift succession by Tommy Rigler, an N.C.O. pilot who had joined just before 609's departure from Warmwell. Then Sergeant Palmer (called 'Goldy' because of his locks), who had chased two of the enemy to Calais, heard on the radio: 'Beauty Leader being fired on.' Michael, who after a long, lone pursuit had shot a second quarry down beside the French cliffs, had suddenly been set upon at the moment he ran out of ammunition by a whole *Staffel* of enemy fighters (he counted nine), which attacked him all the way back across the Channel. It was then that this superb pilot, disarmed as he was, showed the mastery in the air that brought ground staff and other pilots out to watch each time he indulged in aerobatics. But this time it was to save his own life. With split-second judgement, again and again, he turned sharply towards each opponent at the very moment the latter opened fire, and—with some eventual help from 'Goldy', who shot one Messerschmitt off his tail just as he was being attacked himself—got home without a single scratch.

I had been waiting anxiously since 'Ops.' had phoned to say: 'We think 609 have been engaged.' When Michael's Spitfire, PR B, arrived and performed twin victory rolls and the rest appeared in ones and twos instead of sections, it was clear that 'Ops.' was right. As they taxied in, I saw that on nearly every one of them the protective gun-canvasses had been shot away. As the leader switched off his engine, I was beside his cockpit as his crew, already on the wings, asked whether engine, oxygen, radio and guns had functioned satisfactorily.

'Everything O.K.,' said Michael, as if returning from an air test. Some perspiration and a slight derangement of his usually immaculately tied silk scarf were the only hints that he had just missed death many times by a hairbreadth. Then he saw me and smiled, if a little wanly.

'Yes, I got two, Zieg.' He did not sound elated, and his voice was tired. 'The second one tried to force-land on the beach – I hoped he would – but he didn't make it. He crashed into the surf, and I felt sick – it might so easily have been me.'

It was all I could get for the moment. He went over to greet Johnny, who limped in badly shot up, with a blocked aileron and windscreen daubed with enemy oil. He too had temporarily ceased to be his usual aggressive self, and wore a far-away look as if still living the few split seconds when he wondered whether his Spitfire would ever pull out of its dive. Contrast Tommy Rigler, whom I spied leaving his aircraft with confident gait. It had been his first combat, and he had yet to learn – as he later did – what it was like to be in a tight corner, with no other pilots to protect him. 'Got two!' he cried defiantly. 'No doubt about it – both point blank. C.O. saw one go in, didn't you, Sir?'

The Station Commander and 'Sailor' Malan had also arrived and, by joining the little procession that greeted each pilot as he appeared, made my own job of interrogation much more difficult. 'How many do you make it now?' they kept asking me.

In the end I made it six Messerschmitt 109s destroyed, plus two probably destroyed, for two Spitfires damaged. The evidence seemed impeccable, was accepted by 11 Group and Fighter Command, and Air Vice-Marshal Leigh-Mallory sent a signal of congratulations. Yet it now seems, from Luftwaffe records, that I exaggerated by at least a third. Compared with Luftwaffe claims over England in 1940, Fighter Command claims over the Continent in weeks to come, not to mention American Flying Fortress claims in the more distant future, the error was modest – yet enough to show the difficulty of making a true assessment even when only a single unit was involved. If hardly any pilots were given to deliberate lying, some did err on the side of optimism, and there was always the problem of duplication when more than one of them had fired at the same enemy aircraft.

Next day, after an engagement involving only one flight, I could only claim a 'damaged' for the loss of one aircraft and pilot – Sergeant Mercer. Yesterday he had emerged smiling from a combat in which he had given better than he got, and today was killed trying to force-land on the beach of St. Margaret's Bay. 'Hell's Corner' had again begun to live up to its name.

Sometimes, on occasions of Release, Michael would say, 'I think London is the form tonight.' Thereupon he would set off in his official car, taking Paul and perhaps one or two others with him, but not before he had added, 'Rendezvous at the Berkeley at eight.'

Though it was said lightly, it was almost tantamount to an order – and taken as such. For the surprising thing about this young man, when off-duty, was that so far from wishing to escape from the men he flew with day after day into his own well-connected social circle, he now did not feel complete unless he had them round him, polyglot though they might be. 'Joe' Atkinson, one of his most discerning pilots, gives the following character-sketch :

'His whole life, on the ground as in the air, revolved about 609, and its life about him. However hilarious the party he was still the C.O. and respected as such – it was always "Sir", never "Michael". Success in the social world seemed his by right, and anyone meeting him at London's more expensive night-clubs, where he was often to be found, may well have believed that this was what he lived for; that his service duties and exploits were a mere adjunct to the real *douceur de la vie* which related, not to flying, but to the development of a discriminating taste in wine, and the company of amusing, mainly rich, friends. Nothing could have been further from the truth. It was the social round that was incidental, his life in command of his Squadron the thing that really mattered.'

So Michael, probably arriving late with one or two appendages and finding his officers somewhat self-consciously sipping lager at the bar of the Berkeley Buttery, would promptly order 'ryes and drys' all round, and unfasten any top tunic buttons that suggested anything other than a fighter squadron. The 'form' would then be strictly 'Squadron' until such time as someone pointed out the need of eating, whereupon those with private dates or failing purses would disappear, in what Paul described as 'loose pairs formation', until about midnight, the time appointed by Michael for the second rendezvous at the Suivi.

For the West Riding Squadron this was the prince of night-clubs. Though few, if any, of its officers had gone through the formality of joining it, let alone paying a subscription, they were soon all personally known to the staff, and evidently welcome whether they danced, sang or stood on their heads. If some actually had their own bottles of booze somewhere on the premises, these were seldom used, for Michael, choosing a table in the corner, would royally order champagne for his men and any other entourage he had collected, while the former reported on their nocturnal combats to date – such as François assaulting a stranger for allegedly insulting Belgium, only to be told that in reality the man was trying to pay compliments. After an hour or so Johnny and Sidney would disappear to the kitchen, there to consume kippers provided for the sole price of one of Sidney's involuntary winks, and still later some tycoon might introduce himself and offer to pay the entire bill. At about three, by which time the Squadron possessed more than its normal quota of 'weavers', the eyes of the Bish would catch those of a Leading Aircraftman sitting near the door. This was the driver who, after some further Bisdee organization, would drive the company back to base. Johnny and Sidney might get left behind, but they had only to telephone a certain lady of title for her to rise from her bed and become their personal chauffeuse, perhaps getting an unauthorized dawn ride in the Maggie as a reward.

It was still the Battle of Britain tradition, a time when fighter pilots, instruments and symbols of the country's survival, were still welcome almost everywhere, drinking hard, behaving madly – living only for the day, but still able to do their job if they reached the next. A year or two later the breed had become more professional, less spoilt, with numbers increasing in approximately inverse proportion to the supply of whisky saved from going to America to help pay for a war that (in early '41) America was not as yet even fighting. By then even 609 no longer drank 'ryes and drys' at the Berkeley or Suivi – most pilots drank beer or were even teetotal. And after D-Day their linear descendants, though shot down in droves without much glory, were mostly no longer fighter pilots, but airborne artillery.

But in 1941, though few could yet imagine how the war could ever be won, food was still quite good, liquor (at least for officers of the services) fairly abundant, nerves and constitutions still resilient.

Pilots might get back at four, and after only an hour or two's sleep be ready to fly again – the Battle of the Dinghy was fought after just such a night in town. And if it had been a Saturday night Michael, whose allegiance to Roman Catholicism went deep, never missed Sunday's early Mass.

One morning it was not necessary to get up. 'There's a knife outside you could cut with a mist,' drawled Keith Ogilvie sleepily as he returned to bed. When he *did* have to go on patrol with a hangover, he referred to the hammerings in his head as 'The Mac-Gillicuddy Boys'.

Two nights after the Battle of the Dinghy there was another 'Imperial Blitz' on London, and forthwith for three successive nights 609 was sent to West Malling to stand by to patrol the Berkeley and the Suivi from the air. Beforehand, all pilots came to the Station Intelligence Office, where with the aid of a map studded with pins I endeavoured to explain the rather complicated way in which Spitfires were supposed to muscle in with the A.A. barrage and the regular night-fighters. As a result their minds were brought back to night flying with a jerk as they wondered which of the perils of A.A. fire, collisions, balloons or getting lost without R.T. was the worst. The first evening quite a party assembled at Dispersal to wish them all godspeed, the effect of the line-abreast take-off being heightened by the Bish, hot from London, leaping from his car to his cockpit at the last moment – and somewhat marred by the Welshman David Hughes-Rees getting stuck in an old bomb crater till we all went and pushed him out. As they disappeared into the distance I breathed a silent prayer – appropriately without a hat, for Sidney, playful to the last, had taken this with him.

As it turned out, it was a three-day holiday, for the Squadron was not called upon. Pilots would do a little night-flying practice, sleep and fly back again in time for breakfast. Then, released for the rest of the day, they would scatter (some of them) in search of recreation. Michael flew to his home near Bristol in the Puss Moth, taking Hal, who later reported on his C.O.'s unsociable flying habits:

'The only time he speaks is when he looks over the side and says, "That must be Newbury – another sixty miles to go." Then he goes on reading his bloody book until it's time to land, which he goes and does in a field, and I – the Adjutant – have to swing the bloody prop when it's time to leave again. And when I've done it, he goes straight back to his bloody book.'

But the return to the state of daylight Readiness brought an immediate resumption of action. It began with the first Belgian – François de Spirlet – being shot down; which, because it ended happily, was treated by himself and others as a great joke. On defensive patrol with Sidney Hill he was distracted by some Hurricanes, lost Hill and then immediately sighted a 'solitary' Me 109. Closing in on the 'idiot' with a whoop of joy, he pressed his firing button and was just admiring the amount of tracer his guns appeared to give forth when he became aware that only the port ones were firing – his starboard ammunition being in the act of exploding. Conscious of many other hits, he rolled over and downwards and saw four other Me 109s flash past him. Somehow he contrived to land beside a dummy Hurricane on a dummy airfield, and found his damage included : starboard ammunition, airscrew and one tyre hit by machine-gun fire, two cannon shells in the fuselage, one on each wing tip, two in the engine and one on the starboard flap. With that François learned that Me 109s were never 'solitary'.

The following afternoon, the whole Squadron was on patrol in the Dover area when someone called up Michael to report that one of his weavers had been shot down. His automatic reply – 'I couldn't be more sorry' – deserved, as I wrote in the Squadron diary, to be recorded in stone, preferably granite. Soon afterwards, some enemy fighters were spied, for once actually below, and Keith Ogilvie and Sidney each sent one smoking vertically downwards. Unfortunately at 500 feet they disappeared into haze, and since in such circumstances I.O.s might not award a 'destroyed' unless the enemy aircraft was actually seen to crash, I spent the rest of the day trying to obtain outside evidence that these two did, and succeeded thanks to the Dover detachment of Balloon Command. As the 'weaver' – the faithful 'Goldy' Palmer – was soon brought back smiling in the 'Maggie' after force-landing at Detling, and Vicki

Ortmans also scored a 'damaged', I was able to chalk up an Anglo-Canadian-Belgian success for one Spitfire damaged. Nearest loss of the day, in fact, was probably Hal. While slow-marching at Hawkinge, where Sergeant Mercer's funeral was taking place, he suddenly found the airfield being strafed by German fighters. Despite a 'Maggie' (from which a Group-Captain had just descended) bursting into flames, he decided the enemy's behaviour was very bad form and continued to slow-march.

The next day is was 'Joe' Atkinson's turn for adventure. Though 'Joe' had joined the Squadron in December, 1940, and was destined to remain with it longer than any other of its war-time pilots, it was only twenty-five years later that I discovered that though his initials were J. A., he only became 'Joe' on being made responsible at Warmwell for the Squadron's defence against gas attack. 'Joe the gas man!' Keith Ogilvie immediately cried (all 'gas men' in Canada being apparently 'Joe') – and 'Joe' he remained throughout the war. By nature modest, scholastic and amusingly introspective, he had been hauled into the air from his studies at Oxford owing, like Noël Agazarian, to having been short- or long-sighted enough to join the University Air Squadron. On this occasion his flight had a brush with some Me 109s over Kent, and Joe, weaving behind, was struck by a cannon shell. Trying to force-land at Rochester, he found his starboard flap would not work, and the other became stuck in the 'down' position, with the result that his Spitfire became all but uncontrollable. After great efforts he finally came to rest in a ploughed field, with a shorn undercarriage and a bumped head.

'There,' he said, 'I found myself being viewed with great suspicion by a labourer, who didn't seem to think it was quite the form to land in his master's field without permission. Personally, I felt so surprised to be alive that I just peered back at him.'

A few days later we lost our first Belgian, a picturesque aristocrat called Rodolf de Grunne, who had flown Me 109s for Franco in the Spanish civil war and told me the pleasant story of a Belgian prince, himself a pilot, who liked to emphasize his superior birth to his colleagues by using the French past definite tense. This riled Rodolf, himself a count, who had his revenge when one day the prince landed an aircraft on its nose. '*Vous capotâtes, prince!*' he said with relish. Shot down at Biggin during the Battle of Britain while with 32 Squadron, Rodolf had sustained serious burns and been off flying till he joined 609, to which he brought a most unseasonable tan acquired during a recent special mission to Lisbon, where Germans in bars told him confidently of their plans for the conquest of North Africa. And now the Germans got him. Just before taking off for the last time, he dashed back from his plane, asked me for his wallet and hurriedly extracted a small silver horseshoe. It was no use : though he was seen to bale out, he was never found, and the only consolation was that his fellow-countryman Vicki Ortmans and John Bisdee shared in the destruction of one of his assailants.

One day two other Belgians, François and 'Strop' Segers, the Fleming, failed to make rendezvous with a Blenheim to escort it over the Channel on a callibration flight. The Blenheim pilot – 609's great friend, Flight-Lieutenant Jock Shillitto—duly reported this, with the result that a Lysander and two Spitfires from another station were sent up to search for them in the 'drink'. Meanwhile, the two pilots were sitting comfortably at Dispersal talking to me. Presently we watched the whole of 92 Squadron take off and the Belgians thought it very funny when later it turned out that all these aircraft had been on the same mission. 92 Squadron were less amused.

By the end of May, there were few pilots in 609 who had not fired their guns 'in anger' at least once. Moreover, like 92 – the first squadron in Fighter Command to get them – one flight had already been re-equipped with the new Spitfire Mark Vb, whose superior operational ceiling and fire-power (two 20 mm. cannon plus four Browning machine-guns in place of the traditional eight machine-guns) made it a match for the new Me 109F, with which the Luftwaffe was now becoming increasingly equipped. Both the recent experience and the new aircraft were needed, for the R.A.F. was about to open its first real daylight offensive.

It started on 17th June, 1941, and continued almost without interruption during the heat wave of the next six weeks. Compared with the mighty American daylight offensives of 1943 and 1944

1936 : First Visit of Inspection. *L. to R.* : Flying-Officer The Earl of Lincoln (Aux. Adj.); Major-General The 10th Earl of Scarbrough (Chairman, The West Riding Territorial Association); Flight-Sergeant Faux (Discip.); Colonel Sullivan (Secretary of the Association); The Earl of Harewood (Lord Lieutenant and Honorary Air Commodore, 609 Squadron); Squadron-Leader Harald Peake (O.C. 609 Squadron). *Yorkshire Post*

1937 : First 609 Squadron officers at Summer Camp, Ramsgate. *Back row* : T. McM. Boyle (M.O.); J. E. Rylands; 'Pinky' Gilbert; Bernard Little; Stephen Beaumont; Peter Drummond-Hay; 'Pip' Barran. *Middle row* : Peter Nickols; Alister Matheson (Assist. Regular Adj. and Flying Instructor); The Earl of Lincoln (Aux. Adj); Harald Peake (C.O.); Norman Odbert (Regular Adj. and Flying Instructor); R. F. Burges (Equipment). *Front row* : 'Presser' Persse-Joynt; G. G. Robinson (Accounts). *Photo* : Treweeks, Ramsgate

Geoffrey Ambler in 1936.

1939 : John Dundas pays an informal visit in his ~~C.O.'s Hawker~~ Hind.

1939 : Joseph Dawson, 'Paul' Edge, Stephen Beaumont and Desmond Ayre.

PR-M seen at Drem, Winter 1939–40. *Earnshaw*

Fg Off 'Hack' Russell shortly before he went missing over Dunkirk, Northolt, Summer 1940. *Rabbidge*

Philip Barran.

H. S. ('George') Darley, fourth C.O., 1940. *From a drawing by the late C. Orde*

1940: Almost the fi␣ Americans to fight in t␣ Second World Wa␣ Gene ('Red') Tobin, Ve␣ non ('Shorty') Keou␣ and Andrew ('And␣ Mamedoff of 609 Squa␣ ron.
Imperial War Museum

Spitfire I, PR-G, possibly P8266. The serial has not yet been re-painted over the newly-applied Sky tail band. *Goss*

609 Sqn, April 1941. L. to R.: Hughes-Rees; Palmer; Green; Rigler; Bennett; Rouse; Malengreau; Wilmet; Tidswell; Mackenzie; Bisdee; Robinson; Richey; Ogilvie; Mackenzie; Hill; Baraldi; Curchin. *Westminster Press*

Keith Ogilvie and 'Teeny' Overton.

The 100th Victory : Part of the Junkers Ju 88 destroyed by Frankie Howell (left) and Sidney Hill (see page 163). *News Chronicle*

Flight-Lieutenant John Dundas,
D.F.C. and Bar. *From a drawing
by the late C. Orde*

Major Helmuth Wick, Com-
mander of the Richthofen Fighter
Geschwader.

Fifteen years after: Battle of Britain reunion at Stanmore, c. 1955.
L. to R.: Bernard Little; 'Teeny' Overton; Michael Appleby; Lord Dowding;
Stephen Beaumont; James McComb (O.C. 611 Squadron, 1940). *London
News Agency*

April 1941 : Fifth C.O. welcomes first Belgians. *L. to R.* : Bob Wilmet; François de Spirlet; Roger Malengreau; Michael Robinson (see pp. 179–82). *Westminster Press Provincial Newspapers*

1941 : The only Drone destroyed by 609 Squadron (see page 177)

1941 : Lord Trenchard greets a wounded Canadian rescued from the Channel (see page 206). *L. to R.* : Tidswell (Adj.); Lawrence (M.O.); 'Moose' Evans; François de Spirlet; 'Duke' Du Monceau de Bergendael; His Lordship. *Photo* : J. Baraldi

The Prime Minister visits 609. *L. to R.* : Air Marshal Sir Sholto Douglas, C-in-C Fighter Command; Winston Churchill; David Hughes-Rees, D.F.M.; Group-Captain Dicky Barwell (Station Commander, Biggin Hill); 'Pyker' Offenberg. *Photo* : J. Baraldi

1941 : Four nationalities. *L. to R.* : Ken Laing (Canada); Maurice Choron (France); 'Cheval' Lallemant (Belgium; in 1944 thirteenth C.O.); Joe Atkinson (U.K.).

1941 : A pilot is interrogated after combat, and his Spitfire rearmed and refuelled. *L. to R.* : Flying-Officer Lawrence (M.O.); Flight-Lieutenant John Bisdee; Flying-Officer Ziegler (I.O.); Pilot-Officer Peter MacKenzie; Pilot-Officer du Monceau. *Central Press*

1941 : Acquisition of Mascot. *Standing* : Bob Boyd; Bauduoin de Hemptinne; Peter MacKenzie; Paul Richey; John Bisdee; 'Pyker' Offenberg; Jimmy Baraldi. *Sitting* : Vicki Ortmans; Tommy Rigler; Keith Ogilvie; Bob Wilmet. Animals : Flying-Officer de Goat, Spit, 'Sailor' Malan's dog. *Central Press*

November 1941 : Savoy Hotel, London. *L. to R.* : Michael Appleby; Air Vice-Marshal Leigh-Mallory (A.O.C. 11 Group); 'Joe' Atkinson; Christian Ortmans; Air Commodore Harald Peake (see p. 228).

G. K. ('Sheep') Gilroy (sixth C.O.); *right*, shaking hands with Maurice Choron, 1942. *Goss*

Paul Richey, seventh C.O., 1942. *Goss*

Sgt Mercer, shortly before he was killed, 9 May 1941. *Goss*

Duxford, 1942: Belgian Minister of War with Belgian Typhoon pilots. *L. to R.*: 'Mony' Van Lierde; Raymond Dopere; Roger Malengreau; André Blanco; Christian Ortmans; Monsieur Camille Gutt; François de Spirlet; 'Cheval' Lallemant. *Author*

Duxford, 1942: Group-Captain John Grandy (Station Commander); Air Vice-Marshal Saul (A.O.C. 12 Group); Air Marshal Sir Sholto Douglas (C-in-C Fighter Command). *Author*

Roland Beamont; *centre*, in doorway, the eighth C.O., 1942–43. *Goss*

Flight-Lieutenant 'Joe' Atkinson, 1940–43. *Author*

January 1943: Jean de Selys after attacking the Gestapo in Brussels (see page 258). *Author*

Manston 1943 : Visit to 609 of Secretary of State for Air. *L. to R.* :
Desmond Sheen (Station Commander and late C.O., 72 Squadron);
Sir Archibald Sinclair; Roland Beamont (see page 260). *Author*

Manston 1943 : *L. to R.* : F. Ziegler (I.O.); Humphreys (N.Z.); R. Beamont
(C.O.); 'Cheval' Lallemant (Belg.); P. Raw and Wing-Commander de Goat;
E. Haabjoern (Norway); 'Moose' Evans (Can.); 'Pinky' Stark; T. Polek
(Poland); Jackson (E.O.); Manu Geerts (Belg.). *Westminster Press Pro-
vincial Newspapers*

1943: Four Belgians. L to R.: M. L. Van Neste; Charles de Moulin (later fifteenth C.O.); Joseph Renier; Manu Geerts (later twelfth C.O.). *Author*

Unteroffizier Werner Öhne, pilot of the second Fw 190 to land at Manston. *Goss*

Unteroffizier Heinz Ehrhardt, pilot of the first Fw 190 to land at Manston (see pp. 268–69); right: Johnny Wells (later eleventh C.O.); centre: Fg Off Treweeks (Station I.O.). *Author*

Alec Ingle; *centre*: The ninth C.O., 1943. *Goss*

Sgt Johnny Wiseman and F/Sgt 'Babe' Haddon standing on R7713 coded PR-Z. Both were to be bounced by Fw 190's of III/JG2 and reported missing, 14 February 1943. *Atkinson*

October 1943: Return from 'Operation Rundstedt' (see pp. 275–6). *L. to R.*: Geerts, Niblett, Van Lierde, MacKechnie (M.O.), Pat Thornton-Brown (tenth C.O.), L. E. Smith. *Author*

Autumn 1943: Last of the Yorkshire Auxiliaries. *Back row*: Eric Ingall; 'Darkie' Hanson; Olaf Priestley; George Ikin; Roland Walker; Bernard Walker. *Middle row*: Geoff Walker; Doug Andrews; Squadron-Leader Pat Thornton-Brown; Harry Simpson; Bob Walling. *Front row*: 'Scales' Summerscales; Les Lindley; Ernie Barker (see page 281).

30 January 1944 : Charles Detal destroys a Junkers Ju 88 south of Paris.

Future D-Day pilots, one Argentinian and four Australians. *L. to R.*: 'Pancho' Pagnam; B. L. G. Foley; George Martin; J. D. McLaughlin; R. E. Bavington. *Author*

'Mony' Van Lierde, 'Pinky' Stark (seventeenth C.O.), Charles de Moulin (fifteenth C.O.) and Johnny Baldwin. *Goss*

609 Sqd. mascots; 'Blitz' (the dog), and 'Billy' (the goat) in front of Typhoon JP843 seen at Thorney Island, June 1944 (this aircraft was shot down 27 July 1944). *Harkness*

The pilots of 609 Squadron as at V.E.-Day, 1945: *Front row*: A. F. Crekillie (Belg.); G. F. de Bueger (Belg.); G. Bell (M.O.); G. J. King (O.C. 'B' flight); L. W. F. Stark (C.O.); J. D. Inches (Can., O.C. 'A' flight); K. H. Adams; A. H. Billam; J. Morgan. *Middle row*: C. H. T. Cables; W. T. Lang (Aus.); A. R. A. Déschamps (Belg.); F. D. Linacre (Aus.); — Bradley; S. E. Hill (Adj.); — Jones (E.O.); A. D. Scott (N.Z.); J. de Bruyn (Belg.); A. Gracie (Aus.); Air Commodore de Goat. *Back row*: G. V. Rémy (Belg.); unidentified; W. E. Corbett (Aus.); D. C. Hellens; R. A. C. Dupré (Mauritius); N. L. Dixon.

1949 : Back to Spitfires (Mk. 16 this time) and Thorney Island. J. Heath, Arthur Hudson (nineteenth C.O.) and J. E. Viles. *Westminster Press Provincial Newspapers*

Pre-War members meet up again post-War; *L to R:* Gp Capt. Norman Odbert (Station Commander, RAF Luqa, 1956), Fg Off. 'Darkie' Hanson and Fg Off. Doug Andrews. *Andrews*

Summer Camp at Oldenburg, 1954: Malcolm Slingsby; Frank Reacroft; Jimmy Heath; Don Dransfield; Peter Hodgson; David R. Shaw, and twentieth C.O., Tommy Evans. *Yorkshire Post*

1955 : Presentation of Esher Trophy to Squadron-Leader Tommy Evans, O.C. No. 609 (West Riding) Squadron, by Major-General The 11th Earl of Scarbrough, Lord Lieutenant of York and the West Riding.

Meteor Mk. 8s : 609 Squadron's aerobatic team.   *Yorkshire Evening News*

11 February 1957: Farewell after the last flight of all. Frank Reacroft, David Shaw (twenty-first and last C.O.), Jimmy Heath, 'Micky' (post-war Squadron mascot). *Yorkshire Post*

1968: After twenty-five years three war-time Commanding Officers – Beamont, Lallemant and Roberts – meet again.

the strike potential was puny : a dozen or two Blenheims or Hampdens would bomb a power station, a marshalling yard or an airfield some little way into France, often more than half of them being hit by *flak* on the coast. Later a few Stirlings were used, the bomb-load of three of them being equivalent to twenty-four Blenheims – 'They don't look British,' Paul Richey once said to me, 'but like some great Russian monster. It's rather terrible to see such a great hulking brute go down in flames.' Afterwards came the faster American Bostons, which were easier to escort. But the main purpose of the operation, which was called a 'Circus', was to engage enemy fighters. For this, up to fifteen squadrons of Spitfires would be used, a number which at that time seemed colossal. Yet if many German fighter formations were soon withdrawn for the invasion of Russia, those that were left behind under Adolf Galland gave a good account of themselves and often opposed even a shallow penetration. And their losses, like those of Fighter Command in the Battle of Britain, were a good deal less than their adversaries claimed – for the bigger the formation, the greater the likelihood of claim duplication, while to confirm the destruction of enemy planes from high altitude over enemy territory was often impossible. Similarly, our own losses were sometimes high partly because a pilot shot down over enemy territory could not normally fight again, nor could his aircraft be recovered and repaired.

For the Biggin Hill wing, led by 'Sailor' Malan, the offensive meant one, two, sometimes even three foreign sorties a day; for few, if any, 11 Group squadrons could be kept in reserve, and often they were reinforced from other Groups. Thus by the end of June 609 (West Riding) had once more become a squadron of veterans, among the top-scoring squadrons of Fighter Command.

The role of the wing varied, the most unpopular being that of close escort, for then the Spitfires, idling along at a speed that deprived them of all finesse, became almost as vulnerable as the bombers themselves. Much preferred was to fly in a semi-freelance capacity, such as that of 'target support' or 'rear support', in which tactics could be adapted to the moment at the discretion of the wing leader. Usually the target would be reached unopposed except by *flak*. Enemy fighters would then be found waiting in its vicinity at great height, and the return journey would seem very long as a few at a time dived straight down through the 'bee-hive', took a quick 'squirt' at the bombers, and continued diving perhaps right down to the deck, with Spitfires after them. Often, in chasing the enemy, a squadron would become split up and it was then that individual dog-fights developed – moments of intense excitement and danger, when life or death hung by split seconds of intuition. Every pilot who fought long enough had them sooner or later, and to the survivors they were not only the most memorable moments of their lives, but crowning gems of experience – for a high percentage of all losses was composed of those pilots who failed to survive their first combat of all.

Looking on death is a lonely affair, and a pilot who landed a few minutes after doing so got back to normal by talking – relief at surviving even making the grim situation retrospectively comical. Thus I remember the soft melodious voice of Jean ('Pyker') Offenberg,* in 1941 the most experienced of all Belgian fighter pilots – while Belgium was being invaded he had actually shot down a Dornier while flying an elderly Italian Fiat CR 42 biplane – recounting with infectious mirth how he found himself simultaneously firing at a Me 109 low over the sand dunes, wiping a frozen windscreen, avoiding *flak* from Gravelines, and watching another 109 'which was floundering around a bit further inland'. And I remember by this time veteran Canadian, Keith Ogilvie, laughingly recounting how, after shooting down an enemy fighter on to Le Touquet airfield, he found his guns jammed and his exit blocked by four of his victim's vengeful colleagues. By employing every twist and wriggle that he had ever learned, he managed to shake them off for the price of two bullet holes in his wing and with a sigh of relief crossed the sands of Dungeness at 1,000 feet – as he thought.

'But I had made a slight error in compass reading,' he slyly confessed to me (meaning that he had flown on a reciprocal course). 'It wasn't Dungeness, it was Boulogne, and there were my friends waiting for me again!' This time he only got rid of them by taking

---

* Offenberg's diary, found long after his death in 1942, was published in English in 1956 by the Souvenir Press under the title *Lonely Warrior* with a foreword by Group-Captain Peter Townsend.

refuge up-sun in the haze over the sea. 'But gee, did I give those Luftwaffe boys the wrong impression!'

The most dramatic reports, however, were those of Sergeant Tommy Rigler. Invariably, after 8th May, when he came back claiming two, my heart sank each time I saw his gun-canvasses gone, for I knew I was in for a verbal barrage that had somehow to be reduced to a cold, factual report. Some said that this balding pilot, who sometimes seemed at war with the world as well as the enemy, had once, as workers' representative, fought for better terms in some factory, and during the Battle of Britain had determined to prove that a working man could be as good a fighter pilot as any wearer of an old school tie. As such he was what the Americans call a 'cinch' to the Press – frequently present because of Biggin's successes, if also (I suspect) because of its accessibility to London – and once they came out with an article, complete with photos, in which our Tommy was anonymously portrayed as 'democracy's typical sergeant pilot'. All of which delighted his colleagues, for anyone less typical than Tommy Rigler was hard to imagine.

The day Tommy performed the hat-trick, however, he was very different. The first I knew about it was when some I.O. at a coastal base rang up to say that he had limped in there, was claiming three, and that frankly he, the I.O., did not believe it. I was busy at the time trying to find out what had happened to François de Spirlet, who had been shot down again, this time into the 'drink', but eventually found him huddled on a chair in the Intelligence Office, with all his bounce gone and Station Commander Dicky Barwell and 'Sailor' questioning him with some incredulity. 'It's no use, Sir, I know I got three,' he tonelessly repeated at intervals. But he did not care whether he was given them, because he was 'through with flying for good'.

The first, I gathered, had been fairly simple, but after that he found himself alone with seven Me 109s above him. Two at once peeled off and came dead astern. He throttled back and turned : the leader overshot, Tommy fired a burst and his adversary disintegrated. Meanwhile, he was hit by No. 2, the others were coming in, and in the course of his avoiding action he suddenly found himself upside down with a dead engine and his head pressed against the roof. 'Tommy,' I said, 'if ever you get out of this, you need never fly again. Then I called, "Blue 2 down below and in trouble!" I saw a Spitfire come down and the nearest 109 dive away in flames. My straps were undone, all set to bale out, when my engine came on again. But just as I got to the coast there was another 109, right on the deck in front. I didn't want to shoot him down, Sir, I'd had enough, but it was him or me.' So he shot it down and nursed his Spitfire back to England. He got his three all right, and he was not 'through with flying'. Two days later, he scored yet another victory, and soon was awarded a well-deserved D.F.M. In the end he commanded a squadron and won the D.F.C.

Here let me add that one of the most beautiful sights of the war was to see the lines of anxiety on people's faces suddenly melt into smiles of thankfulness when the 'phone rang to announce that a pilot who was missing had been rescued. It happened this same day, François's luck still being in. He had been floating about the English Channel in one of the new fighter dinghies with which 609 had practised in a swimming pool.

'I fall out of him twice when I stand up to wave to some aircraft, who do not see. Then after half hour come two rescue boats, and I fear big battle because one he come from France. There *is* battle, and I see one is Navy, the other R.A.F. Navy say, "We saw him first!" but R.A.F. say, "He is R.A.F. man!" I say, "I care not, but please ONE pick me up!"'

In the end the R.A.F. won – to François's disappointment, since the crew had had a party the night before and finished all the rum. Though unwounded, he was taken to Ramsgate hospital and put to bed. He couldn't understand this, and after some hours got up to protest – only to be put back to bed even more firmly on being told that he was suffering severely from jaundice. At that he looked in the mirror and roared with laughter. Yellow he was indeed – from the marker fluid he had released into the Channel.

As Squadron I.O. I was now kept pretty busy. Compared with bomber crews, who however tired, and even if slightly wounded, queued up patiently for de-briefing, fighter pilots were an undisciplined lot. When, as now often happened, the whole Squadron had been engaged, persistence, tact and power of absorption were needed. Persistence because the moment a formation landed after an engagement, all other pilots, 'Ops.', the Station Commander and perhaps even the A.O.C. himself would compete with the I.O., in person or by phone, in getting the news direct. Tact because most pilots had to unburden themselves of a mass of irrelevant matter before getting to the facts I wanted, and to cut them short would result in their closing up like clams. Power of absorption because everyone talked excitedly at once and before you could say knife those who held the main clues to the story might have vamoosed to the Mess bar and would have to be followed there. Meanwhile my notebook became a mass of disconnected jottings. Most of these would be needed, not for the immediate hot-news report, but for the exhaustive one I should have to write later – for with two and three operations taking place daily, detailed interrogation often had to wait till dark, by which time a pilot might well have forgotten the chance, but possibly all-important observation he had made just after his first landing.

Of the formation leaders Paul Richey was one of the best at giving reports, Michael one of the worst. For Paul, though wild at times, was by nature observant and inquisitive – he loved to fly low like a disembodied spirit over English country houses, wondering who lived in them. Once over St. Omer, after shooting down one and probably two of a large formation of enemy fighters which had split up his section and tried to finish him off, he escaped the remainder by flying out of sight behind woods and in valleys all the way to the coast, and took the opportunity to study the French countryside which he had not seen so closely since being stationed there in the era before Dunkirk. On returning he solemnly reported : 'No cows or sheep in the fields, no cars on the roads, only horses and horse-carts – one of them shied into the ditch.' On another occasion he asked me to signal H.Q. 11 Group to enquire about a squadron of fighters over England, whose unusual tactics made him doubt the report that they were friendly. Group drily signalled back : 'Unusual tactics probably friendly, probably Polish.'

Michael was far less objective. 'Oh, we just stooged around,' he would say. 'Some of us took squirts here and there, but there was nothing to get worked up about.' Then, ending the interview with the words, 'Let's discuss it in the bar, Zieg,' he would call his pilots together and for the next twenty minutes give them a terse lecture on their errors of formation – in which, to use his manner of speech, I couldn't have been less interested. If, on the other hand, something occurred that interested *him*, as when he discovered how to stay with a Me 109 in a dive by turning his Spitfire upside down (thus presumably giving its engine the benefit of negative '*g*'), he took pains to see that I got the details right so that pilots of other squadrons might benefit. Indeed, this German pilot must have been surprised at being caught : 'I automatically ducked when his parachute flew past me,' said Michael.

I always rejoiced that fate had finally made me a Squadron, rather than a Station, Sector, Group, Command or Air Ministry I.O., all of whom were the static branches of the Intelligence tree. A Squadron I.O., on the other hand, was a living contradiction of the dictum that no man shall serve two masters. I did. One was the S.I.O. at Biggin or Group H.Q., the other the young man who led the squadron on whose strength I was, and with whom I lived and moved from one Station or Group to another. The only disadvantage was that instead of working a shift, like all the above, I felt that to do the job properly one should be around at all times, and begrudged handing my Squadron over to a *locum tenens* when I occasionally went on leave.

In 1941, however, Biggin Hill saw the emergence of Fighter Command's first fully-fledged Sector Intelligence Office. This was the product of the S.I.O., Squadron-Leader de la Torre, known to all as 'Spy' – previously (like 'Brains') a generic term for any I.O., but at Biggin Hill now monopolized by him. Half Spanish, half French, this officer had none of an Englishman's repressions, and possessed a tall stature, an aggressive black moustache, a powerful personality and a stentorian voice that could (and did) dominate any gathering, however noisy. He was also a born showman, and the large and conveniently placed building which he demanded and obtained soon invitingly displayed every kind of 'gen' any pilot might desire to absorb. It also wasn't long before he achieved his aim of making the place the operational hub of the Sector, with Station and Squadron I.O.s sitting at a line of desks as in an American bank, and the Wing Commander Flying sharing an inner office with himself and the station loud-hailer. My only complaint was that after issuing general invitations to the Army, Observer Corps, A.T.C. and Air Ministry Public Relations officers he invariably contrived to be absent when they arrived, thus leaving the onus of showing them around to one of us. For the office was permanently manned, and it was when I was on duty myself one day that I was visited and saluted by General de Gaulle in his search for Winston.

But 'Spy's' crowning achievement was a briefing room large enough to seat three squadrons. Whereas heretofore each squadron, before an offensive operation, had been given a separate and rather sketchy briefing at Dispersal by its own C.O., with last-minute alterations in the operations plan brought by its I.O. panting on a bicycle, 'Spy' now achieved the miracle of getting the whole Wing seated on the rows of plush seats that he had scrounged from a bombed cinema. And from them thirty-six pilots gazed at a vast wall-map on which (as a result of our work for the previous hour) the tracks of the bombers and all the fighter wings taking part were marked with multi-coloured wools and paper aircraft. On another part of the wall, resembling a tote, would be chalked up the number and type of operation, the target, role of the Biggin Wing, courses, times of take-off and rendezvous, and call-signs. When all were seated, 'Spy' would mount the platform and explain the operation with the aid of a billiards cue filched from the Mess, after which 'Sailor' Malan or his deputy would detail the order of battle, tactics and formation to be employed, and perhaps the Station Commander would give a short pep-talk. With about fifteen minutes to go before take-off, pilots would then bustle out and be conveyed to their widely separated Dispersal points, and Squadron I.O.s strolled out on to the tarmac jealously to watch the 'form' of their own squadrons as they left the ground. 'There goes the 92nd Pursuit!' Tom Wiese, its I.O., would say (he was actually a Norwegian). 'Let's see what the 609th West Riding can do.'

The whole thing depended on split-second timing. Wings from several diversified sectors and stations had to rendezvous at an exact moment, place and height, and if the bombers arrived over the target five minutes too late or early, the whole operation might be thrown out of gear and disaster invited. At Dispersal there was always a bit of last-minute panic : one pilot would have no map, another would have lost his gloves, a third would have forgotten the vital call-signs. Then the Merlin engines would start up, faces would disappear beneath robot-like helmets, goggles and oxygen masks, and the squadrons would become airborne, after which everything moved with machine-like precision until the engagement.

For an hour and a half, perhaps, the aerodrome would be silent except for the sounds of birds or of some of the ground staff kicking a football around, and I might go and have lunch with Hal. But on hearing the drone of the first returning Spitfires we would both start counting and dash back to Dispersal – I to get salient information for the first report before the babble started, he to find out if there were any casualties, for if so various signals had to be sent. Sometimes I would watch the Wing being plotted on its course at the Ops. room, three miles away, and listen in to Michael and Jamie Rankin, high over France, discussing in conversational tones whether an approaching formation of fighters was friendly or hostile. Then someone would cry 'Look out !' and a series of exclamations and curses would show that the battle had begun. Then, 'I've got one, he's on fire !' would indicate a pilot's triumph ; or, 'They've got me, I'm going down,' might be the last time that pilot's voice was ever heard. It all sounded as if it was taking place in the next room instead of over Lille. And when the pilots reached the Channel again, it was time for me to be getting back, for in another ten minutes or so the Spitfires would be landing. Once 609 returned after dusk, still in perfect formation, with red and green navigation lights twinkling against a sky of ultramarine – as pretty a sight as Michael no doubt intended it to be.

There was also night duty, at which each I.O. took turns except 'Spy' himself. This consisted first of answering various queries from Group, clearing up the accounts of the day's activities, and getting things organized for the day following. Here is my log of one night's duty, which I apparently recorded because of its futility :

23.10 Ceased day's work at Intell. office and went on night duty.
00.00 Controller 'phoned to say he was sending tomorrow's ops. instructions (Form 'D') in half an hour.

01.00 Rang Controller to ask why these had not arrived. Told they were just leaving. Went to bed and waited.

02.00 Got up again and made further enquiry. Told despatch rider had had a puncture.

04.00 Awakened by arrival of instructions. Learnt d.r. had had another puncture. Rang Ops. about getting 72 Squadron over from Gravesend.

07.00 Got up and had a bath.

07.30 Roused Station Commander, informed him of coming operation, asked him what time he wanted briefing to take place. Arranged for 609 and 92 to be called and informed.

08.00 Went to Intell. office and prepared briefing map.

08.45 Squadrons arrived for briefing.

09.00 Operation cancelled.

And more than once, with an operation pending at dawn, I remember spending hours ringing up all over London to contact Michael. It always worked out all right in the end.

By the end of June, 1941, 609 was again a team full of confidence born of success. According to a contemporary Yorkshire newspaper account there were still at this time some forty Auxiliary ground staff in the Squadron despite efforts to disperse them since the 'embodiment' of the Auxiliary Air Force with the Royal Air Force at the outset of the war. The anomaly of their continued presence long after all the Auxiliary officers were either dead or superannuated apparently vexed Authority, which seemed unable to understand that these men from Leeds, Bradford and other West Riding cities remained just as loyal and efficient when the West Riding Squadron's pilots were partly composed of foreigners as they had ever been before. Men like 'A' flight's Rabbidge, Eric Ingall, Johnny Payne and Olav Priestley, and 'B' flight's Fitzgerald, Walling, the brothers Walker and 'Darkie' Hanson himself, were now mostly sergeants or flight-sergeants. They were also the repositories of the Squadron's traditions, which they expected new pilots to follow.

Like all other members of the Squadron I was proud to belong to it, and shared in its celebrations and its sorrows – for though during the month of June 609 was credited with the destruction of fourteen enemy fighters, it also lost three pilots. One was Sergeant Chestnut – one of a pair of Canadians (the other was Ken Laing) who had recently arrived. Hit in the engine over the Channel he tried to stretch his glide over the Ramsgate cliffs – and failed to do so by a few feet. The other two losses were the 'heavenly twins', Johnny Curchin and Sidney Hill.

When Johnny ('B' flight's commander) was missing early in the month, no one could quite believe it. 609's most distinguished survivor from the Battle of Britain, with a personal 'score' of at least nine, he had served with the Squadron for exactly one year and one week and become a sort of legend. Without him Sidney lost all his infectious laughter and seemed to turn into a fanatic bent only on revenge, but doomed himself. A fortnight later one of the Belgians (Baudouin de Hemptinne) came back to report that he had followed Sidney as he twice tore into hopelessly superior numbers of Me 109s off Cap Gris Nez. Both extricated themselves, but on reaching Dover Sidney was seen gliding down, and the next thing Baudouin saw was the burning wreck of a Spitfire. Sidney was killed. I claimed for him a 'probable' on the strength of other pilots' observations and his last words on the R.T.

Michael was very tactful that evening. He knew Sidney had been the best-loved member of the Squadron, and he saw that everyone was very silent. It happened that a D.F.C. for 'Pyker' Offenberg had just been signalled, partly for his successes with 145 Squadron in 1940. Tearing off his own ribbon, Michael pinned it on 'Pyker's' breast and decreed a party to celebrate. When spirits had risen somewhat, he took his Squadron on a boisterous nocturnal bathing party, in the course of which six Englishmen immersed themselves and six Belgians refrained. Then he ordered an 'adjutant purge', which consisted of chasing the unfortunate Hal with wild shouts through bushes and over yew hedges till he was caught and delivered to the waters.

It was the right thing to do. In the midst of operations pilots could not afford to grow morbid over the loss of their friends. However demonstrable the mathematical probabilities, they had to persuade themselves (bar a few like Frankie Howell) that it could never happen to themselves. Equally, they must not sympathize with a colleague who lost his nerve – as hens attack one of their number that goes sick, he must be sent away lest the infection spread and the dread and wicked initials LMF ('lacking in moral fibre') applied. I remember one charming and popular lad, who though he suffered from some such phobia was so desperately anxious to prove the contrary that he nearly killed himself doing a 'roll off the deck', and then in tears begged me to intercede with his C.O. to allow him to stay. I couldn't of course, but a few months later he came back to visit his old squadron wearing a D.F.C. ribbon. No one made any comment, but everyone was terribly happy.

For the first fortnight of July the weather grew steadily hotter, and with the long summer days operations sometimes began at 5.30 in the morning and did not end till ten at night. Though I warned them they might be shot as spies if captured, many pilots flew in their shirt-sleeves without insignia of rank. Paul, on landing, would go straight to the 'A' flight office, collect his bathing trunks and whisk his men away to the swimming pool at Brasted. There, relaxing in the sunshine, they became boys again till it was time, perhaps two hours later, to fly back to France.

The tempo was only possible thanks to all the departments necessary to keep a wing of fighters operating – fitters, riggers, armourers, signals, catering staff and ops. themselves working at top pressure. In this a fine example was given by the new Station Commander, Group-Captain Dicky Barwell, D.F.C., who apart from his admin. duties was invariably around to guide and encourage his pilots, and often flew with them himself, usually as Michael's No. 2. The evening he walked into the Mess for the first time he was surprised when two Belgians, Van Lierde and 'Strop' Segers, closed in upon him and insisted on each buying him a drink. Not wishing to offend these new and unusual allies, he felt obliged to accept and only excused himself on the plea that he must go and dine. 'Ve vill dine vith you!' cried the rotund Fleming, and ignoring the disapproving head-shakes of the more respectful Walloons, they did.

On 4th July Paul reported having seen a parachute, and that the parachutist seemed to be wearing black overalls. The only pilot we could think of who wore black overalls was the Station Commander, and for a moment it seemed slightly hilarious to think of a Group-Captain baling out.* In fact it was Keith Ogilvie – Keith who had just written in his diary after typically taking part in every operation since 17th June : 'And so to bed, a plenty tired guy. That leave on Saturday looks pretty good right now.'

The next, and final, entry is dated two days later, though not actually written till he recovered his diary in 1945 :

'How the gods must have laughed ! That leave never came off – and this is why. About noon on July 4th we took off in absolute silence as close escort to the bombers doing Lille, Sailor Malan leading the Wing, Michael Robinson our Squadron, Paul Richey leading one flight, I the other. Over North Foreland the bombers crawled in beneath us and wings of fighters formed up ahead, behind and on either side – an inspiring spectacle, and I never lost the thrill of being a part of the show. Far below we could see the white streaks as the air-sea rescue launches put out from Dover and Ramsgate. On crossing the Channel and progressing inland we were greeted by "ack-ack", first at Dunkirk, then St. Omer. Away to the side tiny specks represented the wary Hun climbing so as to be above and behind us when we turned down-sun for home . . . We had already started when about fifteen 109s floated over us, breaking up into fours, then pairs. A pair came down to attack the bombers and I had turned in to attack them when there was one hell of a "pow" and I was smacked into the dashboard, my port aileron floated away and a great rib appeared up my wing . . . There was blood all over and I felt sick, so I blew my hood off and turned the oxygen full on to keep awake. If I could reach the Channel I'd bale out, because I could not land the kite as it was. But I must have passed out because suddenly everything was quiet and through a haze I could see my prop sticking straight up, and smoke coming from under my cowling. I figured, "This is where I leave", and let go of the stick. . . . Sometime later I came to in a field, surrounded by sympathetic Frenchies who tried to get me up and away, but I could not make it. I had been hit twice in the arm, once in the shoulder, and had lost too much blood. A little while later a sad-eyed German "sanitär" informed me, "For you the war is over" – and he was not kidding.'

The rest Keith recently wrote to me from Ottawa. After nine months in hospital at Lille and then in Brussels – 'The Jerry docs

---

* Soon afterwards Group-Captain Dicky Barwell broke his back in a crash. Then, flying on an operational sortie with his back in plaster, he was shot down and killed by another Spitfire.

fixed my arm up really well, though I can still tell when rain is in the offing' – he eventually reached the notorious R.A.F. camp, *Stalag Luft III*, where he was one of the twenty-four prisoners chosen to take part in The Great Escape under the leadership of Roger Bushell, shot down over Dunkirk when C.O. of 92 Squadron. The last to get free of the tunnel before it was discovered, he was recaptured after two days and sent to a Gestapo prison at Görlitz in Czechoslovakia. There during repeated interrogations 'I stuck to my story that I was a career officer. This must have registered with the Teutonic mind, because I was one of eight returned to camp – the other sixteen, as you know, were shot . . .

'And that, old Spy' – Keith characteristically concluded his letter – 'is I hope my last debriefing – until the big one.' Just a day or two before he was missing he and John Bisdee (who had taken over command of 'B' flight after Johnny Curchin's death), had been awarded the D.F.C.

Keith Ogilvie and Sergeant Bramble were, happily, the only losses 609 sustained in July, 1941, three others being rescued from the Channel virtually unharmed. One newcomer was the Squadron's first Frenchman, or rather Corsican, Maurice Choron—who was yet another crystallization from Michael's past. It seems that in the spacious days of 1937 the latter, already an officer of the R.A.F. and private owner of the (or a) Puss Moth, had flown this to Corsica, met Maurice, then *aviateur instructeur* of the *Aero Club de Corse*, and become the club's honorary president. Maurice was the gayest pilot I ever met, with a fund of French songs and a guitar, all liable to be heard from dawn onwards. Soon he was appointed No. 2 in any section Michael was leading, and remained as such, literally, until the moment they both died.

There were also many visitors. Apart from the Press, who insisted on arranging completely artificial tableaux of Mae-Wested pilots supposedly engaged in cricket, hay-making and archery, there appeared at Dispersal such notables as the C.-in-C. (Sir Sholto Douglas), Lord Trenchard and Winston Churchill himself – last seen by 609 when it escorted him to France in June 1940. During one of Lord Trenchard's visits the Squadron unconsciously staged one of those dramatic situations that a Press photographer would have revelled in. As he talked to the pilots the 'Maggie' landed, flown by François, and out hobbled a large curly-headed Canadian sergeant, 'Moose' Evans, who was returning from a few days in hospital after being intercepted while swimming manfully for the French coast in mistake for the English. As he reached Dispersal, supported by François, he was dumbfounded to find his hand being shaken by an officer whose sleeve carried more stripes than he had ever seen before. Quickly I hustled Jimmie Baraldi, who had a camera, into position, and the necessary 'scoop' for the Squadron album was secured. 'Can't think what he wanted to talk to me for,' said 'Moose' later. But when I showed this and other pictures to his lordship on a subsequent visit, he said 'Thank you,' and put the lot in his pocket.

It was about this time that the Squadron first acquired the services of William – a mascot destined to become a legend. Down the lane was a pub called The Old Jail, run by a Belgian lady called Biddie and much patronized by Belgian pilots, particularly Vicki Ortmans, who evidently so endeared himself by his self-accusative smile that she kept her best bedroom and wine cellar constantly at his disposal. One morning when pilots came to dawn Readiness they found Vicki asleep at Dispersal with a small brown kid on his chest, a gift of the pub. It was promptly given the rank of Flying Officer William de Goat and a special piece of ground in front of Dispersal, where it was taught the use of its horns by 'Sailor's' dog Peter and the Squadron's previous mascot 'Spit' – an intelligent dog who could always pick out his master's Spitfire when it landed and once nearly gave Sergeant Olav Priestley heart failure as he struggled to hold him in the open cockpit of the 'Maggie'. William's introduction to squadron life was being fed quantities of beer from a baby's bottle, after which he was incapable of staggering up the three steps into the Dispersal hut until his morale had been braced by a dozen cigarettes – a diet which he would vary, if I was not watchful, with maps and secret documents. Soon it became unthinkable for 609 to be stationed anywhere without William, whom I last saw in Germany after the war was over – swollen in stature and rank, with Air Commodore's stripes painted on his horns. By then there were only two men left in the Squadron who knew about his origin.

A squadron's Dispersal hut in war-time was its only home – the place where a pilot spent the bulk of his time on duty, often the last place he ever saw on earth. Michael made sure that 609's was as pleasant as possible, with comfortable chairs, bunks for those who had to be at dawn Readiness, and some gay little curtains made by Teresa. From its walls the Orde portraits of former Squadron heroes challenged their successors to emulate them, while now on the flagpole outside there floated not only the flag of 609 but the Belgian pennant as well. But the actual H.Q. of the Squadron was its C.O.'s office. There Halliday Tidswell, tunic unbuttoned and feet on desk, might be surprised reading a novel, or senior squadron officers be discovered gossiping. Occasionally, however, when Hal could divert Michael from flying matters, it was miraculously transformed into a court of law. The stentorian voice of the Flight-Sergeant Discip. would then be heard drawing nearer: 'Escort and accused, at-ten-shun! Quick march! Right wheel! Halt!' – and flanked by his escort (always of the same rank) the prisoner (always without a hat) would find himself confronting the desk where Michael sat in judgment, while Hal, tunic now meticulously fastened and hat on head, stood gravely at his elbow. After the charge had been read out and the prisoner had muttered his defence, Michael would decree the punishment, the prisoner would be marched away, Hal would unbutton his tunic again, and everything would return to normal.

July, 1941, was perhaps the zenith of Michael's career. To quote 'Joe' Atkinson once more, 'He had reached a point of fulfilment when experience and aptitude were so closely matched to opportunity that all that had gone before seemed to be mere preparation and anything that came after, mere epilogue.' Not only had he himself scored half the Squadron's dozen or so victories for the month, but as deputy leader of the Biggin Wing he had shown himself to be a master of tactics. Once, anticipating those of a formation of thirty–forty enemy fighters manoeuvring to intercept, he suddenly changed course and height and enabled the Wing to take them completely by surprise, 609 alone scoring four destroyed, two probables and five damaged without loss. 'A proper bounce!' commented the Station Commander, who was among the scorers. But to Paul belongs the credit for having introduced a new type of tactical flying known as 'Three Snakes', to which John Bisdee attributes much of Biggin's – or at least 609's – success during this period. In place of the traditional four sections of three aircraft in 'vic', as used during the Battle of Britain, there were three sections of four aircraft in line astern, staggered in altitude and all weaving, with the result that the squadron was continuously covered visually against attack from any angle. 'I don't think we were ever seriously "bounced",' says Bisdee, who later employed the same tactics as C.O. of 601 Squadron in Malta. 'The only trouble there was that other squadrons thought we were Messerschmitts!'

Towards the end of July, with a total personal – and in his case almost certainly genuine – score of sixteen enemy aircraft destroyed, Michael Lister Robinson was awarded the D.S.O. and soon afterwards promoted as Wing-Commander Flying of the Biggin Wing in succession to 'Sailor' Malan. The Belgian government in exile also gratefully awarded him the Croix de Guerre (as it did to five of its own pilots), so that Michael had to re-sew his ribbons twice in a few days. Other fresh awards were a bar to Paul Richey's D.F.C. and D.F.M.s to David Hughes-Rees and 'Goldy' Palmer – till finally Hal dryly remarked that the Squadron resembled a Christmas tree, and that he personally felt more distinguished without a decoration.

On the last day of the month John Bisdee, who had served with 609 without a break since the far-off days of December, 1939, was posted away for a well-earned rest from operations. He had been in the Squadron a year longer than any other contemporary pilot.

5

SHEEP

To Michael Lister Robinson no one would have been more welcome as his successor to the command of 609 than his own brother-in-law, Paul Richey, who shared both his operational and social ideas. Many of the Squadron felt the same, not least Paul himself. So when, with the succession (so far as I knew) still open, the A.O.C., Air Vice-Marshal Sir Trafford Leigh-Mallory, attended a Biggin party to mark the departure of 'Sailor' Malan, it seemed an ideal moment for the new Wing leader to champion Paul's candidature. Finding Michael seated on the staircase between two Hambro sisters, with Paul and Teresa near by, I said as much. To my horror he replied, 'You do it, Zieg', and Teresa said 'Oh do!'

It was a fantastic mission for a squadron I.O., but no one was 'feeling much pain', and the A.O.C. himself seemed in jovial mood. Waiting till he emerged from the telephone box, I asked if I might have a word with him. 'Your name?'

I never gave it, though looking back I might conceivably have saved some skin if I had; for his sister was one of my parents' oldest friends, and as a boy I had heard his brother talking about the Everest expedition of the year before he was lost. But none of this occurred to me now, and I merely said that as its I.O. I was well informed about my Squadron's thinking. 'In other words, Sir,' I concluded, 'they would like to have Paul Richey as their new C.O.'

We had been pacing the corridor. The A.O.C. had listened, apparently sympathetically. 'It's a bit late now,' he said. 'Arrangements have been made. However . . .' I forget how he ended, but believe it was something about seeing what he could do. At any rate I had seen what *I* could do – and that was, as it turned out, to have put up 'Imperial Black' No. 2. Some time later the A.O.C. appeared at Gravesend, to which 609 in its turn had moved, for the formal investiture of 'Pyker' Offenberg with his D.F.C. – it being contrary to protocol for King George VI to do this in the case of a foreign national with a King of his own. Incidentally, it was the first time the Squadron had been on parade since the famous gas parade at Warmwell, and now as then there was a contretemps, for the A.O.C. was kept waiting to inspect the ranks by Flight-Lieutenant William de Goat deciding to do so first. On reaching the smartest pair of boots he approvingly lay down on them, and with everyone stiffly at attention the Squadron was powerless to remove him until the ops. clerk, Leading Aircraftman Hinchcliffe, grasping the situation from the window, rushed out and coped with it. But I myself was not on parade, having arrived back from a trip to Biggin after it was already lined up. Feeling slightly guilty I concealed myself with 'Strop', who had been excused as being likely to impair the symmetry of the ranks. But as the Squadron was dismissed the Station Commander found me in the lavatory.

'The A.O.C. wishes to see you, Ziegler – out on the tarmac. Got a hat?'

Surely the great man had more to worry about that the absence from parade of the Squadron I.O.? Wonderingly I marched up to where he now stood alone with his Personal Assistant. 'You wish to see me, Sir?' I said saluting.

I received a long, unfriendly, stare. 'Are you the officer who spoke to me three weeks ago at Biggin Hill?' His voice was brimmed with fearful augury.

'Yes, Sir.' I saluted again, while his P.A. eyed me as he might a rare but repulsive zoological specimen.

'Well, I take an *extremely* grave view of what you said to me on that occasion. Do you think I am going to tolerate officers dictating to *me* about who shall command them? Do you think *I* do not know what is best? Paul Richey needs a rest, and I have sent you an excellent man. I expect you to serve him to the best of your ability. Understand?'

'I intend to, sir.'

'Right!' And I received another long look which posted me half way to West Africa.

A year later at Duxford, when he was C.-in-C., I was formally introduced, along with all 609's other officers, by the Squadron commander. 'Yes, I remember you,' he said, with the ghost of a smile. And I smiled a bit too, for the Squadron commander by then *was* Paul.

Meanwhile Paul did need a rest, as the Squadron M.O., Flying-Officer Lawrence, had no doubt recommended. He in fact nearly perished on his last operational sortie as flight commander. As usual the Wing had been over France, sweeping round St. Omer at 29,000 feet. Paul reported :

'I admit I was flying sloppily. I was bored and cold and troubled by icing; so I really deserved it when I was shot up in no uncertain manner by a gaily coloured Me 109. My glycol tank was pierced and all my coolant lost. I throttled back and got into a spin – a nasty flat one – and could see nothing for smoke. I opened the hood to bale out but couldn't undo my harness pin, partly because of "*g*", partly because I wasn't looking what I was doing. Then the smoke abated and I changed my mind. By exerting all my strength on the stick I recovered from the spin with about 5,000 feet to go ... Half way across the Straits of Dover at 1,000 feet I found that by cutting revs and boost to a minimum I could still use a bit of engine.'

He force-landed at Manston, and a few days later was posted to take over 74 Squadron, now recuperating in the north. As leader of 'A' flight or the Squadron he had never lost a pilot.

I was also at Biggin on the day that 609's new C.O., Squadron-Leader G. K. Gilroy, D.F.C., arrived there to take over. Michael, his flying boss to be, was over at Gravesend 'liaising' with his old squadron, so I rang him up. 'Give him lunch, Zieg, and tell him the form.' By the 'form' I understood I was to give the new C.O. an account of current operations, a thumb-nail sketch of Squadron personalities, and lead him mentally to the Berkeley and the Suivi.

I was confronted by a seemingly very dour, ruddy-faced Scot, whose language was very hard to understand. On each lapel was the letter 'A', not seen in 609 since the death of John Dundas nine months before, and meaning that at this late stage of its develop-

ment the West Riding Squadron was once more to be commanded
by an Auxiliary officer – one of only a handful still left on active
service. G. K. Gilroy, or 'Sheep', as he was (and is) universally
known – he owed his name either to being in real life a sheep-
farmer or (according to Richard Hillary) because of his features –
had a long and distinguished record with No. 603 (City of Edinburgh) Squadron dating back to 1938. On 16th October, 1939,
he had shared in the destruction of the very first enemy aircraft
of World War II – a Heinkel 111 raiding the Firth of Forth – and
had even been hit by a bullet from one of Mussolini's Fiat CR42s
during their one so unwise attempt to raid English soil. If, unlike
so many of his Squadron, he had survived the Battle of Britain,
this was due in part to his extraordinary eyesight. Hillary, who
served with him in 603, wrote in *The Last Enemy*: 'Sheep's experience on the moors of Scotland proved invaluable. He always
led the guard section and always saw the Huns long before anyone
else.' Later in his book Hillary describes the occasion when 'Sheep',
after 'taking off from his bath without a tunic', was hit by an
incendiary bullet, and his plane caught fire :

'He baled out, quite badly burned, and landed in one of the poorer
districts of London . . . He was at once set upon by 200 silent and
coldly angry women, armed with knives and rolling-pins . . . a har-
rowing experience, until he finally established his nationality by producing all the most lurid words in his vocabulary.'

I just don't know how he did it, for one of the words that he
must have uttered many times was 'Och !' – which after all sounds
very much like 'Ach !'

What I discovered now, however, was that when it came to
'silences', 'Colonel Bramble' had been positively garrulous. With
the soup I gave my synopsis of operations : my new C.O. said
nothing. My sketch of personalities lasted until the sweet : his
eyes twinkled, but that was all. 'And if they're not rabbit-shooting,
they rush off to the Chatham Hippodrome or go on a thrash in
town', I concluded my review of social and sporting life over the
coffee.

My C.O. looked thoughtful; the word 'Hippodrome' seemed to
remind him of something. 'Are there any horses at Gravesend ?'

he enquired. I said I didn't know. 'Well, see if you can find out, and if we are released hire six for tomorrow evening.'

My C.O. had spoken. Thenceforth the term 'West Riding' assumed a new significance as, led by their squadron commander in rat-catcher, a motley collection of officers – the 'Duke' and Roger Malengreau in close-fitting cavalry boots, others in flying boots and some in no boots at all – were seen cantering about the Kentish countryside. They became known as 'The West Riding Drag'.

In deference to 'Spy', I had myself reluctantly remained at Biggin for about ten days after my Squadron had moved to Gravesend. After all, he had said, the whole Wing was being briefed at Biggin before an operation, and the whole Wing would land there afterwards to be debriefed. This assessment greatly underestimated the spirit of independence of 609, for whom baths and beer usually took precedence. One morning when they all did land back at Biggin to await another operation in the afternoon, it was announced that the C.-in-C. was coming to lunch and therefore officers would wear ties. Having left these at Gravesend, there was nothing for it but to fly over and get them, at a cost of perhaps 500 gallons of valuable aviation spirit ('and I can't get *two* for my car,' said one pilot). Some were still absent when at Biggin the sound was heard of 92 Squadron taking off. Unknown to 609, the second operation had been brought an hour forward. Those who had returned promptly rose from their lunch and took off, but were late. Their leader, 'Pyker' Offenberg, returning with engine trouble, was followed by the rest of his section who thought the take-off had been a false alarm; Roger Malengreau and his No. 2 tried to rendezvous with some non-existent bombers over Manston; Vicki joined a Polish squadron and flew with it over St. Omer, while another pilot attacked some enemy E-boats off Dunkirk. But they all respectfully wore their ties.

As has been mentioned, 74 Squadron had left Biggin Wing and been replaced by 72, whose place 609 took at Gravesend. These two squadrons had last been together during 609's final summer camp at Church Fenton in August, 1939, when the Regular pilots of 72 Squadron had lent 609's Auxiliaries their own precious aircraft for the latter's first flips in Spitfires; and their present C.O., the veteran Australian Desmond Sheen, had even earlier, so he told me, helped teach a few West Riding pilots about fighter tactics. And now 609 had shown base ingratitude. The day after 72 had moved into our old Dispersal buildings I innocently went over to enquire whether the new squadron was comfortable. I learnt that it was decidedly not, and became the butt of a pithy Australian harangue about my Squadron's infamies:

'At Gravesend we left you all our furniture and games, and what have you left for us? Just four walls! It's an absolute scorched earth policy – I'm told you even tried to get away with the starter motors and equipment benches!'

I departed, resolved to inform Hal that this time he had carried squadron loyalty a bit too far. Two years later, when Desmond Sheen was 609's Station Commander at Manston, we seemed to have been forgiven.

Cobham Hall, seat of the Earls of Darnley and (in part) Officers' Mess of 609 (West Riding) Squadron during the months of August and September, 1941, was a stately home of best Tudor vintage, complete with room slept in by Queen Elizabeth, oak furniture, a library of leather-bound classics, spacious yew-treed lawns, a deer park and floral lavatory basins. In a panelled alcove, the bar, hung 609's china beer mugs, leaving present from Michael, who had had painted on them the Christian or nickname of each recipient – a touching act of faith in the longevity of both fighter pilots and china. Perhaps it was well that the Earl was not in residence, for some of the Belgians like 'Strop' and Bob Wilmet spent all their spare time shooting rabbits in the park – they would have shot deer too had they been allowed. I sometimes wonder whether pilots, flying off to a hostile continent from surroundings steeped in so much English heritage, gave a better account of themselves than if their quarters had been nissen huts. I still don't know the answer.

At Gravesend airfield itself the station personnel could hardly have been more friendly to the single squadron that supplied their *raison d'être*, even apart from the fact that most of the station's functions took place in one and the same building, right beside the Spitfire park. Entering this building via a balcony you would find yourself at the bar, to the right the dining room, to the left a room that was at once the anteroom and pilots' Dispersal, with the Pilots' Order Book nestling up against thrillers by Edgar Wallace. At one end of it the Station Commander would be reading *The Times*, at the other the Squadron ops. clerk – Leading Aircraftmen Kay, Hinchcliffe or Barker – would be awaiting the ring of the 'phone that would launch 609 into the air. If that moment came just after lunch, station officers would rise to deliver up the 'Mae Wests' on which they were sitting and newspapers would become airborne in a search for a pair of missing gloves which at the last moment might be found being used as a mute for the gramophone. Following the pilots out, the station officers would watch them take the air, after which there was time for a club-room nap before the hubbub of their return. Any pilot who was not flying – or reading a book in the shade of the Cobham Hall garden – might pick his way past the recumbent bodies and find himself in the cool sanctum of the Intelligence Office, where he might learn how near he could approach His Majesty's ships without receiving resentful fire, brush up his aircraft recognition or study the distribution of the German Air Force. He might even take the I.O. on one side, as young Peter did one day, and confess that, unable to use the approved air-firing range, he had fired his guns at random into the sea and been startled by the explosion of a mine. What would the Navy say? Well that, said the I.O., depended on whether the mine was 'ours' or 'theirs'. He would look into the matter.

Another important function of the building was to supply a 'Mappin Terrace' for Flight-Lieutenant William de Goat – who, amongst all the stations of his war service, must surely have classed Gravesend as 'tops'. Upstairs were the offices of the Station Commander, Adjutant and others. These he rightly avoided, but continuing upwards he would find himself in the control tower. From there it was simple to climb out of the open window, and to the plaudits of the crowd below progress backwards along the front of the building on a six-inch ledge until, reaching the middle, he resolved himself into stone, causing visitors to think he was part of the statuary. Bored with watching, the audience would then go in to tea – whereupon William would sneak down again, quietly enter the dining room, and in a flash be on to the table, gobbling up as many lettuce sandwiches as he could before pandemonium focused itself into the action of ejecting him. But later he might be found curled up repletely in an armchair. Once, during an inspection by a rather senior Air Ministry officer, the tannoy was heard to boom 'Remove that Goat!' and William was seen standing guiltily on the roof of the Station Commander's car.

Useful though the tannoy – or loud-hailer – was, it had the demerit that you couldn't ask it questions. On another occasion, while 609 was airborne over France, the voice of the Station Commander suddenly proclaimed: 'Enemy aircraft approaching from three o'clock – man defences!' The sirens wailed, a Bren-gun carrier moved out along the perimeter, and Hal and I solemnly put on our tin hats. The voice continued: 'Parachutists dropping near the north-east corner of the aerodrome!' Eyes strained upwards, fire and gas parties went to readiness. I considered setting fire to the Intelligence Office, thought better of it and rang up Biggin ops. to suggest the loan of a few Spitfires for local defence, only to be told they had no 'hostiles' on the board. Finally the voice said: 'Danger now over.' It had been a practice, but the voice had omitted to say so.

One day, after a visit to Belgian headquarters in Eaton Square by such social elements as Roger Malengreau and 'Duke' du Monceau, it was announced that their Minister of War and Finance, Monsieur Camille Gutt, had invited the officers of 609 Squadron to a dinner in the Pinafore Room of the Savoy Hotel. It was a sumptuous affair, and after plentiful wines and liquers, speeches merged with anecdote, and anecdote with song. Finally, as symbol of the alliance now cemented between Belgium and the West Riding, a beautiful and valuable ebony cat was spirited away from the mantelpiece, paraded in triumph at the Suivi, and next day added to the other trophies at 609 Dispersal.

Unfortunately I was one of the chauffeurs responsible for getting the Squadron back to base, my passengers being 'Duke', young Peter MacKenzie, Paul Richey and Teresa (who was coming on a final visit just before her husband's departure). The three men promptly went to sleep in the back, and though Paul alone knew the way and I once roused him when lost near Blackheath, all he did was to get out, pick up the business end of a crossing-beacon lying in the gutter, and go to sleep again with the orange orb lying across their laps. Two policemen, who flashed their torches on this strange picture of still life, were so astonished that they could hardly tell me the way themselves. Finally Paul and Teresa, having failed at five a.m. to gain admission to the Dickens Pickwick Leather Bottle Hotel where they were booked in Cobham village, had to be given my double-bedded room at Cobham Hall. A few hours later, choosing our moment, Peter and I smuggled Teresa out again, unobserved except by the batman who had not yet recovered from the shock of serving breakfast in bed to a married couple. Fortunately only one section that morning was required at Readiness.

If 609 was now commanded by a Scot, by the end of August both its flight-commanders were Belgian – 'Pyker' Offenberg and François de Spirlet. In fact by the end of autumn 1941, British officer pilots were reduced to three: 'Sheep' Gilroy, 'Joe' Atkinson and Dennis Barnham – an intelligent and artistic young man who later commanded a flight in Malta under John Bisdee. While one or two Belgians departed – Baudouin de Hemptinne to take up a flight-commandership elsewhere – new Belgian officers soon included Alex Nitelet, Morai, Giovanni Dieu, van Arenberg, Baron de Selys Longchamps, and Vicki Ortmans' younger brother Christian. But if officer strength was mostly Belgian, N.C.O. pilot strength came mostly from Britain, Canada and New Zealand. Two of the new intake here included Peter Nash and John van Schaick (the latter despite his name as British as the former), who along with such veterans as David Hughes-Rees (Welsh), 'Moose' Evans (Canadian) and Tommy Rigler would be commissioned before the year was out. There also came one Belgian sergeant-pilot known as 'Cheval' Lallemant, who was destined three years later to command the Squadron.

Deterioration in the weather from August onwards resulted in less operations involving several Wings ('Circuses') and more by single squadrons or even flights. These included attacks on enemy shipping, or supporting such operations (code named 'Roadstead') by Blenheims, Beauforts or Beaufighters. Compared with the Hurricane pilots of 615 Squadron under Dennis Gillam, who as specialists were I believe ultimately successful for all but closing the Straits of Dover to enemy shipping by daylight, 609 had as yet little experience in this field, and on their first single-handed attack off Dover its pilots failed to agree whether the target had been fifteen R-boats or five minesweepers each with two paravanes. Though one was claimed as damaged, Sergeant Boyd, a veteran from 1940, was hit by *flak* and baled out. Picked up by a naval launch five minutes later, he had to stifle his lurid references to the temperature of the water on finding aboard a female reporter from the *Toronto Star*. More galling still was being accused by the watchers at Dover of having baled out for a newspaper stunt.

Though a state of defensive Readiness was still observed by daylight, and as winter approached Spitfires stood by yet again for *Fighter Night*, defensive patrols, except in aid of convoys, were now rare. So when weather prevented large-scale offensive operations, and the other two squadrons of the Wing were respectively at Readiness or Released, a new 'state' was created for the third known as 'Released for Rhubarbs'. A 'Rhubarb' was an offensive patrol by a single pair of aircraft, which eluded enemy radar by crossing the French or Belgian coast at 'o feet' and sought targets of opportunity – the while protected from attack from above by low unbroken cloud. The technique was not yet highly developed as 609 was to develop it later, and damage to the enemy was slight ('I fire on armour car,' Vicki reported one day. 'He stop, but I think this was mistake'). What 'Rhubarbs' did do was to bolster pilots' confidence in themselves and their navigation – the penalty for error being a gauntlet of *flak* from Boulogne, Calais or Dunkirk. Sheep – the amount of whose operational service in World War II can have had few parallels – himself set a shining example, and sometimes had as many as four pairs operating at once. Perhaps his keenest follower was that indomitable individualist Tommy Rigler, who attacked factories, gun positions and vessels with equal fervour. One day, while the Squadron was flying east near the French coast, he called excitedly :

'Hullo, Red Leader, this is Red 2 reporting a ship at three o'clock.'

'You mean nine o'clock,' Sheep replied. He had of course already seen it, and three o'clock would have taken it well inland.

'Three o'clock, Sir,' Tommy persisted.

'Above or below?'

'Below'.

'Well, blow me down!'

Sheep had a distinguished habit of appearing at Biggin briefings wearing a raincoat beneath his 'Mae West' and carrying a small Gladstone bag,* causing him to resemble a Ruritanian commercial traveller on a wet day rather than a leader of Spitfires. Apart from pipes and tobacco, of which he used a great deal, its contents remained undisclosed, and I consequently viewed it with some suspicion. For apart from seeing that pilots took off equipped with the necessary 'gen', it was also my job to ensure that they left behind such things as letters and diaries which might provide useful clues in the event of capture. Not that I was really worried: any enemy interrogator, confronted with the task of getting anything out of Sheep, would have shot himself quite soon. Even friendly interrogators sometimes despaired:

'What happened after Hazebrouck?' I would ask him.

'I've told you twice, Zieg.'

Probably he had. I just hadn't understood. He was also unduly modest. When, like Michael a year before, he opened his score with 609 by bagging two enemy planes, he made no claim at all. Fortunately I had other, quite convincing, evidence.

A worse headache than the search of pilots' pockets was the up-hill struggle to keep a tally of the purses of foreign currency issued to pilots to help them escape if forced down on occupied territory. Altogether these must have represented quite a drain on Britain's war-time stock of foreign exchange and were strictly accountable to Group H.Q. Yet no matter what system I devised for their return after landing, the number was always short. Some pilots would refuse to give them up on the grounds that they had

---

* Twenty-seven years later I mentioned this bag at the Leeds reunion. 'I've got it with me now,' he said. Incidentally, he didn't look a day older.

to go immediately to Readiness, and argued that in chasing the enemy from these shores they might get carried over France. Others would draw a second purse, having left the first in their bedrooms; still others would swear they had never had one at all, or had given it to someone else. And in the pandemonium of take-off there was often no time to obtain the vital signature. The only thing to do was to write one off each time a pilot was shot down, whether he came back or not, and thanks to the efficiency of the Air-Sea Rescue service this nearly balanced the account. I duly did this when Alex Nitelet was missing, believed killed; and when, months later, he returned to 609 Dispersal after a long journey via Spain, I tried to take some credit for his escape.

'But you didn't give me a purse that day!' he said. 'I had to go to Brussels to borrow from my mother.' He also claimed a Me 109, which was tardily added to the Squadron score at the instance of H.Q. Fighter Command. But he lost an eye.

Vicki Ortmans, D.F.C., won me two purses by being shot down twice within a couple of weeks. 'What! You again?' cried the crew of the same rescue boat on hauling him aboard by his hair and the seat of his pants for the second time. 'Oui, oui! Me two lives!' he replied. By then we were back at Biggin, and the night before Vicki had earned much disapproval from station officers by tap-dancing on the billiards table. Sheep, who next day wondered what punishment would satisfy them, was heard to mutter as Vicki again returned from the 'drink': 'Perhaps he has suffered sufficient inconvenience already.'

Vicki's first immersion occurred on the day a new tin leg was dropped for Wing-Commander Douglas Bader, lately leader of the Tangmere Wing but now a prisoner-of-war. The teleprinted 'Form D' on this occasion began:

OPERATION LEG (Circus 81). To take place a.m. Tuesday 19th August 1941. INFORMATION: The leg is to be dropped by a Blenheim when W. of St. Omer. The leader of the Tangmere escort wing is to report by R.T. when the parachute has opened, 'Leg gone'. Tangmere controller is to report to Group controller immediately he receives this message.

And afterwards the Intelligence report ran:

During this operation the leg for Wing-Commander Bader became airborne at 10.51 hours, and was last seen floating down gracefully S.W. of St. Omer. At 11.00 hours a message was broadcast to the enemy that the leg had just been dropped by parachute. The message was acknowledged ... No bombs were dropped during this operation. All the bombers returned safely.

But Vicki lost his favourite aeroplane. 'Poor "D",' he mused wistfully, 'she is dead.'

Flying-Officer Vicki Ortmans, and *Sous-Lieutenant* Maurice Choron, the lone Frenchman (he was once delighted to receive an official letter addressed to '*Le chef du détachment français, escadrille No. 609*'), were at this time two of the Squadron's outstanding warriors and characters. Being also close friends, they held a position similar to that once occupied by Johnny Curchin and Sidney Hill. In the air they were fighting terriers that worried the Luftwaffe; on the ground mischievous terriers that brought bones into the house and got into trouble. On 17th August Vicki and 'Goldy' Palmer, D.F.M., were cut off and furiously attacked by some twenty of the enemy, emerging damaged and exhausted after the most violent dogfight of the month. When Vicki swore black and blue that one of his assailants had been 'a Me 109 with a radial engine', and I reported this to 'Spy' on the telephone, he regarded it is such arrant nonsense that I only just persuaded him to mention the matter in the initial Wing report. In fact, Vicki's may have been the very first combat with the new German fighter, the Focke-Wulf FW 190, which appeared without warning and was soon to be respected (except at high altitude) even more than the Messerschmitt 109 F and G.

Maurice, who continued to fly number two to Michael whatever squadron the latter put himself at the head of, thereby occasionally made nonsense of my reports; for after writing that 609 hadn't seen a thing, I might have to refer to the destruction wrought on the enemy by one of its members. Like Michael, Maurice was also prone to sing into his microphone. Once, when he gave away the Wing's position as it approached Rouen by singing, '*J'aime à revoir ma Normandie*', he was curtly told to shut up; but when Michael treated thirty-six pilots to a rendering of *Little Miss Muffet*, there was no one senior enough to give him the bird.

One day, when at Cobham Hall, I was instructed on the 'phone to place both Maurice and Vicki under close arrest and bring them to the airfield. With prisoner Vicki at the wheel of his little Morris Eight called 'Caroline' we arrived at the Intelligence Office, which had become a Court of Inquiry. It appeared that the two culprits, on a recent trip in the Tiger Moth, had had their number taken near Northolt by a dutiful warrant-officer of the service police, who reported that not only had they circled a house at extremely low altitude but, contrary to all regulations, had 'dropped an object from the aircraft', and waited till it was collected by a woman. In evidence it turned out that the lady was a friend of theirs, and that they were returning a fur coat that she had left behind. If they avoided court-martial it was probably only because of their indispensability to 'ops', and when weeks later Maurice proceeded to 11 Group H.Q. to have a 'strip torn off' by the A.O.C., Vicki was no longer around.

The increased efficiency of the Air-Sea Rescue service was a great boost to morale, for pilots knew that there was now a better than even chance of being picked up, at least from the Straits of Dover – 609 had six rescues in two months. As soon as a pilot got into trouble, or saw a colleague in trouble, he would call *M'Aidez*! – spelt 'Mayday' for simplicity – on a special frequency on which all stations kept a listening watch. This would enable the approximate position of the pilot's inflatable dinghy to be fixed, and rescue boats would be sent to the spot, often with aircraft to guide them. Once the 'Duke', in defiance of the Pilot's Order Book, 'corrected' a boat that was a bit off course by firing a burst of canon in front of its bows – 'a very good idea,' said the skipper, whom he later met. It was not unknown, even, for one side to help the other : I remember the skipper of another boat saying that he had actually seen a single Focke-Wulf 190 approach a flight of searching Spitfires, waggle its wings and lead them to their own pilot's dinghy – without being attacked.

Joe Atkinson probably owed his life to a pilot from another wing. Turning to rejoin his formation after an abortive chase over France, he found himself being shot at from behind :

'I thought it was a Spitfire, and as it was shooting damn badly I ignored it. Then my air-speed indicator blew out – there must have been another type shooting from above.'

He finished his avoiding action 2,000 feet above Boulogne beach with his engine on fire; and though he managed to glide to mid-Channel before baling out, he had given his 'Mayday' too low for proper reception. Unaware of his fate, the Squadron had flown home; and it was beginning to get dark. 'I felt so lonely and small bobbing about out there in my dinghy,' said Joe.

But another lone Spitfire pilot, from the Kenley Wing, had seen him and went on orbiting until, with his petrol nearly exhausted and the light nearly gone, Joe was picked up.

At Gravesend black depression turned to whoops of joy when we heard that Joe was safely in the hands of the Royal Navy based at the Lord Warden Hotel, Dover; and at ten p.m. Hal, Roger Malengreau, Peter MacKenzie and I set off in the 'Belgian Barouche' * to retrieve him. It was nearly midnight when we arrived, Dover was deserted owing to an air raid, and we couldn't find the way. It was cold and we were all wearing fleece-lined flying jackets. Eventually we drew abreast of some members of the Salvation Army, whom Roger, at the wheel, addressed with his slightly foreign accent. No, they stoutly maintained, though they had been in Dover nine months, they knew of no Lord Warden Hotel; but if we cared to wait they would go and find out from the police. They did not return, and meanwhile two naval officers came by, themselves headed for the Lord Warden, so we gave them a lift.

It was awesome to meet a friend whom one had thought was lost; and Joe, thanks he said to a benzedrine tablet consumed in his dinghy, was in excellent form. Dressed in a polo-necked sweater and a blue tweed jacket, he was at the bar surrounded by Navy who promptly plied us too with drinks. But Joe had hardly started

* A large Ford estate car recently presented by the Belgian government in London for pilots' recreation. At a time of strict petrol rationing it had the unique privilege of being able to fill up at any R.A.F. petrol pump, and later (after the R.A.F. had put its foot down) at any Army one. Needless to say other squadrons were both mystified and jealous, for its mileage was terrific.

on his story when there was a commotion in the hall and I was summoned to meet a whole bevy of policemen. During the air raid, they told me, a German bomber had been shot down, and its crew after apparently requisitioning a car, had asked the Salvation Army the way to the Lord Warden Hotel. Now, after changing into R.A.F. uniform, it seemed they were drinking with the Navy. It took me at least five minutes to convince the police sergeant that all this was unlikely behaviour, and that the foreign accent the Salvation Army had heard was not German, but Belgian.

Next morning I despatched signals of gratitude to the rescue launch skipper and to Kenley. The latter ran :

'Grateful thanks of 609 (West Riding) Squadron to the pilot whose initiative and persistence resulted in the rescue of Flying-Officer Atkinson.'

Eighteen months later I happened to meet this pilot at Manston and introduced him to Joe. 'I've still got that signal pasted in my log book,' he said.

As for Joe's brine-soaked uniform, he took it back in a sack and asked the batman we shared to put it on the stove — to dry. Next day he asked for it.

'But you told me to put it on the stove, Sir !'

Like coal.

The third time Vicki Ortmans was missing, he did not return. It was 21st October, a fortnight after he, like Offenberg, had been decorated by the A.O.C. at a parade that included eighteen tassle-capped Belgian cadets attached to 609 for training as ground staff. Michael Robinson, taken off operations 'to be fattened up for the spring', as he put it, was now P.A. to Air Chief Marshal Sir Arthur Longmore, Inspector General of the R.A.F., and Jamie Rankin, late C.O. of 92 Squadron, had inherited the Wing. He was leading it today at the head of 609, whose own C.O., Sheep Gilroy, was accordingly leading Blue Section. With Biggin detailed as Rear Support Wing off Boulogne — considered a mere 'stooge' job — Sheep took Vicki's brother Christian on his first operation as his own No. 2, with Vicki and 'Goldy' Palmer, D.F.M., as a strong rear-guard. Suddenly the C.O. spotted fifteen–twenty Me 109s

coming down on them, and called that he was going down too as
there were too many to deal with. But though he was followed
by Christian, Vicki and 'Goldy' evidently never got the message,
and though the latter landed on the water, he never got out of his
plane. No one saw what happened to Vicki, though the rest of the
Squadron searched for him for the rest of the day, and I shall
never forget the look of anguish on Christian's face as the last
Spit landed in the gathering darkness and reported no trace. With
difficulty he was restrained from taking off yet again, alone – for
not only was Vicki his brother : he was his hero and instructor
who had been teaching him dog-fighting all over the sky, as David
Crook had once done with his friend Geoffrey Gaunt.

Vicki, in fact, was alive, though the discovery of this was a near
miracle. One day the faithful Biddie (I think it was), reported that
while listening to a German broadcast giving the names of prisoners
of war, she thought she detected the name 'Vicki Ogilvie'. Without
much hope I got in touch with the Air Ministry and asked if by
chance they had the name of such a prisoner. They said they had
a postcard so signed but were puzzled because no one of that name
had ever joined the R.A.F.

The following January Christian received a letter. Vicki had
in fact survived the Me 109 attack, but had then been assailed by
five FW 190s, one of which he shot down before having to bale out
himself, badly wounded. He had spent no less than two days and
a night in his dinghy, longing to die, before being picked up unconscious by the Germans after falling out of it. Later, remembering the rule that to protect their families at home captured Belgians
should give false names and say they were French Canadian, Vicki
had given the name of Ogilvie – only to find the real Ogilvie
(Keith) in the camp to which he was eventually sent. Writes the
latter :

'I had briefed Vicki on his "French-Canadian background" and
this was never questioned – either the Jerries knew or just didn't care.
But prison was hard on Vicki : he worried about his family, and became very moody and depressed.'

And having survived the war, Vicki killed himself, inevitably,
soon afterwards by trying one too many air stunts. The last time

I heard his voice was three days after he was missing: on the
B.B.C. with Offenberg and Dennis Barnham – a recording. It was
the last time Christian heard it too.

Vicki and Palmer were the first experienced pilots to be lost to
the Squadron since Keith himself three and a half months earlier.
In August Pilot-Officers Nitelet and Cropper and Sergeant Pollard
were killed or missing, and Sergeant Folkard injured, soon after
they had joined the Squadron; and in September another new
pilot, Pilot-Officer Saunders, just escaped with his life when, out
of petrol, he hit a gun emplacement full tilt. Next month Pilot-
Officers Van Arenberg and de Selys both managed to get down
after an air collision, though this put up 609's accident rate to
four in eighty hours' flying, against its previous record of one in
ninety (what would Cloves have said!)

Operationally 609 was luckier than the other squadrons, even if
its pilots were now more experienced. At the beginning of October
92 Squadron lost five pilots in two days, and soon afterwards were
sent north; while on the 27th their successors, No. 401 (Canadian)
Squadron, lost five pilots and 72 one. Before a conference of enquiry could be convened, 609 was sent off again to protect two
rescue launches searching for the missing pilots, and might well
have been wiped out itself. For while Sheep called vainly for reinforcements, 'ops.' plotted no less than three enemy formations
of fifteen-plus, two of twelve-plus, a nine-plus and a three-plus
coming in to attack. The Squadron was saved largely thanks to
Wing-Commander Jamie Rankin, D.S.O., D.F.C., who after ap-
pointing himself as solitary 'high cover' engaged and drove off
two successive enemy formations. In the end there was no loss to
609, while for Jamie I claimed one FW 190 destroyed and one Me
109 probably destroyed, and for Sheep two Me 109s destroyed –
largely on the evidence of a pilot of the 'Jim Crow' Squadron,
No. 91, who saw three enemy aircraft hit the sea. On this day
German newspapers reported that a Luftwaffe fighter ace, back
from the Russian front, achieved his hundredth victory. Such
aggression by such numbers over the English coast suggests that
he and his unit had not been told that this was no longer quite
'the form'.

609's long spell of service in the south was almost up, yet in the last twelve days before on 19th November it followed 92 Squadron to Digby, Lincolnshire, they were the only scorers in the Wing, claiming four enemy fighters destroyed and two probably destroyed for the loss of Sergeant Ken Laing, who was hit by *flak* while helping to escort Hurricane bombers of 615 Squadron attacking an alcohol distillery (one of Fighter Command's new targets). Ken Laing was said to have been the last of a batch of thirty Canadians who had crossed the Atlantic together, and before long he wrote to say he was a P.O.W. On the same operation 72 Squadron lost a pilot in an air battle in which Sergeants van Schaick and Nash put up a brilliant display, the latter single-handedly repulsing with loss simultaneous attacks by three FW 190s and three Me 109Fs that went on for ten minutes. Victors next day were Sheep and Christian Ortmans, still his No. 2, while on the last day of all Dennis Barnham obtained the Squadron's last victory of 1941 during a battle with three FW 190s which lasted from Cap Gris Nez to Dover. But with 72 and 401 Squadrons each losing two more pilots, the aggregate Biggin–Luftwaffe score for this November period was six-to-four in favour of the latter.

Before the dreaded departure for the north there occurred two events which gave the Squadron a feeling of public recognition and pride of continuity. On 14th November Air Commodore Harald Peake, Director of Public Relations, Air Ministry, formally presented the West Riding Squadron on parade with its official Badge,* approved by the College of Heralds. And it was right that

---

* The original design for the Badge – according to Cloves and confirmed by Hanson – arose from a competition set in October 1940 by Michael Robinson, who offered £1 to the winner. Cloves' own design – a bugle with the White Rose of York, in the drawing of which Corporal Summerscales is said to have helped – was duly submitted to the College of Heralds, who suggested that the single bugle be replaced by twin hunting-horns, crossed. These in turn led, after vain attempts to put the word 'Scramble!' into Latin, to the motto 'Tally Ho!', a call common to huntsmen and fighter pilots. Soon after the presentation, 609 received a letter from a Mr. Will Friend, one-time Master of the Holderness Hounds, offering it a pair of actual hunting horns made in 1847. These were duly presented by his widow after the war, and are now amongst the Squadron's mementoes. But Flight-Sergeant Cloves never got his 'quid'—he left the Squadron too soon.

it was Peake who did so; for though the post of 609's Honorary Air Commodore may still have belonged to the Earl of Harewood, it was Harald who since the war began had voluntarily shouldered its burdens. And four days later, on the very eve of their departure, the officers of 609 found themselves once again dining in the Pinafore Room of the Savoy Hotel, this time as guests of Harald Peake himself. Seldom can so many past and present members of a war-time fighter squadron have sat down together. Besides the host himself, they included its early Adjutant Gordon Sudworth, and such survivors from Dunkirk and Battle of Britain days as Jarvis Blayney, David Crook, Michael Appleby, John Bisdee and Michael Robinson. Distinguished guests included Air Vice-Marshal Sir Trafford Leigh-Mallory (A.O.C.), Group-Captain Barwell (station commander, Biggin Hill), Group-Captain Sir Willoughby de Broke and Colonel Wouters (Belgian Air Force Commandant). After the toasts of the King and the King of the Belgians had been drunk, the A.O.C. said he was honoured to have been invited to 'such a family gathering', stated 609's successes in figures, and added that he was sorry the Squadron was leaving his Group – to which Squadron-Leader Gilroy responded that every effort would be made to return to it soon.

Late in the evening, after all the guests had gone, a residue of the Squadron sat planning its last and perhaps most difficult operation in 11 Group : how to recapture the famous ebony cat* which again defied them from the mantelpiece. Difficult because this time the defence, recognizing its adversaries, was fully alerted. So first there was a feint : the cat disappeared and Peter Mackenzie was sent out with bulging tunic. Promptly intercepted by several waiters, he opened his tunic and empty wine bottles cascaded to the floor. This diversion enabled the real operation to be mounted. Out went François de Spirlet, carrying a bag, and in the corridor was engaged by the enemy commander, the manager himself.

'Excuse me, sir !' the latter fired. 'A most valuable ebony cat has disappeared. I must really ask you to open that bag !'

'You insult me, yes? You say that I, a Belgian Flight-Lieutenant of the Royal English Air Force am a thief? I will *not* be searched !'

* After its first capture this cat had been returned to the Savoy to save embarrassment to the Belgian minister, M. Gutt.

The dogfight continued down the stairs to the front door, where the manager fired his last shot : 'I must INSIST, sir !'

'*Alors!*' Disdainfully François dropped the bag, and the manager stooped to open it. Inside there was only some photographic apparatus of mine. 'I . . . I am very sorry, sir !'

I was just behind and we walked out without further opposition, the cat nestling under a raincoat over my arm.

Some weeks later Sheep received a letter from Harald Peake, explaining that he could no longer lunch at the Savoy in peace because of reiterated managerial inquiries. So finally, with an ebony ear repaired in station workshops, the cat was flown back from Lincolnshire in the 'Maggie' and returned by Joe Atkinson and me. Joe says we were received by the Savoy management with open arms, as if we were making a presentation instead of returning stolen goods – and Sheep even got a letter of thanks. Long after the war I read that this same ebony cat, 'Kaspar', had for years been a favourite of Winston Churchill's at dinners of 'The Other Club', held in the Pinafore Room : if there were thirteen he arranged for it to join them at the table. *The Evening News* added that during the war it had been taken to the Middle East !

In ten months to a day 609 Squadron would return to Biggin Hill. Meanwhile it left, as I wrote in its war diary, 'not as a tired squadron of declining morale – as other squadrons leave – but with its pilots still at the top of their form', and only 'to allow another squadron to gain experience'. During its nine months in the Biggin Hill sector it had been credited with fifty-three enemy fighters destroyed, nineteen probably destroyed and forty-one damaged for the loss (as in 1940) of fourteen pilots—'a gain-loss ratio that has probably not been equalled in Fighter Command this year'. During 1941 it had been awarded one D.S.O., five D.F.C.s, four D.F.M.s and numerous Croix de Guerre, and finally went north after eighteen months' continuous service in front-line sectors. No other fighter squadron, I believe, had been so long in the firing line.

6

RECESSION AND TRANSITION

The further a war-time fighter station was from the war, the more strained relations were apt to be between the station authorities and the squadrons based there. Digby was in 12 Group – a Group where daylight operations, mostly limited to precautionary patrols, yielded pride of place to training, more aircraft were 'pranged' in accidents,* and disciplinary regulations retained some of the holiness of peace-time. Pilots' leave was reduced from once in four weeks to once in six, scarves and flying boots were taboo in the Officers Mess, and a £4 maximum monthly bar bill reflected not only a shortage of spirits but disapproval of their consumption. Accustomed to being lionized in 11 Group, 609 Squadron took an instant dislike to Digby, where its reluctance to conform earned so many reproofs that someone suggested that its motto be changed to *Semper In Excreta*.

Digby, which previously had housed No. 2 Central Flying School, at this time was a Canadian Sector airfield commanded by a Canadian Group-Captain, where newly formed all-Canadian squadrons were introduced to operational flying, and even Wing-Commander 'Cowboy' Blatchford, D.F.C. – a seasoned Canadian, once of 41 Squadron, whom Stephen Beaumont had briefly befriended in October 1939 – reluctantly found himself more an instructor than the leader of a wing. Thus if 609 was itself initially disliked, one reason may have been that its personnel were something outside the station's previous experience. For one thing most of its officers were Belgian, for another many of its ground staff

* At a conference held on the morrow of 609's arrival the Station Adjutant actually suggested that any pilot involved in an accident should be temporarily deprived of his 'wings'.

were Yorkshiremen, who indicated that as something called 'Aux-iliaries' they could work very well, thank you, without all this 'bull'. One day thirteen 609 airmen were marched in front of 'Pyker' Offenberg, acting C.O., charged by the station with a technical infringement of the black-out. Penalty : three days' de-tention 'retrospective from the date of the offence'.

Apart from the affront to good order and discipline caused by the sight of the Squadron's uniquely privileged transport, the 'Belgian Barouche', dashing all over the country burning service fuel, what really got the goat of the (British) Station Adjutant was . . . 609's Goat. Hardly had this mascot regained *terra firma* from the Harrow aircraft which had flown him north, than he made his way to the station orderly room and reduced it to a shambles. He then proceeded to the Adjutant's own office and consumed the station's Christmas cards. 'My office has become a pig pen !' declared that officer, for once gaining a little sympathy. It was a bad start, and William did nothing to improve his squad-ron's popularity by subsequently nibbling the shoots from the Station Commander's prized ornamental trees and – after appar-ently overcoming the sentry by sheer brute force – penetrating the Operations Room itself and reducing East Anglia's air defence to chaos.

If 609 was difficult to bully it was because, unlike most squad-rons on being posted away from the firing line, it managed to pre-serve both its spirit of continuity and its fighting strength. The reason was simple : while other squadrons such as 92 were stripped of experienced pilots for service overseas, Belgians were exempt because their country had no interest in either the Mediterranean or Far Eastern theatres. Thus whereas during four months at Digby three outstanding British officer pilots – Dennis Barnham, John van Schaick, D.F.M., and Peter Nash * – departed, and only one British officer (Pilot-Officer Osborn, later to be killed in a motor smash) was posted in, the Squadron gained three more Belgians and lost – by posting – only one. At the same time perhaps a dozen N.C.O. pilots – from Britain, Canada, Australia and New Zealand, plus one from France (Maurice Choron had

---

* On 21st May 1942 there was an obituary notice of this pilot in *The Times* (on which he had served), quoting his eleven victories in Malta.

left before the Squadron's move), arrived, were trained, and mostly sent on to other units.

In this way 609 fulfilled the task expected of it, and when weather permitted seldom worked harder in its life, once reaching an all-time high of sixty hours flying in the course of a day that began at dawn and ended well after dark. New pilots became operational by day and into dusk, all experienced ones night-operational as well. (Once, when fog threatened the landing of four aircraft on a dusk patrol, their leader 'Pyker' half humorously gave the order: 'Prepare to bale out in formation.') Apart from that, there were endless exercises conducted for the benefit of G.C.I. controllers, bomber gunners and searchlight operators – while 609, 92 and 412 (Canadian) Squadrons took it in turns to observe a state of defensive Readiness and mount constant patrols over the North Sea convoys. François, who with Christian Ortmans once carried out two in succession after missing breakfast, cal-culated that for this protection of millions of pounds' worth of goods, plus ships and seamen, he would probably be paid about 1/6d.

If convoys and fighters could now communicate by means of a common radio channel, the latter spent much of their time in-vestigating 'bogeys' (unidentified aircraft) which nearly always turned out to be friendly bombers. Once a confused convoy leader called up Joe Atkinson with the words, 'Hello, Bogey Red 1 . . .' But occasionally, when cloud conditions made interception diffi-cult, enemy bombers did attack, and on two occasions in February, 1942, 609 was engaged. On the first a particularly large convoy was attacked at two-hour intervals by Dornier 217s which dropped out of cloud cover singly or in pairs, and were set upon successively by pairs of Belgians. Though only one of the enemy planes was damaged, the interceptions prevented any bombing accuracy and the convoy was unscathed. The second occasion was similar, ex-cept that this time three pairs of fighters (Wing-Commander Blatchford leading one of them) were successfully engaged with an estimated total of eight Dorniers, of which one was shot down by the 'Duke' (convoy confirming), and two others damaged by Joe Atkinson, Moose Evans, Christians Ortmans and the Wing-Commander, again without damage to the convoy. Moose, who

earlier in the day had been called 'an awful clot' by his senior
fellow-Canadian for taking off and landing down-wind, was now
warmly commended for having driven off another Dornier attacking a second convoy after his ammunition was exhausted –
and even won headlines in the Canadian press. Incidentally the
'Duke's victim was the first enemy *bomber* shot down by 609 since
1940.

With the nearest enemy territory well over a hundred miles
distant even from the coastal airfield of Martlesham Heath,
'Rhubarbs' were barely feasible operations – yet Tommy Rigler,
now commissioned and back from a pep-talking campaign to encourage the munition workers of Birmingham and Wolverhamp-
ton, decided to carry one out. Hugging the surface of the North
Sea, he set off with Christian Ortmans to attack an enemy airfield
in Holland, but two miles from the Dutch coast they met two *flak*
ships, and judging surprise to have been thereby lost, attacked one
of these instead. They hit it all right, but Tommy was hit too in
shoulder, arm and leg, yet pressed home his attack with his right
arm out of action, just as two Me 110s appeared above them.
Bleeding freely, and unable to get a homing, Tommy only just
made it back, and was lifted from his cockpit more or less unconscious. When he returned from hospital a fortnight later Jean de
Selys said to him unkindly : 'What about a Rhubarb, Tommy?'
'Piece of cake, but *flak* ship bloody silly target.'

And occasionally 609 went south again to reinforce 11 Group.
On 12th February, 1942, Sheep, both flight commanders and two
other Belgians were surprised on returning from a Belgian ceremony at Northolt (which at a vital moment also absented the
A.O.C., Leigh-Mallory, from his H.Q.) to find that Wing-Commander Blatchford and the rest of the Squadron had been part of
the force trying to stop the German battleships *Scharnhorst* and
Gneisenau passing through the English Channel – even if, like
most other fighter squadrons concerned, all they did was to charge
about in the murk with little idea of what their mission was. But
on 8th March it was an old-time 'Circus', with 'Cowboy' Blatchford leading 412 (Canadian) and 609 (West Riding) Squadrons –
92 had gone overseas – as rear-support wing off the French coast.
It was like manning the least favourable butt on a grouse drive,

and nothing would have happened but for Sheep's amazing ability to spot the Hun. As they returned towards Kent he reported to the 'Wingco' some dozen FW 190s just below and headed north. At once 609 became involved in a series of savage dogfights resulting in two enemy fighters being destroyed, one probably destroyed and two damaged without loss, the 'Duke' and Giovani Dieu being the most successful pilots. Nearest casualty was Blatchford himself who, 412 having turned the wrong way, was attacked by the enemy when all alone, and limped back to West Malling badly shot up. Flying home alone rather late in the dark, but failing to get down at Digby owing to bad visibility, R.T. failure and prowling enemy bombers, Sheep spent an enforced night at Wittering, but returning next morning, seemed in excellent form. Asked why, he said: 'What makes me so happy is to see all the boys return!' He had reason to be pleased, for the Focke-Wulf 190 was in most respects more than a match for its current opponent, the Spitfire Vb, and on the one day it had been allowed to help, his team's score was more than that claimed by the whole of 11 Group, which also suffered some losses.

But although while at Digby 609 lost no pilots on operations, in January it suffered a very serious loss in an accident. Flight-Lieutenant Jean ('Pyker') Offenberg, D.F.C., was training a new Belgian, 'Balbo' Roelandt, when a pilot of another squadron, probably practising a mock attack, misjudged and cut the tail of 'Pyker's' Spitfire clean off – both aircraft hurtling to the ground and killing their pilots. It was one of the worst shocks 609 Squadron ever endured, for apart from being a superb pilot and a leader of vast potential, 'Pyker' was loved by Belgian and Briton alike for his utter modesty, kindly humour and consideration for his fellows. Even his funeral, attended by Belgian friends from London H.Q. and other squadrons, was fitting. At the outset it was snowing hard, but when the flag-draped coffin, with 'Pyker's' cap and decorations, was borne through Scopwick cemetery gates by his Belgian Squadron colleagues past a guard of honour of his British and Commonwealth ones, suddenly the sun came out, and uniforms, wreaths and priestly robes became lustrous against the newly fallen snow. Standing apart was a lady in black with a single snow-white lily. The burial service was read, the bugles sounded the Last

Post, the rifles of the firing party cracked; and finally, starting with
the Station Commander, each officer and senior N.C.O. saluted the
grave and departed, leaving a brave Belgian to sleep, far from
home, in a corner of an English shire. It was all very beautiful,
and very sad.

The lady in black was Marigold, Countess of Londesborough,
the best friend 609 Squadron ever had during its sojourn in Lincolnshire. Many of its officers had come to regard her residence,
Blankney Hall, as a home from home ever since she had invited
them to Christmas dinner and afterwards led them via a complicated cross-country route to Fulbeck, there to attend a dance given
by Air Vice-Marshal Willock of Cranwell, his charming wife, and
stunningly beautiful daughter. Hospitality was so lavish that it was
quite difficult to get back to base. 'Shall I drive now?' said one.
'No, you're too drunk.' 'Well, you've been driving in a field for
the last half mile.'

After Christmas, 1941, the Digby Operations Room was moved
from station headquarters to a wing of Marigold's residence –
though whether this precaution was against enemy bombers or
609's Goat was never disclosed. More important was the fact that
the Countess was Master of the Blankney Hounds, and to no-one
did this position endear itself more than to that equestrian fanatic,
Sheep Gilroy. Horseborne, as airborne, he was followed o'er hedge
and through spinney by his faithful No. 2, Christian Ortmans, and
once returned to the Mess with bloodied face to receive the solici-
tude of the A.O.C.

In mid-February 1942, Sheep quietly announced to his officers
that they would be leaving the station Mess to take up quarters at
a mansion called Ashby Hall, which he had just requisitioned.
Patient though he was, he too was a little tired of the sour faces of
the W.A.A.F. waitresses if, after night flying, his pilots appeared a
few minutes late for breakfast, and of all the other complaints he
had received on behalf of his Squadron. Certainly he never endeared himself more to his officers than he did by taking this action
on their behalf.

The first night the mansion, not having been inhabited for some
time, was very cold, mattresses at Sheep's suggestion were dried in

front of stoves, and frigid Joe Atkinson next morning said, 'You needn't think I'm going to wash! You needn't think I'm going to shave!' – but spent five minutes massaging his scalp as an anti-baldness precaution. Everything in the end thawed out, and as sudden squires of an estate the inhabitants exploited such amenities as tennis, skating on the lake and shooting partridges (sitting). Soon 609 resolved to celebrate its newly won independence with a mammoth house-warming party on 28th March – only problem : how to raise enough spirits for an estimated seventy hosts and guests at an estimated half-bottle per head. But it was done : Jean de Selys got some from Belgian H.Q.; a friend of Sheep's (Flight-Lieutenant Morton, D.F.C.) flew down in a Boston with some from Acklington; Offenberg's successor, 'Digger' Cotes-Preedy, G.M., flew to Cumberland and got a friend to fly to exploit a source in Northern Ireland; François somehow got some bottles through a girl friend; Hal got some from the N.A.A.F.I., and three eighteen-gallon barrels of beer were added – Jean, as drinks officer, keeping all the hard liqour locked in his bedroom cupboard. Then, ten days beforehand a signal arrived posting 609 Squadron to Duxford on the very day the party was due.

'Carry on,' said Sheep. 'I'll try to get the move put back.'

He did, by two days. But now the wording of the invitation had to be changed, and finally ran :

The West Riding Squadron prior to their departure from Ashby Hall, Ashby de la Launde, in the County of Lincoln, frigidly invite you and your lady to a HOUSE COOLING on . . .
Train : Kings Cross 3.50 p.m., Grantham 6.02 p.m. Dancing 9–2 a.m.

To which the Station Commander replied :

Group Captain Campbell coldly accepts the invitation of the West Riding Squadron for Saturday next; but would prefer to come direct rather than via Kings Cross as you suggest.

And astonishingly when, as Ashby P.M.C. I asked his permission for a female dormitory, it was granted, and the Countess at once brought flowers, a cheval glass, and loose covers for the Ante-room. Yet when Michael Robinson signalled his arrival by 'beating up' station headquarters at low level in a Spitfire, and Maurice Choron did the same in a Master, the latter was promptly booked for a court martial. Other old boys : Bisdee, Richey, Barnham and MacKenzie – plus Hugh ('Cocky') Dundas, younger brother of 609's hero John and now C.O. of 56 Squadron. At 2 a.m. the last paled visibly on passing a huge Goat on the staircase – for after breaking into the W.A.A.F. Mess and eating their nighties, William now lived at Ashby too, together with the white goat of the Welsh Fusiliers, kidnapped by Hal to keep him company. By 3 a.m. Maurice had persuaded the Station Commander, who by then had formed an *entente cordiale* with the Belgian air chief, Colonel Wouters, that it would be a good thing to forget about the court martial, and by the following evening N.C.O. and W.A.A.F. reinforcements had to be sent for to drink up the rest of the beer. The day after that the Squadron, all but one man, departed for Duxford. Staying behind to clear up accounts and return glasses etc., to their various sources, I spent another night all alone in sudden silence, then handed a not too tidy Ashby Hall over to the Adjutant of the incoming Canadian squadron, No. 411. He took one look and said, 'My boys aren't used to running a place like this on their own. They won't like it – they're pampered.'

'It's fun !' After saying which I drove the 'Belgian Barouche' slowly south, with 609's pictures wrapped in cotton wool in the back. The man mainly responsible for their existence, Michael Robinson, we had just seen for the last time. A few days later, on 10th April, both he and Maurice Choron (his No. 2 to the last) were killed while Michael was leading the Tangmere Wing at the head of a French squadron whose first operation it was. The French C.O., Scitivaux, was also shot down and wounded, becoming a prisoner of war. What happened will never be known. Though a report on the Paris radio said Maurice had been picked up dead in his dinghy by the Germans, the Germans never confirmed it, and no trace was ever found of Michael. Almost at the very moment of the tragedy his brother-in-law Paul Richey was driving back to H.Q. Fighter Command, where he was currently Squadron-Leader Tactics, with the C.-in-C., Air Marshal Sir Sholto Douglas. Says Paul :

I happened to mention to him how strange it was that some pilots repeatedly managed to return to base in damaged aircraft, while a few never got a bullet hole but suddenly disappeared. When we arrived, Sholto was called to the telephone, then turned to me and said : 'Michael Robinson is missing.' It was Michael I had mentioned as an example when I said, 'Some never get a bullet hole,' for up till then he never had.

It was Michael who had encouraged me to introduce into the war diary something of the Squadron's life and character in the hope that future pilots, reading it, might adhere to the pattern. He himself had obtained a copy of the document for the period of his own command, and during his period of service at a desk had shown this both to Sir Arthur Longmore and the Duke of Kent, who in turn had shown it to his brother, the King. Thus, when a certain Wing-Commander came hot-foot from No. 12 Group H.Q. demanding that much of what I had written for the preceding month be blue-pencilled, he was at first indulged; but when it happened a second time the following letter was sent :

Flying-Officer Ziegler . . . has been writing R.A.F. Form 540 in the style complained of for eighteen months. It has been read by, amongst others, the Director of Public Relations, Air Ministry, the Inspector General of the R.A.F., H.R.H. the Duke of Kent and His Majesty the King, none of whom have taken exception to what Flying-Officer Ziegler . . . has written. It is not understood why Wing-Commander . . . should do so.

There were no more complaints.

*

Entering a Duxford hangar, Sergeant 'Darkie' Hanson stood amazed at what he saw. It was full of fighter aircraft of a type he had never seen before, and not only were all of them unserviceable, but each had the letters 'US' painted huge and permanently on its fuselage. Then the penny dropped, and he realized that just as 'PR' represented his own squadron, 'US' stood for 56 Squadron – however technically apposite, to a fitter, the letters might be.

Recently No. 56 had been the very first squadron to re-equip with the new 400-m.p.h. Hawker Typhoon – long before that aircraft was ready to go into service. As such it bore the brunt of the teething troubles that inevitably developed. Under 'Cocky' Dundas this squadron was now quartered with such serviceable aircraft as it could muster at the satellite airfield of Snailwell, while at Duxford itself was No. 266 (Rhodesian) – the second Typhoon squadron, commanded by a Rhodesian of powerful physique named Charles Green. And now 609, one of the earliest and most distinguished Spitfire squadrons, was to become the third. It was changing horses in mid-stream with a vengeance !

Typhoons, however, were in short supply. During the first month 609 received just one, and meanwhile was the only operational squadron in the Sector – on Spitfires. As such, and with six weeks of fine weather, it was extremely busy. On 3rd April, with five Spitfires still unserviceable at Digby, I wrote :

Demands suddenly pour in : Two pilots required for Readiness, two to train 154 Squadron at Fowlmere (the other satellite), two to dogfight with Typhoons, two to intercept Liberators at Polbrook, two more to pep-talk the Daimler works. Flight-Lieutenant Cotes-Preedy is about to go on leave, while his deputy and Flight-Lieutenant de Spirlet are summoned to a court-martial in Scotland. The C.O. is already there.

(He always tried to take a short leave in April when his sheep, of which he was said to own some ninety score, were lambing.)

From the 11th till the 25th the Squadron was even cut in half, and 'A' flight sent out of the Sector to Coltishall for dawn, dusk and convoy patrols. Everybody wanted 609 : Duxford ops., Coltishall ops., the Wing-Commander Flying (Dennis Gillam, D.S.O., D.F.C., A.F.C.), and last but not least 11 Group, to reinforce its continuing offensive. On one such occasion François, whom I had deputed war diarist for his Flight, wrote : 'Coltishall ops. do not like us going away, and plead with us on the R.T. But we do not hear.'

Six times the Squadron took part in large-scale operations from West Malling in Kent, and four times they were attacked by very skilful opponents, mostly Focke-Wulf 190s, on three occasions being saved largely by Sheep again spotting the enemy planes in time. Once, stung by an 11 Group report that implied he had seen them in his mirror, he told me to send the following signal :

SQUADRON-LEADER GILROY TAKES VERY GRAVE EX-
CEPTION TO THE PHRASE 'KEEPING AN EYE ON HIS
MIRROR'. SQUADRON-LEADER GILROY ATTRIBUTES HIS
LONGEVITY AS A FIGHTER PILOT LARGELY TO THE
FACT THAT HE HAS NEVER RELIED ON HIS MIRROR AT
ALL EXCEPT FOR TAXYING AND CONSIDERS THE
ABOVE STATEMENT MOST MISLEADING TO OTHER
PILOTS.

Appropriately he and Tommy Rigler scored 609's last two victories as a Spitfire squadron, the former with only two MGs and
one cannon working, and that for only twenty rounds. The last
time Sheep led his Squadron, his own Red section comprised a
Scot, a Rhodesian, a Belgian and a Frenchman. The Frenchman
(Sergeant de Saxce) and the Rhodesian (Sergeant Innes) were the
only ones of their kind. On a subsequent operation the latter (a
newcomer) was lost – and that day, significantly, Sheep was not
there.

Strange to relate, the West Riding Squadron's final operation as
a Spitfire squadron was at night. Six pilots – François de Spirlet,
Roger Malengreau, Jean de Selys, Tommy Rigler, Moose Evans
and Christian Ortmans – carried out *'Fighter Night'* patrols in
defence of Norwich during one of the enemy's so-called 'Baedeker'
raids; but the enemy came in well below 609's appointed patrol
heights. As the six landed, a long and glorious chapter came to an
end. Close of play score (credited): 161 enemy aircraft destroyed,
fifty-nine probably destroyed and ninety damaged for the loss by
enemy action of thirty-one pilots.

On 1st May, 1942, the Squadron had on its strength thirteen
elderly Spitfires Vb (still used for numerous 'co-op' jobs), plus
fifteen brand new Typhoons Ia (twelve Browning machine-guns)
and Ib (four 20mm cannon). Though the Spitfires' airframes and
engines averaged 201 and 173 hours respectively, the engineer
officers – Pilot-Officer Yates and Warrant-Officer Abrahams –
were about to find that it was a lot easier to keep these serviceable
than the new Typhoons, especially with a ground staff that owing
to overseas postings had shrunk from about 150 to 109.

Pilot strength, too, was down to nineteen, the lowest for a year and seven below establishment. Recently, indeed, the Squadron's integrity had been menaced by none other than John Bisdee, now C.O. of 601 Squadron at Digby, which had recently converted to Spitfires and which he wished to strengthen. Though he failed to seduce away such veteran stalwarts as Joe Atkinson and Moose Evans, he did somehow manage to capture the two excellent New Zealand N.C.O. pilots, Dixon and McConnell. He already had Dennis Barnham as a flight commander, and even 609's Welsh veteran from 1940, David Hughes-Rees, though he had already departed, soon joined the Bisdee outfit. As it turned out, the robbery was in a good cause, for on 20th April, 601 (County of London) and 603 (City of Edinburgh) Squadrons flew off the American aircraft carrier *Wasp* and landed in Malta, thereby contributing much to that beleaguered island's salvation. McConnell perished and the Bish himself only just survived after a 6-hour paddle to shore in his rubber dinghy.*

The pilots that remained to 609 represented possibly the most experienced nucleus a fighter squadron ever had, and when in May two Belgians and one Englishman arrived, each with over 1,500 hours flying behind them, there were no less than fifteen pilots with an average of over 1,000 hours. The two Belgians were Raymond Dopere, who had been badly treated in a Spanish prison on his way to Britain, and Jean Creteur, a man of irrepressible humour known as 'Le Canard'; the Englishman was Johnny Wells, who had so far worked his way up the R.A.F. ladder from Leading Aircraftman to Flying-Officer, and would end the war as a Group-Captain. And soon, if only to keep up 609's traditional heterogeneity, there would also be a Canadian (Flight-Sergeant Spallin), a voluble Pole (Flying Officer Solak), three re-mustered Army officers – Peter Raw, Roy Payne (veteran of Dunkirk) and Gilbert (once a Hollywood make-up artist) – and a former Bomber Command pilot, John Skett, who was immediately appointed navigation officer. Strangely, it was the Canadian, not the Pole, who was wont to play the Warsaw Concerto on the piano.

But by the end of May, 1942, 609's commanding officer and Tommy Rigler had departed after respectively ten and fifteen months with the Squadron. Incredibly, Sheep Gilroy seems to

* See *The Flying Sword* by Tom Moulson, Macdonald 1964.

have been in squadron harness – with 603 and 609 – since 1938, and if any pilot deserved a rest, he did. Even so it was only a pause, and before long he would be in command of a mobile wing of five squadrons that operated with enormous success in North Africa, Malta and Italy and with whom he doubled his personal score to 22. Having won a bar to his D.F.C. for his service to 609, he went on to win a D.S.O. and an American D.F.C., and ended the war as a Group-Captain – a classic and well-nigh unique example of a pre-war Auxiliary 'amateur' who survived to lead and command a very professional Allied aid force contingent. In 609 he made no attempt to court popularity, yet won great respect and deep affection.

He was succeeded by Paul Richey, who thus returned to 609 after an absence of nine months. Though the three squadrons did not know it, (and he himself did not then know that he would be one of their commanders) Paul had been largely responsbile for their selection as the first to re-equip with Typhoons; during his six-months stint as Squadron-Leader Tactics at H.Q. Fighter Command, Sir Sholto Douglas had simply asked him to pick the squadrons. At the moment, faced with an aeroplane whose fighting qualities were still unknown but whose unreliability was notorious, they were hardly sensible of the honour. Seeing for the first time something that was about twice as heavy and powerful as a Spitfire, and a good deal less graceful-looking, 609's youngest and smallest pilot, 'Babe' Haddon, remarked : 'I'm not going to fly a big bastard like that !'

But like the rest, he did – and once having been trained, Typhoon pilots became a sort of monastic brotherhood, as immune from posting as Belgians (and doubly so if they were both), till other Typhoon squadrons began to be formed. At the end of June 1942 there were no less than three pilots on 609's strength who would one day command it : R. P. Beamont, Johnny Wells and 'Cheval' Lallemant.

Meanwhile there were quite a lot of things to get used to. Apart from occasional undercarriage troubles and the tendency of cannon to fire themselves against the station Intelligence Office in the act of landing, the two main troubles were the tail unit, which was apt to come off in a power dive, and the Napier Sabre engine, which was liable to cut or even catch fire. On the ground this did not much matter, because by regulation there was always an air-man standing by with a fire extinguisher when an engine was started. But in the air it was different, and at almost the exact moment that Paul Richey arrived to take over command Jean de Selys became the first Typhoon pilot to bale out – his safe return late at night leading to a double celebration. Before long Bob Wilmet and Paul himself had managed to land Typhoons with their engines on fire, while earlier 'Mony' Van Lierde saved his by some-how making a belly-landing when his rudder pedal became stuck against the priming pump. Before the year was out there would be few pilots who had not made at least one forced-landing.

For two months 609 was a virtually non-operational squadron while it practised formation flying, interceptions, air firing, ground attack and co-operated in large-scale exercises with the Army. With a number of new aircraft types flying about, including American, a new drive in aircraft recognition training was ordered by the C.-in-C. In conducting this, I.O.s now had the assistance of a magic box in which they could 'fly' a number of selected aircraft types at different ranges and angles and even obscure them in fog and clouds. Many pilots took a pride in their powers of recogni-tion, but a few were almost unteachable. 'Balbo' Roelandt, a some-what stolid Belgian, always tried to evade the classes, saying they were all right for boys of eighteen, but he was too old. And once I carried enthusiasm too far. A smiling and fairly senior little Bel-gian called Joseph Renier (in peace-time he had been Offenberg's flight commander), arrived still clad in the uniform of the Belgian Air Force, with rows of ribbons which Anglo-Saxon colleagues unkindly referred to as 'swimming and diving medals', and which Belgians only wore on their R.A.F. 'best blue' uniforms. Finding him (as I thought) next day, I submitted him to a test, found him deficient and ordered him to report to me again on the morrow. Later Jean Creteur, who had been watching with considerable glee, said : 'You know, Ziegly, that wasn't Renier; that was an officer from Headquarters.'

Ironically, what Typhoon pilots were most keen about was that Spitfire pilots should learn to recognize the difference between a Typhoon and a Focke-Wulf 190 – the lamentable tendency being for the former's giant air scoop to be confused with the latter's radial engine. In this way 56 Squadron had already lost two pilots in one day, and more such disasters were to follow.

As a station Duxford, near Cambridge, was pleasant enough; so was its commander, twenty-nine-year-old Group-Captain John Grandy (later to become Chief of Air Staff). Thanks to a Belgian chef and a catering officer said to be a brother of Michael Balcon, the film producer, the Officers' Mess boasted probably the finest table of any R.A.F. station in Britain—which made Duxford a popular place for visitors to have business at. One Air Ministry visitor turned out to be Wing-Commander Norman Odbert, 609's original Adjutant and flying instructor at Yeadon, who was delighted to be brought up to date with its subsequent history. Another was Eric Kennington, the war artist, who came to paint portraits of such distinguished Belgians as François de Spirlet, Roger Malengreau and 'Duke' du Monceau (who came over for the purpose from Debden with another 609 'old boy', Jimmy Baraldi), and stayed to paint the Squadron badge on the cowlings of its new Typhoons. A third was Monsieur Gutt, the Belgian minister, who at the second attempt found the way, piloting himself. When Lord Trenchard appeared and delivered to 609 perhaps his fifth pep-talk of the war, there ensued the following conversation piece:

Christian Ortmans : 'What rank is Lord Trenchard?'
I.O. : 'Marshal of the R.A.F.'
Christian Ortmans : 'Is there nothing higher than that?'
I.O. : 'No, that's the top.'
Christian Ortmans : 'There is no future for him, then.'

On 9th and 10th June, after a tremendous effort on the part of the ground staff, the three squadrons flew together as a wing for the first and second times in honour first, of the Duke of Kent, second, of the C.-in-C., Air Marshal Sir Sholto Douglas, and the 12 Group A.O.C., Air Vice-Marshal Saul – after which François, with his usual caustic penetration, remarked that to have crammed thirty-five Typhoons into the air was likely to give these high officers a very misleading picture of Typhoon serviceability. He was right : though the C.-in-C. startled the Squadron by saying he hoped to get the wing operational by 15th June, no complete wing operation in fact took place till 19th July.

Meanwhile its pilots vented their frustration in warlike nocturnal games that took place in the Mess anteroom after the furniture had been cleared. Usually it was just 266 v. 609, but sometimes officers of the Navy, Army and R.A.F. Regiment became involved, and apart from bruises, cracked ribs and twisted ligaments were not unknown results. For some weeks the braces of 609's C.O. became a feature of the 20ft. high ceiling, after being festooned there during a human fly act by Jean Creteur. For late at night Paul himself tended to become highly aggressive, and even when the games were over felt it necessary to lead a few henchmen in persecution of those who had retired without his permission. One victim was his flight commander, R. P. Beamont, who was forced to drink a potion composed of soap and vinegar. When another intended victim, Sub-Lieutenant David Bey * of the Fleet Air Arm, defended himself by firing off his revolver, I myself became the alternative target, and after being drenched with soda syphons was carried out and laid in the middle of the main road, minus one pyjama leg. When shortly afterwards one of the Squadron's dogs caught a large rat in my room, I knew where to hang it.

It was only one facet of Paul's complex character. On 26th June François de Spirlet was killed when one of his Typhoon's tyres burst on take-off and he and 'Cheval' Lallemant collided. Though Cheval was miraculously unhurt, he was so shocked that he vowed never to fly again. Paul was magnificent. After talking to him like a father, he made him repeat the take-off with himself in François' place and also Christian as before. Thus was Cheval's confidence restored † and a crisis in Squadron morale averted. For the loss of a colleague in an accident was felt more deeply than his loss in combat, and François, the second flight commander so to die, had in many ways, after fourteen months, become the

---

* David was both the only Turk and the only Naval officer ever to fly operationally with 609, on attachment from Duxford's Air Fighting Development Unit. I could not but think of the puzzle he would have caused German Intelligence had he been captured flying an R.A.F. fighter.

† See *Rendezvous With Fate*, by Colonel R. A. Lallement, Macdonald 1964.

Squadron's corner-stone. Of the many Belgians he was perhaps the one I personally got to know and like the best. Shortly before his death I accompanied him on an errand to Church Fenton in the 'Maggie'. Having probably flown already that day he said, 'You fly, Zieg,' and went to sleep. For an eternity I battled incompetently against a strong cross-wind, just managed to remain on course, then pin-pointed Doncaster about 600 feet below. At that moment on the 'inter-comm' I heard a muttered quotation from the Pilots' Order Book, the contents of which it was one of my jobs to ram home : 'To avoid alarming the population pilots are forbidden to fly over industrial areas below 1,000 feet' – saying which François went to sleep again.

Once, at Biggin Hill, he had asked me to try to find out details about a certain Channel combat from which he had heard his half-brother had failed to return. François, I think, had also been engaged, and may have had the dreadful thought that he could have been responsible. For his half-brother was flying a Messerschmitt 109, for the Luftwaffe.

The not very offensive sweeps by the Duxford wing that for 609 began in late July were either independent operations planned mainly by its leader, Wing-Commander Gillam, or were phased in with 11 Group 'Circuses'. But however astute the planning they failed to entice the enemy into putting himself in a position to be shot down – except on one occasion. This was on 19th August, 1942, the day of the historic Dieppe raid, when the Duxford Wing made three sorties. During one of these 266 Squadron made three claims but lost a flight commander and another pilot, one probably owing to tail-unit failure and the other to a Spitfire, and 609 made the discovery that even the Luftwaffe could not always distinguish a Typhoon from one of their own Focke-Wulfs. Seeing one of the latter and Bob Wilmet flying side by side, Frenchman de Saxce mentioned the matter on the R.T. but the Fleming failed to understand his French. When the two suddenly regretted their friendship and broke away, 'Fifi' de Saxce became the first pilot of 609 (Typhoon) Squadron ever to fire a shot in anger.

The first Typhoon success had been ten days earlier, when the Rhodesians, from the Coltishall satellite airfield of Matlaske, shot down a shipping and/or weather recce Ju 88 over the North Sea—a success repeated four days later when 266 Squadron shot down the first specimen of the new Me 210 east of Cromer. At this time the Luftwaffe, at Hitler's insistence and despite diminished resources, was reverting to small-scale attacks not only by night but (when cloud cover permitted) by day. On 23rd July a section of 609 was scrambled after a Dornier 217 that bombed Bedford, and on the 27th R.P. Beamont, after making the first Typhoon night patrol when Cambridge was bombed, identified another Dornier crossing Duxford itself with navigation lights burning. On 3rd August, with all senior officers away, Flight-Lieutenant Joe Atkinson found himself O.C. Duxford at the moment when the tannoy shouted: 'Stand by to take cover!'— whereupon the acting Station Commander was seen bicycling frantically towards Dispersal to defend his Station in the only aircraft available, 609's Hurricane conversion trainer. On that occasion the 'enemy' turned out to be an American transport with sixteen passengers which was peppered by light Ack-Ack.

Sightings of the enemy were, however, becoming more frequent, and there was a report that he was now using a new high-altitude reconnaissance-bomber called a Junkers 86P1. On 5th September, while trying to intercept one of these which dropped bombs at Luton, Roelandt and Creteur reached probably an all-time ceiling for Typhoons of 34,500 feet, only to see their quarry an estimated 12,000 feet higher still. A fortnight later one was intercepted and damaged by the Russian prince, Flight-Lieutenant Emanuel Galitzine, in a specially polished and pressurised Spitfire armed with two cannon only, during a running fight at about 45,000 feet all the way back to Cherbourg. Unfortunately, he tells me, one of his cannon jammed, and he fell out of the sky each time he fired.

But in the south enemy tactics were very different. There he was deploying Focke-Wulf 190 fighters and fighter-bombers which strafed and bombed with impunity just above the ground – either after a dive from about 20,000 too fast to be intercepted, or by approaching at sea-level and so evading radar detection altogether. (Recently one of these redoubtable aircraft had been landed intact at Pembrey in Wales by its pilot, who after a dog-fight near Exeter

mistook north for south and the Bristol Channel for the English
Channel. Borrowing my camera, Paul Richey at once flew over and
took pictures which I then had to supply in centuplicate).

It was at this point that Paul wrote a paper, a copy of which
reached the C.-in-C., expressing the view of himself and the other
two squadron commanders that the deployment of Typhoons as
an offensive wing had proved a failure, and urging that their speed
and fire-power could be far better exploited by distributing the
three squadrons near the eastern, south-eastern and southern
coasts as a defence force against the so-called 'tip-and-run' raiders.
For the Rhodesians of 266 Squadron this paper seems to have been
just in time, their leader, Charles Green, having confided to Paul
and Dundas that they were on the point of resigning *en masse*. In
the event, the Typhoon Wing was broken up within a week, and the
last of its three squadrons to re-equip was the first to go – back to
Biggin Hill. On its blackboard at Dispersal its C.O. chalked his last
message: 'Tally Ho! Gone away!'

7

MASTER TYPHOON SQUADRON

At Biggin Hill, after a few days in temporary quarters, 609 managed to regain its former Dispersal buildings, with crew room decorated and furnished by Michael Robinson eighteen months before. Peeling paint and dilapidated easy-chairs reflected the more casual attitude of subsequent occupants, and even the pegs in the kit-cum-sleeping cubicle still bore the names of 609 pilots long dead or departed. Incredibly, however, there were still eight of them – two Englishmen, one Canadian and five Belgians – who could now use their own pegs again.

As 609 moved in, so 133 (American Eagle) Squadron – doomed within days to lose eleven out of twelve pilots on one tragic operation – moved out, while the incoming 340 (French) Squadron took over the temporary quarters being vacated. Though during this triple operation no important items of equipment were knowingly exchanged, 609's assistant Engineer Officer, Warrant-Officer Abraham, was so dazzled by the gold braid on the Frenchmen's dark blue uniforms that he repeatedly addressed his opposite number as 'Sir' in the belief that he was the C.O. And in the middle of it all, Squadron-Leader Bill Igoe, famous Battle of Britain Controller and head of Biggin 'ops.', came along for a talk about R.T. procedure, and 609's 'arch-binder', Polish Solak, had to ask: 'Supposing, Sir, I want a homing and my R.T. set isn't working and my compass has been shot away...?' Bob Wilmet, *sotto voce*: 'And he bales out and finds there's no more water in the Channel...' End of talk, continuation of move.

A day or two later two other Spitfire squadrons changed places, 401 (Canadian) being replaced by 611 (West Lancashire) Squadron – thus for the first time placing the Red and White Roses on one station. But the Squadron of the White Rose – a year ago perhaps the most favoured of 11 Group – had not replaced anyone: it had simply added itself, and was in the way. For the religion of both 11 Group and Biggin Hill was the Spitfire. What could this single squadron of Typhoons do that the Spitfires couldn't? Tag along on offensive operations? Try to help cope with the raiders?

During the next six weeks both types of employment were tried, particularly defence. In all weathers up to a dozen pairs of aircraft patrolled sections of the coast ranging from Ramsgate to Selsey Bill, with others operating from Hawkinge, the advanced base selected by Paul. But though 609 flew more hours than any other squadron in the sector, something always went wrong. Either the enemy disappeared in cloud, or did his bombing just after 609's aircraft had landed, or the latter were themselves shot at by the coastal guns, or they chased their own plots, or 'ops.' just said, 'Don't bother, we've got Spitfires in control of the situation.' Once in heavy weather Jean de Selys, hearing Christian Ortmans (on a separate patrol) shout 'Tally-Ho!' chipped in with the words: 'Don't get excited, Christian – take steady aim!' At that moment his own cockpit canopy was blown off. Could it be . . .? Perish the thought! Christian's intended quarry turned out to have been a Ju 88.

And then, less than a month since his paper had brought about the dispersal of the Duxford Typhoon Wing between Biggin Hill, Warmwell and Matlask, Paul Richey received a direct Air Ministry posting to India to take command of a Hurricane wing. Not only that, but somehow he persuaded the Belgian authorities in London to make a glaring exception to their national policy: to permit Christian Ortmans – his own, and previously Sheep Gilroy's – No. 2 – to go with him. Thus Christian became the only Belgian ever to fight the Japanese – and die, shot it is believed, on his parachute.

At almost the same moment there departed the last two Belgians of the original batch that had arrived in April 1941—Roger Malengreau and Bob Wilmet (to form a Tomahawk squadron to protect the Belgian Congo). Bob did not survive the war, but Roger was Belgian ambassador in various countries since.

To speed them all on their way, the Squadron was visited by

the Inspector General of the Belgian Forces, the somewhat elderly but charming General le Chevalier Van Streidonck de Burckel, Colonel Wouters, Commandant of the Belgian Air Force, and one or two more. With no flying possible owing to thick mist, a magnificent lunch was served in the Officers' Mess, both the General and Paul made speeches in French, and 609's entire repertoire of French songs was sung. Somehow the party ended in London, where late at night Moose Evans found himself being closely interrogated about the details of Typhoon operations by two suspicious-looking individuals dressed as R.A.F. officers. Convinced they were Fifth Columnists, he felt it his duty to ring up the Provost Marshal's department to check their credentials:

'What are their names?'
'I don't know, but one is a Squadron-Leader.'
'Are they wearing campaign medals?'
'Champagne medals? That's the whole trouble, they aren't drinking at all!'

609's eighth C.O. – and the seventh had recommended him – was Roland P. Beamont, D.F.C., whose term as flight commander at Duxford had abruptly ended in hospital when he 'pranged' himself on some parallel bars in Cambridge. Though the youngest C.O. the Squadron ever had, his operational experience was already vast: with 87 Squadron he had served continuously right through the Battle of France, the Battle of Britain, and later when it became a night-fighter and 'Intruder' squadron. As Joe Atkinson once said to me at Duxford: ' "Bee" is an anachronism; he ought to be either a Wing-Commander or dead.'

In retrospect, it is probably true to say that had Beamont not been appointed to command 609 Squadron at this moment, the Typhoon might well have been lost to the Allies as one of their war-winning weapons. Earlier in 1942 he had spent his first 'rest' from operations as a production test pilot at the Hawker factory at Langley. There he had not only discussed the new fighter intensively with the acting chief test pilot, Philip Lucas, but helped the experimental test pilots (one of them Bill Humble, an original pilot of 609) to fly it intensively. As a result he not only knew the aircraft better than any other fighter pilot, but – more important –

believed it had a future when few others did, particularly those in authority. Only some ten weeks after taking command of 609 on 19th October he was directed by the new 11 Group A.O.C., 'Dingbat' Saunders, to attend a meeting called by the C.-in-C. (now Leigh-Mallory) at H.Q. Fighter Command.

At this meeting I was astonished to find that the whole future of the Typhoon was at issue, with a strong lobby mainly of Engineering Branch officers backed up by Spitfire men expressing in the strongest terms their opposition to the continuing production of the Typhoon on the grounds that it was an inferior machine and unsuitable for Fighter Command.*

To which 'Bee', aged twenty-two and the most junior officer present, firmly answered that so far from this being the case, the Typhoon was 'undoubtedly *superior to the Spitfire* for all purposes at low level' (author's italics). When it was found that none of the opposition had ever flown one, the Typhoon was reprieved, at least for the moment. Meanwhile, let Squadron-Leader Beamont and his squadron show what they could do with it.

This meeting, I believe, took place on the very last day of 1942, and only in the last few weeks had 609 done anything to justify itself, defensively, at all. On 1st November, less Orderly Room and Servicing Echelon, it had moved for an experimental week to Manston, only thirty-five miles from the enemy, in response to what had happened the day before when the Luftwaffe launched its biggest daylight raid since the Battle of Britain – by thirty FW 190 fighter-bombers supported by as many fighters – on Canterbury. 91 Squadron at Hawkinge claimed the destruction of five, and 122 Squadron one, for the loss of two Spitfires; while the coastal Ack-Ack, opening up in all directions, claimed to have destroyed or damaged two more. The last claim was accurate, except that the targets were patrolling Typhoons of 609 Squadron, who were thus deprived of their best chance yet to make an interception. Happily Roy Payne successfully force-landed in shallow water, waded ashore with second-degree burns, and only lost his temper when a coastguard addressed him in German.

*From *Phoenix Into Ashes*, by Roland Beamont, C.B.E., D.S.O.*, D.F.C.*, William Kimber, 1968.

Had it happened a day earlier, Roy would never have been filmed (and sound-recorded) playing the clarinet. For recently 609's crew room at Biggin, while continuing to fulfil its normal purpose, had been transformed into a film set while Pilot-Officer John Boulting of the R.A.F. Film Unit, with some guidance from me, endeavoured to dissect for the silver screen the strands that bound the West Riding International Squadron together. Introduced by Joe, Roy of England, Moose of Canada, Jean de Selys of Belgium, de Saxce of France, Turek of Poland, and Corporal Roland Walker of Yorkshire all explained how they had got there, while the camera roved around their other colleagues and environment. How John Boulting stuck it, I don't know. After rehearsing a scene half a dozen times he had only to say, 'O.K., let's shoot,' for an aero engine to start up outside and ruin the sound track; or else one of the actors would say, 'Sorry, I've got to go on patrol now.' He was not even deterred by the 'unkindest cut of all', when the whole cast suddenly moved to Manston: he simply built an exact replica of the crew room at Elstree Studios, where the film – title *Between Friends* – was finished as and when the actors could attend. Yet for all his efforts, the public never saw it: the last scene showed the Squadron taking off in the distance to the sound of a moving ditty on Roy's clarinet – but it did so in Typhoons, and these were still on the secret list, even though by the time the film was due for release the enemy had seen them much closer, and one at least had been shot down over France.

If Biggin Hill had been crowded, Manston was more so, with Whirlwind fighter-bombers, Hurricane ditto and Albacores of the Fleet Air Arm already in occupation. But 609 never returned to the parent station, and soon its officers acquired sleeping quarters at 'The Nook', two miles away at Westgate-on-Sea, with Doone House, in real life a girls' school, as Manston's off-duty Mess near by.

On duty no squadron worked harder, flying up to fifteen patrols a day at lower and lower altitude and in ever more atrocious weather, while others pairs stood by to answer an alert. Finally, overcoming the opposition of Biggin 'ops' by appeal to higher authority, 'Bee' moved the standing patrols two to six miles out to sea, just over the wave tops. Though this was to prove half the answer, it also intensified the Ack-Ack problem, for recently the guns had obtained permission to fire on any aircraft approaching the coast below 1,000 feet. Thus although the Typhoons' noses were painted white to differentiate them from radial engines, and their wing undersides, painted in black-and-white stripes like zebra crossings, screamed 'FRIENDLY!' they continued to draw the fire of coastal batteries, the Navy and even other fighters, almost as often as the FW 190s for which they were mistaken. Once, after I had telephoned the Duty Gunnery Officer, North Foreland, with the usual complaint, he actually rang back and said : 'Could you ask your pilots tactfully – *very* tactfully – whether we got anywhere near them?'

What with having to keep one eye on engine temperature, scan the air for enemy raiders, watch each gun position and Spitfire with suspicion, and guard against crashing into cliffs or balloons, the whole enterprise seemed unprofitable. By the end of November, with nothing to show for it, the Ack-Ack had claimed one Typhoon, the weather two Typhoons and their pilots. After all his sufferings in Spain, Raymond Dopere flew into a cloud-decked hill almost on the site of the Battle of Hastings before he had once sighted the enemy he had come so far to fight; while Warrant Officer Spallin of Canada crashed into a Dover balloon cable when the balloons themselves were in cloud, and left just a patch of oil on the sea. Then, with morale at a nadir, two things happened: 'Bee', entirely on his own initiative, started a completely new, if additional, type of operation; and 609 regained the services of its luck-giving mascot, the Goat.

This officer had been absent without leave for two months owing to Hal Tidswell's failure to include him in the movement order from Duxford. Returning to make enquiries a fortnight later I learned that the Station Adjutant had immediately given orders for his disposal or destruction, that he was now with a farmer, and that the latter had already sold him to a butcher. Judging by letters I later received from them, he was saved in the nick of time by Corporal Clough of the Duxford Guard and Lieutenant Guthrie of the Fleet Air Arm, the latter eventually launching him on a complex train journey from Wittlesford, Cambs., to Ramsgate, Kent, costing 10/1d. 609's luck changed almost at once, the Goat was promoted to Wing-Commander, and one of the remaining Auxiliaries, Corporal Summerscales, was assigned as Goatmaster and A.D.C., with the duty to groom and feed him, and the privilege, on official parades, to stand beside him in front of the Squadron. Once, as it marched past, I actually saw the A.O.C. chuck the 'Wing-Commander' under the chin. The mascot was rapidly becoming a fetish.

Bee's new morale-boosting type of operation was offensive patrols by one or two aircraft against the enemy's communications system in France and Belgium, Saunders the A.O.C. having promised him a free hand, provided the Squadron fulfilled all its defensive commitments. On 17th November Bee had caused astonishment by demonstrating that the Typhoon could be used in this way *at night*. Others followed suit, and soon 'locomotive-busting' by moonlight or under cloud cover by day, by single aircraft and in pairs, had become the Squadron's spare-time speciality. It was more fun than standing patrols, and the results were dramatic. It was even less dangerous, for though there was *flak* by day, and searchlights and *flak* by night, experience brought knowledge both of where these were located and how to evade them. Bee's moonlight technique was to 'brew up' the locomotive on the first run so as to produce a cloud of steam to act as a marker for an attack on the *flak* car. To help the enterprise Fighter Command Intelligence even provided a time-table of German troop trains, and on his first day 'Rhubarb' Jean de Selys had the satisfaction of shooting up some fifty enemy soldiers as the train stopped and they leapt for cover – only two days later to help rescue some enemy sailors by directing a Walrus amphibion to their raft. Strain though the added commitment was on serviceability, with the Typhoons sometimes shot up or damaged by flying so low that they returned with telephone wire or timber in their radiator scoops, the fact that they usually did return demonstrated what punishment these aircraft could take and still fly. In technique such operations were very smiliar to those which the Squadron, in its defensive capacity, was trying to stop the FW 190s from carrying out – the difference being that so far the Typhoons had no bombs and were discriminating as to target. Soon they became so popular that there was hardly a pilot who would not gladly give up a day's leave rather than miss his turn in one of the few available aircraft for a lone sortie over enemy territory.

Then, on 5th December, 'Babe' Haddon – the young pilot who had once declared he would 'never fly a big bastard like that' – scored the Squadron's first Typhoon success against the Focke-Wulfs when four of them, in weather much too clear for a 'Rhubarb' by either side, tried to attack their opponents on the ground. Just as the station sirens shrieked there was a crackle of cannon and machine-gun fire and a 'whoosh' that shook the Dispersal hut, and out rushed the bunched pilots of 609, exclaiming, 'Look! 190s' – thus presenting a fine target had the latter come round again. Then 'Bee' came tearing out of his office, and four Typhoons hurtled into the air too late to do anything. But Balbo Roelandt and Haddon were on standing patrol at 400 feet, and set off in pursuit as the enemy belted for home at sea-level, 'Babe' in the faster machine catching No. 2 of the second pair just as they reached the French coast. After several bursts he had to turn to avoid a collision, just as the Focke-Wulf reared up in the air and fell – and when he came round again only the No. 1 was crossing the sand dunes. Though a near certainty, I could only claim for him a 'probable'. It was enough. At a party at Doone House that evening the Goat celebrated his success by consuming thirty cigarettes, two bowls of chrysanthemums and the C.O.'s mess bill.

Ten days later 'Babe', again on standing patrol, was the first to be awarded a 'definite'. By now there was a system whereby the Royal Observer Corps, as soon as they spotted the enemy, drew the attention of defending pilots by firing so-called 'totter' rockets. Peter Raw now took off on seeing these from the ground; 'Bee', just back from a 'Rhubarb', broke off a conversation with the Station Commander and took off without helmet or parachute on seeing a Whirlwind being attacked by a FW 190, and Johnny Baldwin, practice-firing over the Goodwin sands, joined with only ball ammunition in a dog-fight that had been taking place off Ramsgate between the Whirlwind, two Typhoons and an unknown number of FW 190s. The two Typhoons were Flight-Sergeant Haddon and his No. 2, Pilot-Officer Amor – it was not unusual in the air for an experienced N.C.O. to command a less experienced officer – and just as the latter called, 'I've hit him!' both 'Babe' and Raw saw him attacking with his own aircraft ablaze. 'Bale out!' cried 'Babe', and too low and too late he did so. Haddon himself then battled with five of the enemy and shot one into the sea, while Raw and Baldwin chased others back across the Channel.

Thus Amor, a very popular and charmingly naïve young pilot, became the first victim of enemy action since 609 had become a Typhoon squadron. In its diary I wrote : 'His performance in continuing to fight while he was himself on fire at only 900 feet is one of the finest actions in the Squadron's history.' On the evidence I could only claim for him one FW 190 damaged, though its pilot probably shared the same watery grave.

Next day Polish Turek and Belgian Jean de Selys scored, three days after that 'Cheval' Lallemant and Haddon again, and then Turek again. By Christmas the score stood at four FW 190 destroyed, three probably destroyed and three (also one Ju 88) damaged, plus eighteen locomotives (seven of them Beamont's) and one tug, for the loss of two pilots – the second, Sergeant Davis, having been jumped while orbiting a dinghy. Letters and signals of congratulation combined with Christmas greetings poured in from the C.-in-C., the A.O.C., Belgian H.Q., Hawkers and Harald Peake. And on Boxing Day 609 defeated the rest of the station at Rugger with the M.O. (Flying-Officer MacKechnie) playing in 'blood'-stained shorts, Moose Evans in long combinations, and Pilot-Officer Gilbert in pyjamas, despite being attacked with soot bombs dropped from an Albacore.

Flight-Lieutenant Baron Jean de Selys Longchamps had started the war as a Belgian cavalry officer, but got aboard a British destroyer at Dunkirk despite being held up at revolver point by a British major. Then, at the age of twenty-nine, he first learnt to fly. Now, for some weeks I had been trying to get permission from 11 Group for him to carry out a cherished idea : a single-handed attack on the Gestapo headquarters in the heart of Brussels. But consent never came, and early on 20th January, 1943, he took off with his fellow-countryman, André Blanco, on a normal

'Rhubarb', but with a cockpit full of flags. When, seventy-five minutes later, he climbed out again and with shamefaced excitement said, 'I've done it, Ziegly!' I knew just what he meant.

'The weather was so tempting – cloud just right. South of Bruges there was a locomotive – a sitter – and a two-second burst was enough – clouds of steam and smoke. But my mind was on Brussels. I kept saying, Shall I? Now's the chance! Blanco had gone off after another engine. I told him to return independently. And then I was flying east over Ghent at nought feet.'

He had never seen his native Brussels from the air before, and must have felt a bit like an avenging angel as his Typhoon brushed the Cinquantenaire memorial and his old cavalry barracks. His target lay at the end of the Avenue de Louise, two miles in length. No *flak* yet, but he mustn't make a mess of it, mustn't kill any Belgians, must riddle all those windows behind which the Gestapo was weaving its deadly web.

Up to 2,000 feet. Plotted now, no doubt. But still no flak, and thank goodness no balloons! Get aligned with the Avenue target . . . concentrate . . . DIVE!

The building on either side rose up menacingly. A tram seemed to take off to meet him. Keep your sight on the target. *2,000 yards . . . 1,000 yards . . . 700 yards . . . FIRE!*

The Typhoon shook from the recoil of the four 20mm cannon. *Strikes! Stick a shade forward for the lower windows; now weave a bit for the sides. Now stick back or you'll ram!*

With a *whoosh* Jean cleared the roof and went straight up in a climbing turn. Wisps of smoke drifted up from the windows. All the traffic had stopped, everyone was tumbling out of the tram. A crowd of people in a square, with upturned faces. *Now literally to show the flag!* Sliding open his cockpit, Jean pushed out first a large Union Jack, then the flag of Belgium. One caught momentarily on his tail-plane, then both floated serenely down.

Farewell Brussels! Farewell family and friends down there! It was me, Jean!

In 1944, after Brussels had been liberated, I met a lady who had actually been on that tram. She described the jubilation of the Belgians and the fury of the Germans. And no wonder, for soon we heard via the Belgian 'underground' that the Gestapo had suffered some thirty dead. But Jean, though he later got a D.F.C. was hauled before the A.O.C. and lost a stripe for disobeying orders. Amongst the Gestapo dead was a British secret agent, unfortunately carrying a list of names that led to the arrest of a hundred others.

If no enemy fighters tried to intercept Jean, it was probably because, by sheer coincidence, the Luftwaffe had chosen this day to launch its biggest daylight attack on London since 1940 by a swarm of FW 190 bombers and fighters, and two diversionary sweeps by Me 109Gs. In fact, before Jean even reached Brussels, 'Cheval' Lallemant had already dealt successfully with one of the advance guard. Then at 12.45, distracted from report-writing by deafening anti-aircraft fire, I saw the sky festooned with convoluting smoke trails, plus one or two parachutes, and was nearly run down by 'Bee' driving furiously towards Typhoon PR G. Next moment I was horrified to see another Typhoon, coming in to land, being fired on by one of a Spitfire squadron that had been told thirty enemy planes were attacking Manston – the Typhoon pilot being Jean de Selys, landing now from a *defensive* patrol.

Defensively, on this memorable day, 609 only managed to achieve nine sorties, out of a total by Fighter Command of 214. Yet of the thirteen enemy aircraft destroyed, 609 Squadron's share was six, of which three – Me 109Gs – were accounted for by a single pilot, Johnny Baldwin, in a much higher than usual fight at 20,000 feet over Margate, while 'Mony' Van Lierde after a series of combats in and out of cloud, bagged a FW 190 at 27,000 feet, and Joe Atkinson got the last.

Baldwin's 'hat-trick' was only confirmed ten days later when he helped to interview in hospital two of the enemy pilots he had shot down – one of them only picked up two days after the event. Though expressing surprise at having been defeated by a 'worm' like Johnny, they presented him with souvenirs in the shape of a handsome clasp-knife and a Luftwaffe 'Mae West'. But asked what aircraft had shot them down, one said a 'Vultee Vanguard', the other a 'Mustang'. Focke-Wulf pilots would have known better.

During both January and February, 1943, 609 stood well ahead of all other squadrons in Fighter Command, both defensively and offensively, with a score of fifteen enemy aircraft (mostly FW 190s) destroyed, three probably destroyed and five damaged, and about forty-five locomotives, plus a few barges and road vehicles, destroyed or damaged – for the loss by enemy action of three pilots. With the Typhoons operating singly or in pairs well below 1,000 feet, it was a different story to that of 100 or more Spitfires operating up to 30,000 feet. In other words, with the fate of enemy planes usually ascertainable, and duplication of claims ruled out, the score was far more accurate.

So now, after being the 'pariah' of 11 Group, 609 suddenly found itself almost embarrassingly famous again. Early in February the Under Secretary of State for Air, Captain Balfour, expressed a desire 'to meet the C.O. of the Typhoon squadron at Manston', and 'Bee' was summoned to Hornchurch, to whose sector control he had successfully changed from Biggin's three months before. Six days later the Secretary of State himself – Sir Archibald Sinclair – appeared at 609 Dispersal, where he displayed considerable knowledge both of the Squadron's successes and its aircraft. Shortly after that the press floodgates were opened when the place was invaded by no less than thirty-five journalists ('Who are all these people?' asked 'Cheval', descending from a patrol), who stayed on for lunch at Doone House. Basil Cardew of the *Express* then put such nonsense into the mouth of Squadron-Leader Beamont (who hardly spoke to him) that a protest was sent to his editor, even though his article brought 'Bee' some bust measurements and an invitation to meet their owner.

On 17th February the West Riding Squadron decided it owed itself a celebration. Held at the West Cliff Theatre, Ramsgate, this was attended by an estimated 500 persons who consumed about 100 gallons and 1,200 bottles of beer, the costs being defrayed by, amongst others, Belgian H.Q. in London. Climax of the evening was when the Goat, his Wing-Commander's stripes painted on horns and collar, stood in glory beside the Squadron commander on the stage as the latter made a speech.

'Give us more aircraft and more pilots,' 'Bee' had said to Sir Archibald Sinclair. And certainly the pilots appointed to 609 round about this period included some of the most experienced available. One was Flying-Officer L. E. Smith (known as 'Smithy'), who like Wells had joined the R.A.F. as an Leading Aircraftman in 1936, and in the Middle East had successfully fought Me 110s with Gladiators during a long period of service with 94 Squadron. Another was Flying-Officer 'Paddy' Cameron, a humorous Irishman who had last flown operationally during the Battle of Britain and now said, 'Going on patrol tomorrow, so I'd better get this aircraft recognition brushed up before I meet the blighters' – and promptly met two sorts of 'blighters' at the first attempt. There was Manu Geerts, a greying thirty-six but a brilliant pilot, perhaps the most experienced of the former Belgian air force, and 'Cheval's' one-time flying instructor. There was also a balding 'airman of fortune', Flight-Sergeant Aitken-Quack, who had lost a pre-war R.A.F. commission by taking unauthorized leave, flown a Boeing fighter for £200 a month during the Spanish civil war on the opposite side to Rodolf de Grunne, and later served with the Finnish Air Force against the Russians, during which time he had courted a niece of Goering's. With 609 he was eventually missing over France, but survived as a P.O.W.

Younger, but already rich in flying hours, were Eric Roberts, recently a Flight-Lieutenant in a twin-engined Beaufighter squadron, Flight-Sergeant 'Pinky' Stark, a former gunnery school staff pilot, and Flying-Officer Nankivell, who had been a Flight-Lieutenant in Training Command, and was one of the most competent, intelligent and charming men I ever met. Sad to say, he perished on 7th February shot down over enemy territory during a 'Rhubarb'. By 20th March, the 'closed shop' known as 609 Squadron included no less than six future C.O.s, three British and three Belgian: Wells, Roberts and Stark; Lallemant, Geerts and Charles de Moulin—in 1941 one of the eighteen tassle-capped Belgian Aircraftmen 2 apprentices. It also included Johnny Baldwin, destined to command 609's sister squadron, No. 198, but who meanwhile was shot down in flames by two FW 190s that I myself saw from the ground, and was so badly burned that he nearly drowned owing to inability to inflate his dinghy.

Besides Nankivell, the other two victims of the enemy in January-February were 'Babe' Haddon and Sergeant Johnny Wiseman : they went out to protect an M.T.B. disabled and under attack in the Straits of Dover, and its skipper saw them 'jumped' by two of the enemy and shot successively into the sea. But an hour later they were avenged. Belgian 'Cheval' Lallemant and Polish Tony Polek, taking off on the same mission, promptly became involved in two desperate combats, separated by only ten minutes, with two separate formations each of four FW 190s; while almost simultaneously Jean de Selys and Roy Payne, 'scrambled' directly by 'Cheval' on the Dispersal R.T. as reinforcements, were attacked by three more off Calais, the former sustaining some damage during a mutual head-on attack. The end result was:

F/O Lallemant (Belgian) :   2 FW 190 destroyed, 1 probably
                            destroyed
F/O Polek (Polish)   :   2 FW 190 probably destroyed.
F/O de Selys (Belgian)   :   1 FW 190 destroyed.
F/O Payne (Scottish)   :   1 FW 190 destroyed.

These engagements (and they were Polek's first) marked a departure from the usual process of trying to catch the enemy as he dashed back home after a raid, with the trick of firing out of range to make him weave. This time the much more numerous FW 190s were either the attackers or at least stayed to fight, and showed again that the Typhoon not only had the edge in speed, (if not in climb) but also in manoeuvrability, 'Cheval' in particular stressing his ability to out-turn his opponents – though he also did some fine deflection shooting and for the three of them used only fifty rounds per gun in five one-second bursts. The result confirmed the assurance given to 609 by its old friend Jamie Rankin five months earlier, after he had flown the FW 190 captured at Pembrey as well as a Typhoon.

But the FW 190 was still the more reliable aircraft. Though modification had improved the stability of the Typhoon's tail unit, its Napier Sabre engine was still prone to fail – Irish Cameron, after an 'engine handling' course at the factory, reported he was stood a pint of beer each time he said how good they were – and by the end of April four new pilots had been lost since the new year due either to this cause, inexperience or both. The more experienced still managed to get away with it. Once, after seeing 'Cheval' crash-land quite near the Swingate G.C.I. station, his

No. 2 called up anxiously for information, only to be told by the Controller, 'At the moment he's drinking whisky with me.' And on 9th March 'Bee' himself, scraping over the Dover cliffs with a failing engine, crash-landed near Deal, sustained a fractured skull and two very black eyes, but continued to run his Squadron from a bed in Deal hospital.

By April, 1943, someone in P-staff must have noticed with a shock that, by some oversight of themselves or the enemy, a pilot who had been posted to 609 way back in November, 1940, was not only still alive but still on his original tour of duty – my old room-mate Flight-Lieutenant J. A. Atkinson, D.F.C. Though it was already a record, 'Joe', but for this piece of vigilance, would have gone on unprotestingly till he dropped dead, either from enemy bullets or exhaustion. Recently he had confided to me that he couldn't drive a car. Would I teach him, if in return he taught me how to fly an aeroplane? Lessons were exchanged, and though when he left neither of us had achieved solo status, when I next met him over twenty years later, he was driving a car with competence and verve, whereas I never flew as a pilot again. 609 was to miss him greatly, not least for his wit, of which the last recorded example was on the R.T. Baldwin had just been shot down, there was a 'Guns Alert', and at the same time several Dover balloons were struck by lightning. Seeing these go down in flames, Joe, who had just relieved another section, thought it was the enemy and hopefully asked the cause. 'Nature,' said the Controller. 'Oh,' said Joe. 'Shall I now relieve Nature?'

His departure was followed some weeks later by that of the veteran Canadian, 'Moose' Evans, who had joined early in 1941. Though I have never seen him since, he has sent me a Christmas card from Toronto every year since the war ended. And then, on 8th May, 'Bee' himself was urged by members of his own ground staff, Sergeants Eric Ingall and 'Darkie' Hanson, to accept the offer of another spell at Hawker's 'before', as Darkie put it, 'he killed himself'. Till a month before, when 198 Squadron began to share the defence commitment, 609 had hardly ever been released from duty or even been at thirty minutes' stand-by since it had come to Manston, and meanwhile those pilots off duty had queued up for the privilege of risking their lives, like their C.O.

in private missions over enemy territory that no one had asked them to undertake. To keep enough Typhoons serviceable for the dual role would have been impossible but for 'Jacko' Jackson, the Engineer Officer, his assistant 'Abe' Abraham and the whole of the servicing and maintenance staff, amongst whom no C.O. had inspired such devotion since Darley in the crisis of the Battle of Britain. 'If Bee wanted it, Bee got it, even if it meant working all night,' says Darkie, adding, 'He handled us with the head of a man of forty.' And before he left he treated them all to a flying display such as had not been seen since the days of Michael Robinson, when he tackled and vanquished an American Thunderbolt in a thrilling 'dog-fight' at roof-top height.

Once, apropos of I forgot what, I said to my twenty-two-year-old C.O., 'You ought to read history.' 'Read history?' he retorted, 'I'm *making* it!' I looked at him, and he had the grace to smile at the enormity of the remark. But it was, in fact, true. R. P. Beamont made history with the Typhoon, as a little later with the Tempest, and after the war as test pilot of the Canberra, the P-1, Lightning and the ill-fated TSR 2. During the period of his command 609 had accounted for twenty-four enemy aircraft destroyed, eight probably destroyed and thirteen damaged, plus a variety of ground and sea targets that included III locomotives, twenty-five of them dealt with by the C.O. himself. And whereas in 1942 the Squadron had won but two decorations, by June 1943 eight D.F.C.s and one D.S.O. had been awarded, one of the former as well as the latter to 'Bee' himself.

*

To take over a squadron at the crest of its wave was an invidious task. Would not the new leader be blamed when the wave became spent? So thought Alec Ingle, A.F.C., who had fought the Battle of Britain with 605 Squadron and now succeeded 'Bee' after a long spell in Training Command.

Circumstances, indeed, seemed against him. The A.O.C. came down and told 609 that it had put the Typhoon on the map; but when he added that it had flown more hours per engine change than any other 'Tiffy' squadron, his words were ominous. The increase of Typhoon squadrons (there were now five between Manston and Tangmere), meant an acute shortage of new, modified engines, and for all its enthusiasm 609 was actually rationed, during May and June, to 300 hours flying a month. Though the ration was never adhered to, standing patrols were replaced by cockpit readiness (up to twenty hours daily) and private offensive action was for a time prohibited.

Nor was the enemy co-operative. Finding the south-east now too 'hot', he shifted his daylight raids to the east, and (taking a leaf out of 609's book) launched his fighter-bombers by night. Here the Army stepped in. It demanded that 609's pilots, night operational almost to a man, be used to patrol its 'searchlight boxes' – a method of defence, said the Brigadier, which was quite infallible. In practice it proved otherwise; more often than not it was the hunter, not the hunted, who became illuminated, and so the target for 'friendly' Ack-Ack.

Alec Ingle remained philosophic but determined – determined that 609 should not lose its private offensive role. Finding that his Squadron's previous natural prey – enemy supply trains – now confined their movements to the darkest nights, he thought up something new. 'Give me some bombs!' he demanded. 'I want to bomb airfields, marshalling yards, barracks – by night!'

After much 'binding' he got a few, and Johnny Wells and 'Abe' Abrahams even designed the Squadron's own bomb sight. Plastered with 'Wings for Victory' stamps the first two bombs were dropped on an enemy hangar by 'Cat's Eyes' Van Lierde. On the way back this redoubtable warrior, who a few weeks earlier had fulfilled the 'Rhubarb' pilot's dream by shooting down a three-engined Ju 52 transporter over its own territory, actually spotted in the dark the first Heinkell 111 seen by 609 since 1940 – and shot that down too.

But Alec was not content. On a dawn patrol of the Dutch Islands he had spotted an enemy convoy entering Flushing harbour. 'Who's doing anything about these convoys?' he asked. Apparently no one was, so he would. Maps went up at Dispersal, recces of the Scheldt were made, and the daily dawn position of shipping established. Coasters, minesweepers, 'E' and 'R' boats – they were there for the 'taking'. And opportunely he had a flight commander who knew all about shipping – Erik Haabjoern, a tough blue-eyed Norwegian, whose membership of the Squadron now raised to three the number of royal toasts to be drunk on formal occasions.

The first attacks were made with cannon only, then by four Typhoons firing cannon and four dropping bombs, the two formations being invariably led by Alec and Erik. Soon there were *flak* ships, and then 'Ingle's Tours of the Dutch Islands', as I euphemistically christened them, became perhaps the most dangerous operations that 609 Squadron had yet embarked on; for as usual the altitude was low, the target was across a lot of sea, and the chances of getting back if hit were hardly rosy. Yet on 1st June both leaders did so after their Typhoons had been shot almost to pieces. Following is from what I wrote in the Squadron diary:

Taking off at 04.54 the four 'fighters' – C.O., de Moulin, Smith and Payne – first set a 600-ton coaster on fire off Walcheren Island, then find a 'stationary blunt-nosed vessel' and tender, and two go for each. But the first turns out to be a *flak* ship, and all its guns concentrate on Squadron-Leader Ingle in such an intense cone of fire that evasive action proves useless. One cannon shell pierces his spinner, another explodes in his port wheel bay, setting off the starter cartridges. These in turn ignite the electrical wiring system and melt the port main tank breather pipe, which burns continuously, blistering and buckling the wing skin. Pulling up to 2,000 feet and warning 'ops' to stand by, he heads out to sea, waiting for his petrol tanks to explode. By a miracle they don't, and he lands at Manston with his aircraft still on fire.

Meanwhile Erik Haabjoern, leading the four 'bombers' – himself, Leslie, Lallemant and Geerts – had already attacked one convoy, leaving one smoking wreck, when he sighted another and called 'Target to port!'

Unaware that the other three have lost him, he attacks alone to within fifty yards, becoming the sole target for *flak* from Flushing, Nieuwe Sluis and all the ships, and is hit in the port nose tank, cockpit hood, main oil feed pipe and hydraulic pipe line, and takes evasive action by crossing the enemy coastline and seeking refuge behind the shore dykes. Still incredibly flying, he makes a belly-landing at Manston without a drop of oil.

This very near loss of a gallant C.O. and flight commander – Erik later became the only Norwegian to command a British Typhoon wing, only to perish in an accident after the war – nearly coincided, as a previous dramatic offensive mission had done, with a highly successful defensive one, when the Luftwaffe raided Kent by daylight in strength for the last time. Just two Typhoons – Flight-Lieutenant J. C. Wells and Flying-Officer I. J. Davies – were in the air, and each, single-handed, attacked a whole squadron of the enemy.

Seeing a Margate gasometer blow up, Johnny Wells identifies twelve FW 190s. Engaging, he is promptly hit by light Ack-Ack but continues pursuit of the enemy who streak out to sea almost touching the waves. Deciding it is important to attack the leading 'vic' of three, he finds the rest of the enemy formation flying innocuously on either side of him. Then, as he opens fire at 200 yards, one of the leaders dips a wing and goes in. Flying through the spray, he attacks the second, which responds with a skid to starboard. Closing up, he fires again, and this aircraft also plunges into the sea. At last his 'escorts' open fire on him, but ignoring this, Johnny attacks the third, only to find his ammo exhausted. A steep climbing turn, and his 'escorts' pass beneath. Score : Two.

Davies attacks four FW 190s which are gunning the streets of Broadstairs. Chasing down after them between the houses, with his own guns blazing, he just has time to see one pull up and its pilot bale out before giving chase to another six which are headed out to sea – five in a 'vic', with one in the 'box'. Firing on the last from 600 yards, this aircraft obliges by 'weaving', and closing the range he fires twice more, and it crashes into the sea in a great fountain of water. But he himself has to turn sharply on seeing tracer flash over his wings. On completing his turn, he is alone, but resuming his original course at full boost, spots another pair of 190s, with a third to port. Saving his last second's worth of ammo till he is well within range, he attacks the last and it bursts into flames. They are now exactly over Ostend, and the others turn to counterattack. Time to go home. Score : Three.

Officially, of course, this was what 609 was at Manston for. But now the 'Tiffies' had won, and in future there would be only isolated raiders. Ranging ahead of Headquarters planners, Alec's mind, as 'Bee's' had been, was always on offence. Instead of receiving operational instructions from Group, these were drawn up at Squadron level and sent to Group for approval. Soon the A.O.C. approved both the policy and procedure – so much so that Alec Ingle recruited reinforcements in the shape of a rocket-firing Hurricane squadron (184), a Whirlwind fighter-bomber squadron (137), and one of so-called 'Bomphoons' (No. 3), and together they became Fighter Command's own anti-shipping task force. In two months over two dozen assorted enemy vessels were put temporarily or permanently out of action by 609 alone.

Manston was now easily the busiest airfield in the country right round the clock, for besides at one time having six squadrons of its own, it was also the nearest landfall for shot-up Flying Fortresses and Liberators by day and Lancasters and Halifaxes by night. So we I.O.s, taking turns at night duty, were quite busy too, even though after a bit we received orders from on high to discontinue interrogating the Americans – perhaps because, having been in the war somewhat longer, we declined to support their fantastic claims. But one busy night, with 609's 'B' flight and most of 137's Whirlwinds on 'Intruder' missions over enemy airfields, and a number of bombers limping in, Alec scored a personal victory over a night-flying FW 190 without even taking off. At 03.30, waiting for Johnny Baldwin to return from a trip to Amiens-Glisy, he saw an aircraft being homed by searchlights.

'Surely Johnny didn't lose his way,' said Alec, puzzled, as it landed.

'Sir! Sir! Van Lierde interjected excitedly. 'That's not a Tiffee, it's a one-ninetee!'

'GET IN THAT CAR!' The Focke-Wulf, as the Hillman drew up, was stationary on the runway, but with engine still running. No one, of course, carried a pistol, so in the darkness Alec pointed his finger. 'HANDS UP!' he shouted, making up in volume for lack of lingo—and the dazed pilot, Unteroffizier Heinz Ehrhardt of I Gruppe/Schnellkampfgeschwader 10, obligingly climbed out and was pushed in the back of the car between Van and Joseph Renier.

'What the hell do we do with him now?'

' "All pilots landing from an operational patrol," ' quoted Johnny Wells on the other front seat, ' "must report at the Intelligence Office." '

The duty I.O., Flying-Officer Treweeks, was already far too busy, with Typhoon and Whirlwind pilots, interspersed with bombers crews, one or two of them wounded, stretching into the next room. Looking up to see a Luftwaffe pilot standing before him, he is said to have merely blinked and pointed to the back of the queue. 'Where am I?' asked the bewildered German. 'Here!' said Van Lierde, obligingly pointing to the top-secret map of Fighter Command's Order of Battle, 'where these pins are. Have some cigarettes.'

Next day Johnny Wells insisted on being photographed with the pilot of the second FW 190 to land in Britain – and so, as in the first case, my camera was used again. We discovered him in the quarters of No. 841 Fleet Air Arm squadron, sitting on a bed holding a gun while his guard, an R.A.F. corporal, explained how it worked. Photograph having been taken outside, I found myself still seated on the grass beside the prisoner after everyone including the corporal had disappeared. Unfortunately, he said, he had mistaken the Thames Estuary for the Channel and helped by search-lights, thought he was landing at St. Omer (a month later, Unteroffizier Werner Ohne of the same unit as Heinz Ehrhardt made the same mistake). He was a young lad from Thuringia, and was beginning to pour out his heart to me when a whole platoon of the R.A.F. Regiment, dressed in khaki, with their Wing-Commander at their head, marched up with shouts of command and a great clicking of rifle bolts, till he probably thought he was going to be shot on the spot. The martial display, however, concluded lamely with the words, 'All right, Ziegler, please fall him in,' and I told the prisoner in halting German, 'Now you must go with the soldiers.'

His reply – 'I would much prefer to stay with my blue comrades' – reflected, I believe, the attitude towards each other of many British and German fighter pilots up till 1944. Till then they were rivals, but also 'comrades', who killed each other mercilessly but with mutual respect, plus a good deal of contempt for many people on their own side, both civil and military. Adolf Galland, in his book, *The First and the Last*, seems to agree.

On 15th July I noted that 609, quite exceptionally, had no less than thirty-five pilots, but only six serviceable Typhoons. A week

later, leaving all its Typhoons and its maintenance Echelon behind, it moved to Matlask in Norfolk to take over those of 56
Squadron, who left the following message of welcome on the Dispersal blackboard: '300 miles of sea – it's all yours!'

Once again it looked as if the West Riding Squadron, put out
to grass for a rest, would at last fade into obscurity. Its living quarters were rural indeed. Whereas the most junior officers dwelt in
the servants' wing at Wolterton Hall, seat of the Walpoles – and
(she having the only telephone) had to be briefed by Lady Walpole
herself if required for an early morning operation – the ten most
senior ones took up residence in a converted mill house, beneath
which flowed the most delectable trout stream. Of an evening I
would stand on a balcony, cast a fly and catch trout with one hand,
and reach through the bar window for a pint of beer with the other.
But once I nearly drowned our only American pilot, big Arty Ross
– he preferred the R.A.F. to the U.S.A.F. despite the meagre pay –
when my fly caught in a tree and, climbing up to rescue it, he
brought the branch and himself crashing down into the mill pool.
Meanwhile Belgian gastronomes, guns bristling through the windows, were wont to patrol the estate in the 'Barouche' and blaze
away at pheasants and partridges, most of them sitting and all
out of season.

In the event the 'rest' lasted less than a month, and operationally
was not all that restful. Besides the usual defensive Readiness, during the moonlight period detachments flew back to Manston for
'Night Rhubarbs', there were several shipping recces of Holland,
and once, while taking part in a large-scale 'Ramrod' with Bostons bombing Schiphol airfield, 609's six serviceable Typhoons
were 'jumped' off the Dutch coast by a squadron of Spitfires – only
to find that the Spits were simultaneously being 'jumped' by
Messerschmitt 109s. In the end Erik Haabjoern shot one of the
Messerschmitts down, and Mony Van Lierde, strenuously evading
another, saw this plunge into the sea too without himself firing a
shot. And one day Flight-Lieutenant L. E. Smith, sticking on a
pair of jettisonable fuel tanks beneath his wings, became the first
Typhoon pilot to fly over the German Reich. In over Holland and
out over Belgium, he was hit by *flak* near Brussels, his engine later
cut and he ditched on fire 100 yards off Deal, but got out. Helped

ashore by soldiers and coastguards, he inherited at Deal hospital the former bed and nurse of Squadron-Leader Beamont.

The day before 609 moved back to 11 Group, Alec Ingle, now D.F.C., A.F.C., was promoted to command a Wing of the 2nd Tactical Air Force, now starting to form under canvas, and in a trice Erik Haabjoern was also promoted to lead one of his squadrons. The next time I heard from Alec was from a P.O.W. camp in Germany. 'Irvin beat Newton by two seconds,' he wrote – meaning that his parachute had opened in the nick of time. Later, peering one day through the barbed wire, he could not help laughing when he saw Wing-Commander R. P. Beamont being prodded towards the entrance gate by a German corporal – the only time, as he said twenty-five years later in his reunion speech that followed 'Bee's', that 'Bee' followed *him*.

*

It seemed impossible that 609 should yet again get a leader of top calibre, but it happened. He was Pat Thornton-Brown, the most lovable young man I ever met, and who charmed the Squadron into instant devotion. ('Charming! – what?' was indeed his light-hearted reference to anything unpleasant, such as a storm of *flak*.) It also seemed impossible, with the massive Anglo-American air offensive building up to strategic pitch for the invasion now only months ahead, that a lone British fighter squadron could still plan its own operations. But this happened too.

It was sent to Lympne, a small airfield of pre-war civil aviation fame near Folkestone, where it came once more under Biggin Hill control. Dispersal was an unheated farm house in a sea of mud, but the Mess was the stately home of Sir Philip Sassoon, where although No. 1 Squadron had already acquired the best accommodation, the beautiful gardens included a swimming pool. At night the flash of guns and bombs at Boulogne were clearly visible.

Orders were routine: defensive readiness, shipping protection, sweeps in support of American bombers, occasionally even the rescue of Liberators lost over Britanny – all of them negative. As for the Liberators, Pat remarked: 'Pretty poor show when fighters have to navigate for bombers!' One of them even landed after him at Lympne, and came to a stop straddling the lane beside Dispersal.

His ideas were different, even from those of his predecessors. Training all new pilots in real 'hedge-hopping' flying, he demanded long-range jettisonable fuel tanks, and told me to collect the maximum 'gen' (there was precious little) about airfields deep in enemy territory. The idea: to penetrate his bomber, night-fighter and training belt, so far out of range of British day fighters.

It was an uphill struggle. Serviceability remained low, long-range tanks seemed unprocurable, and Authority was dubious – but for one man. This was Air Vice-Marshal Hill, at this moment, I believe, A.O.C. 12 Group to which 609 still technically belonged, but soon to become Air Marshal Sir Roderick Hill, C.-in-C. of Air Defence of Great Britain, which on 15th November replaced Fighter Command when Air Chief Marshal Leigh-Mallory became C.-in-C. Allied Expeditionary Air Forces. A few days after Pat took over, Hill arrived in a Spitfire and listened to him. And the day after that, 28th August, having obtained just two pairs of L.R. tanks, Pat and Johnny Baldwin, now a flight commander, set off on 'Ranger No. 1', target: enemy aircraft south of Paris.

Flying low enough to read the signposts, they reached an area never before penetrated by British day fighters since the fall of France, and the ensuing combat was not over Margate but on the wrong side of Paris. Yet on their return, Pat bade me send the following signal to Hill:

REF OUR CONVERSATION TEA TABLE LYMPNE YES-TERDAY CONCERNING LONG-RANGE TYPHOON OPERA-TIONS, TWO FW 190 DESTROYED BY 609 SQDN THIS AFTERNOON.

Two days later a Canadian, Flying-Officer Reahil, and a very independent Belgian, Pilot-Officer Detal (he once startled me with the information that he was going to spend his leave in Turkey – till I found he meant Torquay), reached Laon airfield, and despite being hit by *flak* destroyed a Me 110 and a Ju 52 on the ground, with another of each type probably destroyed. This had never happened before; an El Dorado had been discovered. H.Q. 11 Group became interested, and asked the Squadron for a chart showing the range and endurance of Typhoons with L.R. tanks.

The tanks themselves, however, still failed to appear, and in early September most serviceability was devoted to supporting a series of large-scale 'ops' in connection with an invasion bluff to test enemy reaction. So far as 609 was concerned, it was a waste of time; so were numerous autumn sweeps it was ordered to carry out while bombers plastered so-called 'Noball' targets, which later turned out to be V-1 launching sites. And on 20/21 September no less than sixty-three sorties, including thirty-eight by 609, were flown before Pilot-Officer Turek (who rejoined the Squadron with a commission after several compulsory months with the Polish Army) was rescued by a Walrus from off the French coast after a night in a water-logged dinghy. Five days later Charles de Moulin owed his life largely to George Martin (one of 609's first batch of Australians), who called up for a dinghy to be dropped after de Moulin had lost his own. And a month after that the Squadron nearly lost one of its best Belgians owing to a constitutional crisis caused by mushrooms.

These grew prolifically on the airfield, and this Belgian was about to get down to a tasty dish of them in his bedroom when he was called to take a bogus phone call, and returning found the mushrooms consumed. Rightly suspecting a certain other Belgian, he enters the Anteroom and slaps his face. At once all Belgians leap to their feet, the Station Commander buries his face in his newspaper, and 'Smithy' (acting C.O. in Pat's absence) has to try to sort out the pandemonium. Next day the mushroom raider magnanimously informs him that he has decided to overlook the episode, 'but of course ... must be posted'. And sure enough Pat on his return finds a signal, obviously emanating from Belgian H.Q., doing just this. He had not been consulted, and asked my advice. I told him *he* was the C.O., and to fight it, which he successfully did. It was the only time in 609 when the dual sovereignties, to which Belgians owed allegiance, for a moment clashed.

When in October 'Ranger' operations were resumed, and 609's Typhoons all but landed on the enemy's deep-inland airfields, his fighter reaction, not to mention *flak*, was often severe. On one occasion Baldwin, alone without cloud cover south-west of Paris, was attacked from all directions by eight Focke-Wulfs, and only escaped by making maximum use of 'ground cover'. On another occasion he, de Moulin, Geerts and Henrion were assailed by no less than two dozen Messerschmitts, but came back with a score of two Me 109Gs and a Me 110 destroyed in the air, a Heinkel 111 damaged on the ground, plus four locomotives, one tug, three supply barges, two radio towers and a gasometer destroyed or damaged. It was a dramatic moment, for it brought 609's tally of enemy aircraft destroyed in the air since 1939 to 199. Sweep money was at once collected for the pilot who would bag the 200th.

It happened next day – the winner an Englishman destined to become the Squadron's last war-time C.O., 'Pinky' Stark, accompanied by Arty Ross, former American cow-puncher.

South of Soissons they come to an airfield with eight Me 110s neatly parked on the ground. Stark fires a burst, his target bursts into flames, and the servicing party scatters. Ross knocks piece off another. *Flak* having opened up, they do not tarry but a minute later a Ju 88 is sighted five miles away at 3000 feet. Making a sharp climbing turn Pinky gets on its tail, and his first burst sets one engine on fire. The Ju 88 starts to go down. At 500 feet it levels out, and a second burst produces smoke from the other engine. As the Typhoon overshoots, the 88 crashes into a wood and catches fire, one occupant baling out just above the ground. Pinky himself smashes through the top of a tree.

But he only won by a short head. Two hours later the redoubtable Van Lierde, operating singly, destroyed a second Ju 88 in the air and a third on the ground. When, some days later he shot down a Me 110, he had accumulated a mixed bag for the year of six, without once repeating himself : a FW 190, a Ju 52, a He 111, a Me 109, a Ju 88 and a Me 110. The following year, as a pilot of the first Tempest wing commanded by R. P. Beamont, I believe he destroyed a record thirty-seven V-1 'doodle-bugs'.

Strange to say, 'Pinky' Stark's Junkers 88 was the first victim of the species to fall to 609 since Frankie Howell and Sidney Hill had claimed its *first* century almost exactly three years before. Telegrams of congratulation poured in, ranging from Leigh-Mallory ('I am not surprised after the magnificent performance of the Squadron this year') to the Mayor and Citizens of Leeds, and one from a detachment of old boys which ended, 'Awaiting Bottle Orders'.

'Bottle orders' were for 20th October at the Hotel Majestic, Folkestone, whose directors themselves contributed towards the expense of entertaining an estimated 600 celebrating people, while the A.O.C. sent a signal releasing 609 from duty 'until such time as its C.O. decides it is capable of taking over again'. Before the latter did so, he made a speech aptly pointing out that whereas the 100th Hun met disaster on its way to London (not *strictly* accurate), the 200th did so on its way to Paris. Needless to say the Goat, promoted this night to Group-Captain, got much of the press publicity, but that was normal: some time previously famous American author, John Steinbeck, then writing for the *Express*, had visited 609, asked questions and been told everything he wanted to know – and then wrote half a page exclusively about His Goathood.

Pat had won his battle. From now on the 'West Riding Air Force' (as it had begun to call itself), in its tumble-down farm house, kept its own 'war room', whence Forms 'D' were once again teleprinted to Group seeking sanction for forthcoming operations. But on one occasion it was Group, in the person of Wing-Commander 'Johnny' Johnson, then on its planning staff, who invited 609 to undertake a special mission – an attack on a special train, complete with *flak* waggon, known to be due to arrive at Paris from the south at 17.59 hours, with none other than Field Marshal von Rundstedt on board. Wrote Johnson in his book : *

The task had to be carried out by the Typhoons, and it would be on a voluntary basis . . . I consulted with Jamie (Group-Captain Pat Jameson):

'Which Typhoon squadron shall I offer this von Rundstedt job to, Jamie?'

His answer was quick and decisive.

'609 at Lympne. They've done a few long-range jobs lately and are pretty hot at it. Pat Thornton-Brown is their C.O. I should have a word with him and see what he thinks.'

I got Thornton-Brown on the scrambler telephone . . . He accepted

* *Wing Leader*, Chatto & Windus, 1956.

the job immediately . . . From now on the fate of von Rundstedt was in the hands of the half-dozen young pilots.

I left our planning office and walked the few yards to the spacious, underground operations block . . . The afternoon slipped by . . . A coloured counter was placed on the plotting-table near the mouth of the Seine. The controller nodded towards the table and said : 'That's 609 crossing out.'

'Can't be,' I answered, 'They're not due out for another ten or fifteen minutes.'

'We'll soon make certain,' said the controller. 'We'll call them . . .'

It was 609 Squadron, and I phoned their intelligence officer when they taxied in at Lympne. He was excited and said that he could see all six pilots had fired their cannon. I told him to get his squadron commander to the phone . . .

'How did it go, Pat?' I asked.

'Absolutely first class, sir. We had a great afternoon. I think we got two Junkers 88s destroyed, one twin-engined Messerschmitt in flames, two 109s on the Seine, a crane damaged and a gasometer sprayed . . .'

'That's fine,' I interrupted gently. 'But what about old von R.?'

'Oh, yes,' he answered. 'I'd almost forgotten about him. We used up a lot of ammo against the Huns and the weather was lifting – blue sky south of Paris. So I called the show off . . .'

Well, it was certainly *one* way of getting permission to do a fair-weather 'Ranger', I wrote in the diary, for in fact they ran out of cloud only sixty miles inland. But the S.A.S.O. phoned his congratulations.

In November Johnny Baldwin, before long to win a second D.F.C. and a D.S.O. (and years later in the Korean war, post-humously, America's highest award), was posted to command another Typhoon squadron, No. 198, at Manston. He was joined by several experienced 609 pilots, including Niblett and 'Cheval' Lallemant, both to become flight commanders, and soon the two squadrons became A.D.G.B.'s almost official long-range striking force, which in this period destroyed probably more of the enemy than all other squadrons of the command put together. They flew so low that it was not unusual for a Typhoon to be hit by the ex-ploding débris of an enemy aircraft as it crashed – and once, after the victim had set fire to a house in a Brussels suburb, Charles Detal spent a sleepless night worrying whether the house might be his family's. On another occasion two pilots had to avoid becoming entangled with the crew of a Flying Fortress parachuting down from above.

On 4th December, five Typhoons of 609, operating together with about the same number of Baldwin's 198, encountered a whole *Gruppe* of Dornier 217 bombers taking off from Eindhoven in Holland. Led by Pat, 609's five charged into them, and combats ensued right down to the runways amidst a hail of *flak*, leaving the airfield and environs plastered with seven burning wrecks, of which a Briton (Pat), an American (Ross) and a Belgian (Detal) had scored more than one each, while 198 operating as top cover claimed four more.

'I thanked my stars I was not flying that day!' a pilot of the Dornier unit (Kampfgeschwader 2) told me after the war. He himself lived to bomb London a few weeks later, and baled out over it.

Then, four days before Christmas, came tragedy. 609 was detailed as close escort to American Marauder bombers. It only had six aircraft, and with the bombers strung out in three boxes over ten miles, there was nothing for it but to appoint two Typhoons to each box. Again it was the old sad story : they were attacked from astern by a swarm of American Thunderbolts, and recognition signals were given in vain. Arty Ross was hit by his countrymen in both wings, and two pilots nevered returned : 'Chuck' Miller, a Canadian, and the C.O., Pat Thornton-Brown. It was typical of Pat that his last words on the R.T. expressed concern, not for himself, but for Miller. His D.F.C. was announced a few days later, and his wife was due next day to join him for Christmas.

On 15th December 609 had moved back to Manston to be with 198, and Johnny Wells now returned to take command. For two month a friendly rivalry developed between the two Johnnies, both of them reared in the same fold, and their two squadrons as a team superb. A month to the day after the Dornier success there was another, also in Holland at Gilze Rijen, when 609 destroyed four Dorniers in the air, plus two Dorniers and a Ju 88C on the ground, and 198 Squadron this time even more. ('I've just got a Hun !' Flight-Lieutenant Davies boasted to his wife on the phone. 'Yes, dear, baby's just got a tooth').

On 30th January, 1944, when Charles de Moulin, during a dog-fight deep in France, called me personally on the Dispersal R.T. set to claim two FW 190s (in case he didn't get back), the Wing scored the biggest Typhoon fighter victory of the war. Seven aircraft of 609 destroyed three enemy aircraft in the air and two on the ground; six aircraft of 198, attacked by up to forty FW 190s, brought down no less than nine of them, Baldwin and Niblett, both ex-609, scoring two each. It made Baldwin, with thirteen-and-a-half victories, top-scoring Typhoon pilot of the war. The Wing score for the month, forty-three, represented three-quarters of the 11 Group total, and at this stage of the war was fantastic. On 5th February, as the pilots were about to be briefed in the Intelligence Office, the C.-in-C., Air Marshal Sir Roderick Hill, unexpectedly entered, walked down each row, shook hands and spoke to each one of them, seeming to know many by name. They had, he said, 'immortalized the Typhoon', and he brought a similar message from Air Chief Marshal Sir Trafford Leigh-Mallory.

And then, at the end of February, it all suddenly ended. Both squadrons were at last absorbed in the Second Tactical Air Force, and became just two of many Typhoon squadrons preparing for their invasion role of ground attack. Gone was 609's independence gone its own little 'war room' and its own successful war. It was the end of an era, itself an anomaly, which could never be repeated. Since it became a Typhoon squadron it had lost twenty-four pilots, but had destroyed in the air and on the ground seventy-seven enemy aircraft (plus nine 'probables'), and destroyed or damaged 148 locomotives, forty-two ships, sixty-nine supply barges and a miscellany of other ground targets. This score was almost certainly the highest for any individual fighter squadron during the period, and brought 609's total claim of enemy aircraft destroyed since 1939 to 231*. I think I am right in saying that this made it the war's top-scoring R.A.F. Fighter squadron of those based exclusively in the European theatre. Since January 1943 one D.S.O., thirteen D.F.C.s and two Bars, had been awarded.

Almost the last report I took went approximately as follows. Flying Officer Georges Jaspis, later a pilot of Sabena Air Lines, speaking:

*Although the author states 232 confirmed aerial kills, only 227 can be positively identified today—Ed.

South of Brussels I call up Smithy to say I come home later because I must see my fiancée. Smithy say O.K. and I come to my house and I make many dives and I see my mother and I take many photos of my mother and she wave with her arms and my engine cut. I climb and my engine splutter and my mother she is perhaps very worried because she know it is me, yes. Then I see an aircraft and it is a Ju 88 and I am very excited. But only the camera work because I have finger trouble because my mother is looking and perhaps my fiancée, yes. Then I fire and all my shots go poof-poof into the 88 till a piece come off and I fire again and the starboard engine catch fire and then the port engine she explode and the Jerry crash on ground with huge flames and all the time it is near my house. Please do not say anything about this I do not want anyone to know, yes.

Yes, it was the end of an era.

8

THE ROCKET MEN

In the evening of 28th February, 1944, a long column of military vehicles was seen bearing down upon the hitherto front-line R.A.F. station of Manston on the tip of Kent. They belonged to No. 123 Airfield, of No. 84 Group, Second Tactical Air Force, and the message of their arrival was that before long the front line would be transferred across the English Channel. Into this so-called 'Airfield',* two days later, Nos. 609 and 198 Squadrons were absorbed as its fighting teeth – almost the last two Typhoon squadrons to join 2nd T.A.F. Though they would remain sister squadrons for the rest of the war, with constant interchange of pilots and commanders, on this day they ceased to be fighter squadrons.

Under the new 'mobile' set-up a squadron consisted of some two dozen pilots (half officers, half N.C.O.s), their aircraft, a Medical Officer, an Orderly Room and just a few dependent 'erks'. For some months already even the post of Adjutant had been held by pilots – successively by Niblett, Bob Watts and Eric Roberts. I called them 'MacAdjutants', and soon a permanent non-flying officer was reappointed. But the briefing and de-briefing of pilots, like the servicing and maintenance of aeroplanes, would in future be an 'Airfield' responsibility (the former in conjunction with the Army), and so the posts of Squadron Intelligence Officer and Squadron Engineer Officer were now abolished. On 1st March,

* Though actual airfields were to become all but 'portable', this was a misleading designation for a mobile unit, and for two or more squadrons the term 'Wing' was revived, even though it bore the same number as the ground unit, from which it was occasionally detached. After a bit No. 123 Wing seems to have absorbed No. 136 Wing, with 164 and 183 Squadrons, which from then on operated with 198 and 609.

stiff and bruised after being dropped the night before from the top of a two-tier human pyramid after traditionally leaving my footprint on the extremely high ceiling at Doon House, Westgate, I bade farewell to the Squadron I had served for over three years, and with my accumulated baggage was driven away in the almost equally senior 'Belgian Barouche'.

Of West Riding origins there were now few obvious traces – even if till the last day of the war the initials 'W.R.' were still placed in brackets after '609' in official records. Since 1941 or even earlier the R.A.F. had been enticing members of the Yorkshire Auxiliary ground staff away by offers of promotion, but on 5th September, 1943, I noted that there were still fourteen of them, and the problem of their continued presence may even have helped delay 609's absorption into 2nd T.A.F. Two days later however Sergeant Simpson, who had presided over the Orderly Room since before the war, was posted, and from then on bribery was replaced by the threat that unless the remainder signed their willingness to be transferred to other units, they would be discharged and re-called as 'V.R.'s, in the rank of Aircraftmen 2. Many had families to support, and (bar two) none could afford to do otherwise than sign – among them Sergeant 'Darkie' Hanson, perhaps the most devoted and efficient servant a squadron ever had. He was posted to the Middle East where, as he told Air-Vice Marshal Ambler after the war, he 'simply sulked'. Only Douglas Andrews and Leslie Lindley, with the support of their firms in 'civvy street', successfully called the bluff, and I believe remained on Squadron strength till the end. Two others – Corporals Barker and Hinchcliffe, who had been ops. clerks since the Battle of Britain – continued to fulfil their role with the Squadron till November, 1944, though technically on the strength of the Airfield.

Now they provided a thin strand of continuity with a distant past, to which future pilots who joined 609 overseas would only be bound by hearsay. More concrete evidence of their Squadron's history and traditions – its war diary, its photograph albums, its portrait gallery and trophies – had for obvious reasons to be left at home, some in the care of its founder, Air Commodore Harald Peake. That the West Riding Squadron, shorn as it was, and despite all the efforts to reduce it to just one cog in a big war machine, did still manage to preserve its individuality and character was due in great measure to its last seven commanders, all but one of whom, British or Belgian, had served and grown up with it since at least early 1943, and two since 1941.

Meanwhile, for a short time, there was a plethora of flight-lieutenants. Besides the two flight commanders, L. E. Smith and I. J. Davies, both D.F.C., these included Eric Roberts, Bob Watts and Arty Ross – promoted inside the Squadron – and Wood, Pike and Le Grand, who had been posted to it in that rank. By the end of April, however, all would have departed bar Davies, Roberts and Wood – and Manu Geerts became first Belgian flight commander since Jean de Selys, killed long ago in an accident while serving with 3 Squadron. On 14th March No. 123 Airfield left Manston for Tangmere, and for the next six weeks the two squadrons darted about the country like headless chicks. First, for a week at Tangmere, they practised dive-bombing under Group-Captain Dennis Gillam, former Duxford Wing-Commander Flying. For another week they did the same at Acklington in Northumberland, where 609 had been based in 1939 and where that outstanding Belgian warrior Charles Detal was killed in an accident. Meanwhile it was announced that they were not to be 'Bomphoons', but rocket-firing squadrons. So then they settled at Thorney Island – significantly on 1st April, for three weeks later they were sent on a course at Llanbedr in Wales, only to be hurriedly recalled on the 29th. By then, at least, their pilots had been intensively trained in the art of firing rockets at diving angles of thirty and sixty degrees.

At Thorney Island personnel slept for the first time under canvas, and at first, being 'sprog' campers, were very cold. But a fortnight later Eric Roberts confided to his diary:

'The pseudo scout life isn't too bad and merely a question of getting organized in one's own tent. The food cooked over wood fires is really excellent considering, and with the main Mess handy for a bath now and then, things could be a lot worse.'

The time was approaching when they would be worse indeed, when 'camping' stood for noise, dust, dirt and danger – and no Mess for baths. Meanwhile 'softening-up' operations for Operation

Overlord were about to begin, and as a sign of the times General Dwight D. Eisenhower himself appeared, talked to the two squadrons, and listened to a model briefing by 609's C.O., Johnny Wells.

On 2 May operations started for 609 with a rocket attack by eight aircraft on a road bridge on the Cherbourg peninsula. On the 3rd 'ninety-three rockets were fired in rippling pairs' by twelve pilots on railway sheds near Amiens. On the 7th targets included another bridge, a canal lock and shipping in a canal marshalling basin. And on the 9th, as if 60lb. rockets and 20mm. cannon were an insufficient armament, pilots were ordered to carry revolvers as well.

Typhoon squadrons were now exclusively airborne artillery, and ex-fighter pilots of 609 and 198 saw with reluctance their once sprightly planes, weighted, slowed and made more vulnerable with the rails and missiles of their new trade. Ideal targets were fuel dumps, one of which when hit by Johnny Wells spouted satisfactory clouds of smoke up to 6,000 feet. Buildings, too, were fairly easy. But on 11th May 609 was sent against a radar 'chimney' near Fécamp – the first of a series of such attacks that were to continue till D-Day, 6th June. These targets were at most two-dimensional and were heavily defended by *flak*. Wrote Roberts * about this attack :

'Junior' Soesman was hit and baled out about fifteen miles from the French coast. He didn't get into his dinghy and has now had it. 'Woody', Flight-Lieutenant Wood, lately one of my closest pals, was hit in the dive, burst into flames and went straight into a house near the target. I, with my usual luck and by the grace of God, haven't yet been hit ... But it seems like the war has started.

The 'war' had indeed started, and from now on the Typhoons were hit repeatedly by enemy *flak*, sometimes lethally, often happily not. 2nd T.A.F., under Air Marshal Sir Arthur Coningham, comprised three Groups : No. 2, with twin-engined Mosquito and Mitchell bombers; and Nos. 83 and 84, respectively under Air

* In 1968 E. R. A. Roberts was the B.E.A. captain referred to in the Prologue.

Vice Marshals Broadhurst and L. O. Brown, together mustering twenty-nine Spitfire, eleven Mustang and eighteen Typhoon squadrons. Besides these, the Allied Expeditionary Air Force, under Air Chief Marshal Sir Trafford Leigh-Mallory, also included the U.S. Ninth (Tactical) Air Force, with I know not how many additional squadrons. Even so, they were not enough, and 'Overlord' might well have failed but for the diversion to a tactical daylight role of the four-engined 'heavies' of British Bomber Command and the American Strategic Air Force. Meanwhile probably the most effective single weapon in the whole of the Allied tactical air forces by daylight was the rocket projectile carried I believe exclusively by perhaps half of the eighteen British Typhoon squadrons.

The full armament of each Typhoon was eight (later twelve) of these, plus of course the normal four 20mm. cannon, though a compromise between range and fire-power could be achieved by fitting just two pairs of rockets and one pair of extra, jettisonable petrol tanks. The full load of rockets, if fired all at once, was lethal indeed – provided they hit. And of course it was while aiming the aircraft in a steady dive that it was at its most vulnerable. Provided the target had a gun, and the gunner had the courage to aim it straight, he could hardly miss. Before he ever fired his own rockets 'in anger', Roberts wrote in his diary :

We will probably come in for a lot of casualties from *flak* . . . and personally I don't think a lot of damage will be done by the rockets because of the many factors governing their accuracy when there's ten-tenths *flak* around.

He was right about the *flak* – during May 609 lost no less than five pilots – but pessimistic about the damage. Up till D-Day 609 and 198 had a dual role : first to help disrupt the enemy's road, rail and water communications systems, and so minimize the reinforcements and supplies he could bring up against the future bridgehead; second to help in the gigantic deception about where that bridgehead was going to be.

One step towards the latter objective had already been achieved : Allied fighter strength made enemy reconnaissance flights virtually impossible. The second was to make two attacks away from the intended 'lodgement area' for every one inside it; and the third was to cripple and distort the enemy's radar system. Between Dunkirk and Brest there were sixty radar installations, which besides aircraft and shipping reporting stations included those controlling night-fighters and the fire of the Atlantic Wall's formidable coastal batteries. During the week before D-Day forty-two of them were attacked for the first or second time.

The assaults were delivered for the most part by the Typhoon and Spitfire squadrons of Nos. 83 and 84 Groups. The targets were very heavily defended by light *flak* and to attack them 'demanded great skill and daring'. The losses in aircraft and pilots were very heavy. Of the many assaults made, Leigh-Mallory in his despatch selected three as worthy of special mention. There was that of 2nd June carried out by eighteen rocket-firing Typhoons of Nos. 198 and 609 Squadrons on the Dieppe/Caudecote station, used for night-fighter control and the control of coastal batteries. . . .*

Finally, on D-Day itself, the deception was completed by Bomber Command, especially by Lancasters of 617 Squadron led by Group-Captain Cheshire, V.C. By dropping 'Window' and circling some quite small ships carrying balloon reflectors in the Straits of Dover, the impression was successfully given that an armada was approaching across the narrowest part of the English Channel. For though only a fraction of the radar system was still working, enough had been deliberately spared to give false information.

During May 609 had lost Flight-Lieutenant Wood, Flying-Officer Soesman, Flight-Sergeant Fidgin, Flying-Officer Stewart, D.F.C.†, and Flying-Officer Thorogood, although Stewart evaded initially, he was later captured whilst Thorogood was luckier and returned to the U.K. a few months later. But on 2nd June, 'Nibbey' Niblett, once a staunch and cheerful member of 609, and now C.O. of 198, lost his life in an attack on radar, and was succeeded by 609's 'A'-flight commander, I. J. Davies, who sadly also perished a few weeks later. They might have been avenged when, on the eve of

*Royal Air Force 1939–1945, by D. Richards and H. St.G. Saunders, Vol. 3, H.M. Stationery Office.

† Jimmy Stewart had won his D.F.C. as a 'cata-fighter' aboard a freighter on an Atlantic convoy. In an old Mk. I expendable Hurricane he had been catapulted off the deck, shot down a long-range four-engined Focke-Wulf Condor, baled out according to programme, and been picked up again.

D-Day, the two squadrons seriously damaged the chateau H.Q. of Rommel himself on the Cherbourg peninsula, but according to a Swiss radio report the old Desert Fox had left a few minutes earlier.

It was the third mission of the day and the pilots did not land until 21.55. Before they did so they were privileged to see a sight that none would forget, and one unique in history: the setting forth in deadly silence across the Channel of the real invasion armada – four years exactly since that other improvised 'armada' had brought back the defeated B.E.F. from Dunkirk. One wonders whether any pilot saw them both. Now the sight took the squadrons completely by surprise, so wonderfully had the secret been kept. Not one pilot had known that tomorrow was the Day, and still did not know (till he landed) the armada's destination. Without saying a word on the radio they simply looked down and signalled to each other joyfully from their cockpits.

The great Overlord invasion of 6th June has been described often enough. While Coastal Command blocked both ends of the Channel against enemy submarines, and over 1,000 aircraft of Bomber Command had plastered ten of the principal batteries guarding the chosen Normandy beaches, the ships and the landings were covered by no less than 171 squadrons. The Luftwaffe, weak as it was on the western front, scarcely appeared. 609 Squadron, after another mission against radar, attacked two enemy road columns east of Lisieux and south-west of Caen, claiming the destruction of its first two German tanks, with other fighting vehicles destroyed or damaged. Roberts, who had inherited command of 'A' flight, was surprised, after missing a Mark IV tank with his rockets, at the effect of his cannon: 'Boy, did it go up! It just belched flame and black smoke – completely burnt out.'

It was 609's last mission of D-Day, and Warrant-Officer Martin, though missing, probably owed his life to the approaching darkness. One of a first contingent of four pilots wearing the dark blue of the Royal Australian Air Force, George Martin had been with the Squadron some time, and was the most typical 'Aussie' I ever met. Tough, strong and quarrelsome, he was usually in trouble but possessed the heart of a lion. Today his parachute opened just above the ground but in full view of the enemy. It also so happened that the tanks, of which he had pulverized one and no doubt its crew, belonged to an S.S. unit, whose members were evidently determined to exact retribution. Finding his parachute, they systematically raked all the surrounding cover with gunfire. George lay in a hedge and a bullet hit him in the ankle – but he made no sound. After dark he swam a canal, and next morning, unable to move, was taken away by a French priest in a donkey cart and hidden in a barn. Later, with papers designating him as a deaf, dumb and injured basket-maker evacuated from Caen, he seems to have shared another farm house with the S.S. or Gestapo, who shot a Canadian pilot in his presence. Always suspicious of George, they decided on the morning of their departure to make a final test of his 'deafness' as he sat breakfasting at the kitchen table. Cocking a pistol, one of them fired it quite close to his ear – and without batting an eyelid George just went on eating. Eleven weeks later, when I happened to be visiting 609 on the only day I was in Normandy, Johnny Baldwin, now a Wing-Commander on an adjacent airfield, phoned to say George was in Bayeaux military hospital, having been handed over to advancing troops by Madame Le Poutlika and Stephen Chyet of St. Pierre des Ips, whose names should be recorded in gold.

He left three other Australians (Bavington, Gibson, Merrett), three Canadians (Buchanan, Seguin, Inches) three New Zealanders (Harkness, Price, Stellin), five Belgians (Geerts, Cooreman, Blanco, Watelet, Jaspis), ten British (Wells, Roberts, Bryant, Holmes, Royston, Bliss, Rowland, Adam, Cables, Billam), one Argentinian (Pagnam) and one German (Adams), to carry on the war. I had just overlapped with the last, who, being a Jew, had escaped from Germany before the war and was unnaturalized. With that background it was only by the greatest persistence that he got himself accepted in a combat role, first as an N.C.O. pilot, and later, after the intervention of Air Vice-Marshal Brown, as an officer. Recently he had changed his name from Klaus Hugo Adam to Keith Howard Adams – largely for obvious reasons, but also because, confusingly, there was another Flight-Sergeant Adam in the Squadron. His comrades, of course, still lovingly called him 'Heinie', and Dr. George Bell, Squadron M.O. from February 1944 till the end of the war, writes :

We were very proud to have him with us. To other pilots being taken P.O.W. in most cases just meant the end of the war for them, but to Heinie Adams it would be the start of a nightmare. To fly with this knowledge as well as the ordinary stresses must have taken immense courage.

Happily it did not happen, and now, Klaus Hugo Adam – as he is again – is quite famous in the film world, and was responsible for the art direction of the James Bond series.

The most immediate task of the air forces after the beachhead had been won was to combat the approach of enemy reinforcements by road and rail – particularly road, the rail system having been semi-paralysed already. On D-Day plus one it is recorded that all eighteen Typhoon squadrons of 83 and 84 Groups, with help from Mustangs released by 11 Group from the general pool, were on armed reconnaissance far south of the battle area, where at dawn strong enemy forces had been reported moving north. The weather was atrocious, the aircraft had to fly very low, and seventeen were lost to *flak*. But this time 609 was lucky, even though between 07.25 and 21.30 on the 7th it flew three such missions, each of up to two hours, and two more on the 8th, attacking two troop trains and road columns, and claiming several Mark IV tanks and other fighting and transport vehicles destroyed or damaged. 'The attacks became incessant and terrible,' complained Lieutenant-General Bayerlein, commanding the *Panzer Lehr* Division, which on the 7th alone lost 130 supply lorries and eighty-four half-track vehicles including 88mm guns. 'Where,' the German soldiers, must have asked, echoing with more reason their British opposite numbers at Dunkirk, 'is the Luftwaffe?'

Such operations remained the general pattern for 609 for the rest of the month, interspersed until the 15th with more attacks on radar. On the 22nd it gave close support to the American assault on Cherbourg by attacking *flak* positions, barrack blocks and communications. Yet the German Army had an ally much more powerful than the Luftwaffe : the weather, which on many days made flying impossible. And on two days 609 did actually meet the Luftwaffe, however much this was now supposedly 'reserved' for Spitfires. On the 23rd four out of eight Typhoons had just attacked some tank carriers near Evreux when R. K. ('Spud') Holmes, climbing to rejoin what he thought was his formation, found it consisted of six Me 109Fs. Possibly he had never been trained to fight enemy aircraft: as he shouted excitedly into the microphone no one understood what he said, and though he jettisoned his rockets and supplementary tanks, he failed to turn on the main ones. Eventually he did attack, but though he scored hits, he was out of ammo before he could finish the job. Australian R. K. Gibson also got a 'damaged' despite one rocket hanging up, while Canadian J. D. Buchanan was lucky to escape with minor wounds after finding three of the enemy on his tail. R. S. Royston claimed a 'probable', but the only 'definite' – it crashed in a field—belonged to the leader, Eric Roberts, who with it scored 609's 232nd* and last air-to-air victory of the war.

Though tanks and rockets could be jettisoned, the Typhoons' efficiency as emergency fighters was still impaired by the rails on which the rockets were slung. When, four days later, after attacks on rail targets far to the south, Holmes again reported enemy fighters, he was not seen again. This time it was FW 190s, and Geerts was leading, with Roberts in charge of a section. In his diary Eric unknowingly wrote the Squadron's last fighter combat report:

27 June 1944. This morning I went as Yellow leader on a long armed recce and had bags of fun. It all started north of Le Mans when my section straggled, and of course just then we were bounced by 190s! I turned on hearing 'Spud' report them, and saw three up-sun. Not a Tiffy to be seen. I turned into the Huns and they came head-on. After a while (I still had one tank on), two of them got on my tail and a third was in front. I had to break again and after dicing like this for what seemed ages, thought discretion was the better part of valour and beat it down to the deck, there to proceed flat out for about ten miles.

Next day 609 suffered its third casualty for June when Flying Officer C. A. Rowland was missing. A few days later the crash was found, and his body was buried in France.

On 14th June, 1944, aircraft of the West Riding Squadron had landed in France for the first time since 13th June, 1940, when it

*Although the author states 232 confirmed aerial kills, only 227 can be positively identified today—Ed.

escorted Winston Churchill on his final mission to the French government at Tours, four days before it sought an armistice. Now the landing ground was an airstrip bulldozed from a piece of Norman farmland. It was only to refuel, but the sound of near-by enemy gunfire and the transport columns grinding incessantly through the harvest were a presage of life to come. It is recorded that 'Spud' Holmes picked a bunch of continental wild flowers to bring back to Manu Geerts at Thorney Island, just to show him that Belgium itself could not now be far off. New Zealander Price brought a German helmet, and Canadian Buchanan a German diary – promptly confiscated by Intelligence. Subsequent spoils were wine, Calvados and Camembert, consumed with gusto while other members of 123 Airfield looked on enviously.

Finally on 1st July, after ten days 'concentrating' at Hurn airfield near Bournemouth, the 'advanced element' of 609 Squadron moved by Dakota to France, expecting the pilots and Typhoons to follow immediately. The advanced element included the Adjutant (Pilot-Officer S. E. Hills), his Orderly Room, five spare pilots, all pilots' kit – and, of course, the Goat.

Of all the Allied units crowding into what was currently the most thickly populated and uncomfortable strip of countryside in the world, only the West Riding Squadron can have considered it necessary to cram a goat as well. The question of leaving him behind seems never to have arisen, even though his most fervid sponsor, Johnny Wells – who considered that to embark on an operational mission without first saluting Group-Captain Billy was sheer stupid bravado – had a week earlier handed over 609 to its first Belgian C.O., Manu Geerts, D.F.C. Recently the well-known American journalist, Quentin Reynolds, had appeared in order to write yet another article about the Squadron :

He was seated comfortably in the Dispersal hut, gathering information and blissfully unaware of the drama being prepared. Outside, some of the pilots were engaged in working up the Goat into a state of fury. When deemed sufficiently wild he was pushed into the hut, where he proceeded to charge at everything in sight – including the illustrious journalist, who had to take swift evasive action through the other door. I came on the scene as he was sprinting round the perimeter track with Billy just a yard behind, head bowed for the kill.

Fortunately no serious damage was done, but I don't know whether the article was ever completed.

So writes Doc Bell, who incidentally had stopped the Goat's P.A. from painting his rank on his horns (as well as his collar), on finding that the aircraft blue dope used for the purpose was having a toxic effect. And now while Billy in a slit trench in Normandy, faced the enemy with courage beyond the call of duty, for a whole week his pilots slept comfortably in the permanent Mess at Hurn, went swimming, drinking and to the cinema in Bournemouth, and did no ops. at all – 'because,' wrote Roberts, 'the shelling of B.10 by the Hun across the canal was rather consistent and alarmingly accurate.'

B.10 airfield, at Plumetôt, was four miles north of Caen, still in enemy hands, and at first the pilots merely slept there and operated from B.5. 'We've got our domestic site in an orchard just off the landing strip, and sleep in holes in the ground,' continued Roberts, and in a book* which I had the pleasure of translating. 'Cheval' Lallemant, at this time a flight-commander in 198, adds:

In front of us were the German guns; behind us, just positioned, our own heavy batteries, with us 'pig in the middle'. It even became almost a recreation to judge which shell belonged to whom, and after a few days we learnt the drill. If the shell came from our own guns, we heard first a bang and then a whistle; if it was German we heard first a whistle and then a bang. But the ones that landed amongst our trenches were all German . . . the enemy could tell just where we were based by the clouds of dust raised by the Typhoons. When new pilots arrived we laughed at them . . . they threw themselves to the ground at *every* bang and whistle, whereas when we recognised an English one we remained standing, teasing the new arrival sadistically each time he bit the dust.

Dust, or rather sand, at first menaced the Typhoons almost as much as enemy *flak*. 'Blown by the propellers into the great air-scoop, it scoured the cylinder walls of the engines like emery powder.' Eventually Tom Yates, the engineer officer of 123 air-field using 'Cheval' as a 'test pilot' for repeated experiments, de-

* *Rendezvous with Fate*, by Colonel R. A. Lallemant, D.F.C. Macdonald, 1964.

vised an automatically operated 'gate' that effectually deflected
the sand. Whether Yates' invention was circulated to other Typhoon wings, or whether each had to devise something independently, I know not. It should, however, be placed on record
that in the field of serviceability no R.A.F. flying unit can have
owed more to one officer than 609 did to Tom Yates. As E.O. he
had joined it first at Biggin Hill in 1941, and left it I believe at
Digby. A man of charm mixed, it seems, with something like
genius, he was still with the Wing on the day 609 was disbanded
after the war. Meanwhile Roberts was writing :

13 July. The food at B.10 is good. Till 123 get over here we're
attached to Canadian 129 Wing . . . free cigarettes and chocolate,
and the odd pilot flies back to England for bread now and then.

15 July. Cloud yesterday too low for us to get an attack in, so we
sat around on the deck. Fun in the afternoon when showers of 109s
came over and were engaged by our ack-ack and Spitfires. One was
hit just above our tents and crashed a short distance away – I was
hopping up and down with excitement !

18 July. Last night and this morning, the biggest artillery barrage
of all time – probably a prelude to the battle which is to take the
the Army south of Caen. It was helped along by the odd 8,000
tons ! ! ! dropped by Lancs and Libs at dawn – what a sight ! . . . Just
afterwards we broke our lull of a couple of days by pranging a gun
position. Tomorrow we join 123 Airfield at B.7 near Bayeux.

The daylight bombing of Caen has been described as 'the
heaviest and most concentrated air attack in support of ground
forces ever attempted'. It destroyed much of the city, many Germans and many French, and pilots who visited it a little later
were appalled at the grisly sights. But though the Army at last
captured what was left, several more such attacks were needed
before it got much further. Meanwhile the enemy advanced to
within a mile of Plumetôt, and fearing encirclement the two
squadrons hurriedly evacuated B.10 and proceeded north-west
to B.7 at Crépigny near Bayeux, the Goat causing many a passer-
by to start as he glared at them from the back of his lorry.

No. 123 Airfield had at last arrived by sea, and would usually
keep up with the Wing for the rest of the war. It was commanded
by a tall, curly-headed New Zealander, Group-Captain Desmond

Scott, whom I had once known as C.O. of 3 Squadron, while in charge of flying was Wing-Commander Walter Dring. Within the bridgehead, which till the break-out measured about fifty miles wide and eight miles deep, some thirty British and fifty American landing strips had been carved out by the special machines of the Airfield Construction Wings. But B.7 was to remain the home of 609 till long after the break-out – right up till 3rd September, in fact. When I paid my one brief visit on 22nd August, some pilots were playing football, with Charles de Moulin, at this moment a member of 164 Squadron, as goalkeeper. Months before I had sold him for £30 my *sans*-everything car, which had reposed in a derelict Manston shed since 1942, but had later written to say I wanted the St. Christopher off the dashboard. It seems he had carried this about ever since, for as I greeted him from behind the goal-posts, he reached in the pocket of his shorts and produced it then and there! (After the war, being a smooth operator, he resold the car for £200).

Meanwhile, besides attacks on communications and armed recces, in the course of which everything beyond the 'bombline' was a legitimate target, the Typhoons gave closer and closer support to the Army to eliminate the many obstacles – gun positions, strongpoints, tank and troop concentrations – that held up its advance. Instead of missions lasting up to two hours from a base in England, they now owing to the proximity of the targets often lasted only a few minutes. On 24th July eight Typhoons, led by the C.O., Manu Geerts, completely destroyed an enemy H.Q. which the Army had indicated by firing red smoke. Next day was the busiest since the Squadron landed in Normandy, with five missions against gun positions. During one, it was recorded, 'everyone was hit by *flak*'; during another, Australian N. L. Merrett had the distinction of destroying a mortar position single-handed, having been the only pilot to see the marker signal.

Marking the target was extremely necessary, not only to protect our own forces from 'friendly' air attack (to indicate their own positions they used *yellow* smoke), but because the Germans were masters of camouflage. 'Cheval' describes two tanks which he and his section destroyed, after locating them with the utmost difficulty because they were buried in the ground up to their turrets, with green foliage on top :

Later, when we visited the spot on foot, we found zig-zag trenches leading to an underground mess, in which the crew must have rested under fortress-like protection. There were mattresses, petrol lamps, even a gramophone. There were even three small individual chambers, in the interest of privacy and, no doubt, rank.

With the opposing sides sometimes within 150 yards of each other, precision was essential. Even red smoke signals were not infallible, for the enemy would fire them too, hoping to induce the Typhoons to attack their own side. And though there were Army liaison officers at every level from H.Q. 2nd T.A.F. down to Wing, where they played a prominent part in briefing pilots for each mission, the situation was sometimes so fluid as to be already out of date by the time the aircraft reached the spot. The answer was V.C.P. – 'Visual Control Point' – a system inherited from 1st T.A.F. in Italy. After nearly five years of war, it was perhaps a crowning example of how the two services, when put to it, could really co-operate. In essence it meant that an experienced R.A.F. fighter controller travelled about in the front line, sharing a tank or armoured contact car with the local Army unit commander, and equipped with a V.H.F. radio set attuned to the R.A.F. unit. The latter, either at cockpit readiness on the ground or waiting as an airborne 'Cab Rank', possessed the same large-scale gridded maps of the sector, and had only to be given the required grid co-ordinates to pin-point a target fifty yards square and be down on it in a flash.

For very close air support the system became standard, and under it 609 operated for the first time on 27th July, during the Allied break-out. But for the pilots, if anything, it intensified the risks, and on this day the Squadron lost two. Before July was out it would lose two more – making, with one lost on the 11th, five for the month : Flight-Sergeant L. E. Bliss, Pilot-Officer J. D. Buchanan of Canada, Flight-Sergeant P. M. Price of New Zealand, Flight-Sergeant R. Ashworth and Flight-Sergeant R. K. Adam.

The last of them was lost on 31st July. On the second mission that day Roberts led seven Typhoons of 609, supported by eight of 164, against a reported troop concentration in a wood south of Caumont. 609 fired fifty-six rockets into the southern edge of this, but seeing no results, made no claims. They were consequently pleased next day to receive the following message from the Army:

Captured P.O.W. report that elements of 21st Panzer Div. were very severely handled by R.P. Typhoons as they were massing for an attack. As a result the attack was never put in. Congratulations 609 and 164.

The day before Roberts had noted in his diary his award of the D.F.C., and added: 'I thank God that he has spared me this long.' And 'Cheval' Lallemant was to write in his book:

We veterans believed ourselves immortal, believed the danger receded in proportion to the number of missions. The greatest risk was in the first week. If a pilot lived through that, he had a chance . . . Training flights for new pilots were a thing of the past; their very first took them straight into battle . . . and they were swatted down like flies.

In the end both Roberts and Lallemant were 'swatted down', though both survived – one badly burnt, the other a P.O.W. Before the war was over there would be no less than four C.O.s of 609 behind barbed wire. Meanwhile the present one, Manu Geerts – the oldest the Squadron ever had, as well as one of its finest pilots – seemed indestructible. The palm for indestructability must however have belonged to his fellow-countryman, a little Belgian pilot-of-fortune, now in command of 'B' flight, André Blanco, who had joined 609 as a sergeant pilot seemingly a hundred years ago at Digby in January 1942, and who went on flying for the Squadron till the last day of August 1944. Enemy aircraft and enemy *flak* had hit him again and again without apparently causing the slightest emotional reaction. According to the M.O. it was all achieved by tea. He writes:

Tea being something of a luxury, he had sought out the brewing centres. Starting at the Airmen's Mess at some unearthly hour in the morning, he would then take a large mug-full with the patients at Sick Quarters, and would so proceed until interrupted by the need to take off on some history-making mission. Being thus steeped in caffeine, with very little sleep, he was to me a subject of considerable concern, but the only reply I got was, 'What does eet matter, Doc?' We will still ween the war!' He was also intensely interested in the day-to-day movements of armies, and for minutes on end would stare at the map in the Intelligence Room, steaming tea in one hand, cigarette in the other.

When he finally went on rest, he had the job of flying despatches by Spitfire to S.H.A.E.F. H.Q. in Paris – where, it is said, Allied generals were startled to find a junior Belgian officer, hands similarly occupied, studying the most top-secret map of all. Years after the war I was being entertained in a Brussels bar by another former Belgian of 609, 'Duke' du Monceau, when Blanco happened to enter. When he addressed 'Duke' as 'Sir' – in English – I felt I was back in 609 Dispersal and time was meaningless.

On 7th August, I believe for the first time in history, a military operation was defeated by the tactical air force of the other side. The American ground forces had broken through, and now the Germans launched a counter-attack by four armoured divisions in the area of Mortain, with the aim of breaking back to the coast at Avranches and annihilating all the Allied forces thus cut off. Had it succeeded, it would have been serious indeed. While American Thunderbolts and Mustangs attacked enemy communications and transport behind the German front, the rocket-firing Typhoons went for the armour. Wrote General Speidel, Chief of Staff to Field-Marshal von Kluge, after the war:

The armoured operation was completely wrecked exclusively by the Allied Air Forces supported by a highly trained ground wireless organization.

Another chief of staff reported at the time: 'The activity of the fighter-bombers is said to have been well-nigh unendurable.' As for the Luftwaffe, Field-Marshal Sperrle – still head of the once mighty *Luftflotte 3* which 609 had fought from Middle Wallop and Warmwell in 1940 – said he could not even get his 110 fighters into the area. But four aircraft of 609 were prevented from attacking: on take-off Blanco burst a tyre, crashed and blocked the runway.

For the Germans it was the beginning of the end in Normandy, and indeed in France. For on this same day Canadian, British and

Polish forces started their hotly contested push southwards from Caen that was to end at Falaise. Then, as the Americans (and Leclerc's French Armoured Division) advanced east, their spearhead suddenly turned north towards Argentan, while the German commanders, instead of re-grouping their forces to meet the danger, were constantly harassed by directives from Hitler to *attack*. The end-result was the famous 'Falaise pocket', enclosing the whole of the German Seventh Army and over half of the Fifth Panzer Army, and similar to the big encirclements in Russia. Only on 13th August did Hitler give permission for the German forces to retreat behind the Seine. Then they lost no time in getting going.

It actually seems that Manu Geerts, at the head of eight Typhoons on an armed reconnaissance of the Falaise-Vimoutiers-Argentan area, was the very first man in the air to spot them. In the morning beneath mist and thick cloud the enemy may have felt secure. But finding a gap in the clouds and plunging down through it with his Squadron, Manu found tanks, guns, troop-carriers and other vehicles crawling head to tail. Four tanks at once became 'flamers', and the fire spread. There was such a plethora of targets that Manu ordered strict economy in the use of ammunition. About this remarkable pilot's own performance, his friend and fellow-Belgian 'Cheval' Lallemant has added:

A column of military buses, hidden under trees in a sunken road, caught his attention ... He steered straight towards them, lined himself up with the road, enfiladed them with his guns and set them on fire. As he flashed over them, he spotted a great horde of fifty-gallon fuel canisters piled up in three tiers – a petrol dump concealed by foliage. With a maximum-rate turn he managed to keen them in view, then fired his incendiaries at point-blank range. The whole dump – the life-blood of the tanks, the very *sine qua non* of the enemy's forces – went up in flames and dense black smoke.

The mission was recorded as a 'Wizard Prang', perhaps the best that 609 as a rocket-firing squadron had yet achieved. And the squadrons that followed had no difficulty in finding the target, for the column of smoke, rising to 4,000 feet, could be seen from 609's base, forty miles distant. It was Manu Geerts' last mission as C.O. of 609. Now thirty-seven, he next day handed over command to the lad he had taught to fly in pre-war Belgium – 'Cheval'.

Ever since then they had been almost like father and son. They still are.

By 16th August there was such a fluid ground battle going on inside the 'Falaise pocket', together with efforts to seal the ever-narrowing escape gap, that further air attacks inside the pocket were suspended as too dangerous for the Allied forces, and the 'bombline' was shifted east to Vimoutiers. Through this place practically all the enemy forces outside the pocket had to pass, and in military history few localities can have known such carnage as it did. In his efforts to get away the enemy did everything to avert attack from the air. On the 16th the new C.O. was surprised to find half-a-dozen 'haystacks' moving in an orchard – with lorries underneath them. On the 17th he returned to base and reported a whole column of 'ambulances' each marked with a large Red Cross. It so happened that the C.-in-C. of the Allied Expeditionary Force, Air Chief Marshal Leigh-Mallory, was present, and he was asked a bit roughly why he had not attacked them. Grimly he and his men went off again, and at the first attack the road was blocked, and the 'wounded' jumped out and sprinted off across the fields. Short of petrol, the Germans had requisitioned horses. Finding a score of ammunition wagons each pulled by four of them, and not wishing to kill his name-sakes, 'Cheval' instead caused them to stampede across-country.

On the 17th Field-Marshal von Kluge was replaced as C.-in-C. West by Field-Marshal Model. While the former committed suicide on his way back to Germany, the latter transmitted to Berlin his 'immediate requirements'. The first of these was 'Restriction of enemy air superiority', on which 'the very difficult withdrawal from the neck of the pocket and the entire system of supply depend'. The only 'restriction' he seems to have got was the shooting down by Me 109s of four of 609's sister squadron, No. 183, over the Seine.

The width of the escape gap, between Trun and Chambois, had now been reduced to about six miles, and on the 18th the tactical air forces nearly closed it :

Shortly after midday reconnaissance showed large concentrations of vehicles to the south-west to Trun and in the Forêt de Gouffern.

As this was well inside the bombline special arrangements were speedily made with the armies and by mid-afternoon a large part of the Second Tactical Air Force, followed later by a proportion of the Ninth, had been turned on to these exceptional targets. For the rest of the day relays of Spitfires, Typhoons, Mustangs, Lightnings and Thunderbolts were striking at targets both inside and outside the bombline.*

On this day 2nd T.A.F. alone flew 1,471 sorties, claiming 1,100 vehicles and 90 tanks destroyed, with many more damaged. 609 flew four missions, each of eight aircraft, and on one alone claimed seven tanks and twelve lorries wiped out in a permissible rectangle of attack two kilometres square. On the 20th a counter-attack by II SS Panzer Corps and bad weather in the morning permitted more of the encircled German forces to escape than would otherwise have been the case, and there was a tough ground battle round Vimoutiers, involving the Polish Armoured Division. To quote from the official history of the R.A.F. :

The *Panzers*, with a local superiority in numbers, were pressing hard when Wing Commander Dring, at the head of thirty-two aircraft from Nos. 164, 183, 198 and 609 Squadrons, arrived. The German armour, in number about a hundred tanks and armoured vehicles, was debouching from a wood. Dring caught them as they emerged and very few escaped.

'Cheval', who was leading 609, continues :

At briefing each squadron was given just five minutes to accomplish its attack, each leader on withdrawal authorizing the next to go in. Approaching Vimoutiers we saw the sides of the road crowded over five or six miles with vehicles, concealed as much as possible beneath the foliage ... While Wing-Commander Dring went down with 164, the other squadrons twirled around the sky at 10,000 feet as spectators and judges. When 198 Squadron took over the attack, 164 had already left clouds of dust and smoke. The allotted five minutes passed, and it was 609's turn. Three tanks were already burning, but I led Red section down parallel with the road in echelon, hoping to see others, for nothing was more annoying than to use up all one's rockets on soft-skinned targets, and then to be left with only 20mm cannon to deal with the 'crustaceans'. The first swoop was thus a

* From *Victory in the West*, by Major L. F, Ellis, H.M.S.O. 1962.

reconnaissance. On our next I hit a Tiger-Royal at the very moment my No. 3, the New Zealander, Warrant-Officer Harkness, succeeded in scoring a 'double' on two others, with just one pair of rockets – a feat almost unique . . . Further attacks followed, and I had never seen my Squadron so actively employed. . . . I let off my third pair of rockets at a tank in a very difficult position – on a slope under the shade of some tall poplars. I missed and tried the last pair. They fell on the road, a bit short, leaving the tank smoking slightly but not burning. Each attack was made from right above our own troops who, alarmed, sent up orange smoke to show their identity. I looked at my watch : just thirty seconds left before I was due to hand over to the impatient Mulliner and 183 Squadron. As a last resort, I decided to try my cannon. Calling to Mulliner, 'It's yours, chum,' as I approached, I emptied my magazines, then pulled sharply on the stick to avoid the poplars. Passing overhead, I saw flames licking the turret and black smoke joining the great cloud already rising skywards . . . The road from Trun to Vimoutiers was on fire. At debriefing it was established that 609 had destroyed ten tanks.

On the 21st the gap was finally closed in strength. As peace came at last to the Falaise sector, tens of thousands of prisoners were taken, and 609's war diary recorded, 'This is a day of rest.' Eric Roberts flew a war correspondent from the *Sunday Pictorial* over the area in an Auster to witness the destruction, though the stench of death, particularly of horses, is said to have risen to 1,000 feet. 'Cheval' and Manu went on a tour by jeep, pausing first at the petrol dump the latter had blown up :

It was just a mass of carbon. The flaming petrol had burnt up the very trees that hid them, as well as a couple of tanks in the act of refuelling. In the panic, stores of victuals had been abandoned. Loaves of bread and smoked hams still lay strewn about. Within a radius of a few hundred yards we counted twenty-two derelict tanks, four destroyed by rockets, the rest scuttled. Without petrol for them, the Germans had blown the barrels into opening flowers.

They found the wreck of a Typhoon of 198 Squadron, missing since May and belonging to that squadron's one-time C.O., Mike Bryan, who had taken it with him on promotion; near by was a wooden cross, attached to it a Wing-Commander epaulet :

We were surprised at the number of dead horses. Some, wounded, were still standing, but held by their harness were unable to feed.

Manu released them. . . . We discovered new saddles and harness apparently brought from Russia. We found an equipment store – already looted – bulging with artificial-silk underwear, but were not even tempted to take a souvenir. The storekeeper, so swollen in death that his uniform seemed to have grown too small, appeared to stare sadly at his left hand, from which two fingers were missing – cut off, no doubt, by someone who coveted his rings.

In the triumph, as well as the destruction, the West Riding Squadron had taken a prominent share. During the month of August it flew 461 sorties and 410 operational hours, claiming a minimum of forty-two tanks and eighty-eight transport vehicles destroyed. But it also lost another five pilots: Pilot-Officer R. D. Grant, Warrant-Officer F. L. Taylor, Flight-Lieutenant M. L. Carrick, Warrant-Officer J. K. Stellin (N.Z.) and Flight-Lieutenant R. J. H. Roelandt (Belgium). Three of them had only joined the Squadron during the month, and one of them perished on his second flight. But Roelandt was the same 'Balbo' who had joined with 'Mony' van Lierde way back in December 1941, and was 'too old' to learn aircraft recognition. On that tour of duty he had stayed with 609 for over a year, but this time was killed after thirteen days. On the same mission his fellow-countryman Paulo Cooreman, a veteran from Manston, was also hit but just got back – his second narrow escape of the month. On the first occasion he had baled out, deliberately at the last moment, and landed in a desert of bomb craters under enemy fire. Crawling to a wood, he spent the night, and next morning was nearly shot by the advancing Canadians – one of whom however took him back to base on the back of a motor-bike long after his comrades had given him up for dead. It was Paulo who collected me from Group H.Q. in a 'liberated' military Volkswagen on my visit on 22nd August. Happily he survived the war.

*

The second battle of France had ended, this time victoriously. In the words of the R.A.F. historians:

The Second Tactical Air Force had by its presence over the battlefield made victory certain and in the later stages cheap . . . it was ubiquitous and invincible.

Now, as part of the short- and long-range airborne artillery of the British Second Army, and still more of the Canadian First Army, the four squadrons of No. 123 Wing would assist the advance through Belgium into Holland and North Germany. Whether the strike formation comprised four or eight aircraft – and even four soon represented a potential broadside of nearly fifty rockets, of which a single one could destroy a tank – each was a skilled team which had brought the finding and hitting of targets to a fine art.

All rockets concentrated in target area ... H.Q. building left on fire ... Army sent us a 'strawberry' on day's work ... such phrases appear time after time in 609 Squadron's war diary. But it was always as a team; apart from the formation leaders few individual pilots stood far above (or below) their fellows in performance. Thus to discriminate by conferring individual awards would have been unfair, and – again apart from the leaders, most of whom had been decorated for earlier exploits – it seems that between D-Day and VE-Day only one pilot of 609 wore a medal ribbon : the Australian Norman Merrett, whose D.F.C. was announced before the Squadron left Normandy. Three others were awarded after the war.

In the eight months of war that still lay ahead, each type of operation would be repeated time and again. Thus whatever the courage and skill of the participants, and the triumphs and tragedies that continued to come their way, to do more than summarize their battle role would make wearisome reading. Moreover, as the great military colossus swept on to its appointed victory, the story of 609 becomes less that of an individual squadron, and more that of 123 Wing, 84 Group or Second T.A.F. itself. From the survivors of those who joined the Squadron after D-Day I have no memoirs, simply because they have been lost touch with. For all these reasons the rest of the story must be condensed.

On 3rd September, the day 609 and its sister squadrons finally quit their Normandy airfield near Bayeux, the Welsh Guards were already being wildly cheered as they drove through the thronged streets of liberated Brussels. After the crossing of the Seine the advance had been so rapid that conditioning and supplying airfields for the supporting air contingent became a major problem, and in an effort to keep in range of the enemy, No. 123 Airfield (if not the Wing) moved three times within a week – first to Moran-ville (B.23), then to Baromesnil (B.35 near Le Tréport), and finally to Merville (B.53) – till recently a Luftwaffe static airfield, with concrete runways, situated near Armentières, west of Lille. While these moves were taking place, so 609's Adjutant recorded with just a trace of envy, 'the Squadron was taking its ease at Manston and having parties'. Between D-Day and VE-Day it was its only return to England, and from Manston it even carried out an old-style 'Ranger' before returning to continental tented life. The Adjutant's reaction to the final location was mixed :

We have left the decent country for the flat industrial area of France [but] life is more civilized and we are only a few minutes from Merville with real shops and places. We visit Lille and Béthune for nights out, or Ypres in Belgium.

And Roberts adds about Lille, where he went on a 'swan' with his old friend Johnny Wells, 'The shops are well stocked, but prices very high. Still, the French seem to have made plenty of paper money from the Hun.'

At Merville the first mixed party was held since D-Day, seem-ingly by command of Group-Captain Desmond Scott, and on Doc Bell, 609's M.O., it seems to have made an indelible impression :

Some of the Belgians were instructed to collect champagne – several three-tonners full of it – and I was detailed to invite as many nurses as possible. Unfortunately the nearest R.A.F. hospital was fifty miles away, and though the nearer R.A.M.C. units had some nurses, the social calendar of these turned out to be fully booked. As zero hour approached we were thus forlornly gathered together with a Mess stocked with champagne and chicken to feed hundreds. Scotty admitted that at the last moment he had sent some Belgians off in trucks to see if they could interest 'other female company', but if they didn't arrive by 20.00 hours the party would be the usual stag affair. I recall him looking at his watch before giving the signal to break out the champagne – when at that moment the Mess doors opened and into the foyer spilled an assortment of women. There was a wide, winding staircase, on which they arranged themselves in echelon, the better to display their charms to the gaping pilots. It was only too evident from what establishments in Lille they had been invited, and my heart sank when I thought of all my anti-V.D. propaganda being put to the test in this way. To everyone's amazement, however, a hilarious type of Mess night, without debauchery, ensued. Once again the Belgians had saved the day.

Indeed, after years of trying to make Belgian colleagues feel at home in England, the boot was firmly on the other foot. Now, when the Belgians went on leave, they skipped across the currently non-existent border to their own homes, sometimes taking their British or Commonwealth friends with them. 'The transformation of a familiar figure in scruffy battledress into the heir apparent of a vast business was staggering,' recalls Doc Bell. Once, according to 609's diary, the whole Wing practically stood to attention when a magnificent Bentley drew up at the Mess with a Belgian pennant floating from the bonnet. Surely, the King of the Belgians himself! No, it was just Flight-Lieutenant Cooreman returning from home with a bit of property. But, sad to say, J. Vandaele was shot down only a few days after saluting his wife and family from the air – possibly the only time he saw them since joining the R.A.F. One might think that, with their own country liberated, the Belgian contingent would have no more interest in the war. In fact, during September, it rose in numbers from seven to fourteen. And glad though they were, after so many years, to see their families and homes again, they were also sometimes over-lionized :

They did not want to hear the banal truth, but an epic . . . They required not a human being, but an archangel. I was the hero of a romance, master of the sky, impervious to cowardice. Little did they care about the vile and pitiful trembling we had to fight even more than the enemy . . . In the end, surfeited with adoration, I longed to return to Merville. There, back at lunch in the mess-tent, I felt I was where I belonged. I rejoiced to see my pilots again, and return to the world of the present. It was our normal, accustomed community, and as yet we wanted nothing to break it.

So wrote the commanding officer of 609, 'Cheval' Lallemant, and when, shortly afterwards, he led his squadron low over his native village, it was for him, too, very nearly the last time he saw it. On 14th September he was hit by *flak* which set fire to his aircraft and, jamming his cockpit canopy, prevented him from baling out. Somehow he force-landed at base, and with the strength of desperation forced his way out of the blazing pyre just in time. But it was the one day he had failed to find his gloves, and his hands immediately became useless pieces of burnt flesh, inexorably closing. Yet the skill of war-time surgeons mended them, and before the war was over he returned to flying. As C.O. he had lasted just a month.

His arrival in hospital in England almost coincided with the departure from that country of the ill-fated airborne expedition to Arnhem, which Second T.A.F. might have assisted so much more than it did. Writes 'Johnnie' Johnson in his book :

Both planning and control were exercized from a combined head-quarters in England, and little attention appears to have been given to the requirements for close support from our fighter-bombers. During the actual drop on 17th September, and on all the seven subsequent reinforcement and re-supply operations, we of 2nd T.A.F. were banned from the Arnhem area because the planners feared a clash between British and American fighters, despite the fact that we had been fighting alongside each other for almost two years !

So the Arnhem bridgehead was lost, and the crossing of the Rhine and the invasion of Germany had to wait. Meanwhile, what the Twenty-First Army Group needed was a port. On the day Brussels was liberated, all ports from St. Nazaire to Antwerp were still held by German garrisons, ordered to deny their use to the Allies by holding out. By the end of September, however, Le Havre, Boulogne and finally Calais (where 609 also flew one mission) had successively surrendered after heavy daylight atten-tion from Bomber Command. But the finest and for future operations most convenient port of all, Antwerp, had – thanks to the speed of the advance and the action of the Belgian resistance movement – fallen into British hands intact, one day after Brussels itself. Being situated, however, deep inland, with the enemy in possession of both sides of the Scheldt approaches, it clearly could not be used till these were cleared. Thus, while also flying many armed reconnaissance missions as far north as Rotterdam and The Hague directed against the barge traffic on which the enemy had more and more to depend for his supplies, the more immediate duty of 123 Wing during most of October was providing close support to the Canadians hammering the enemy from the Bres-

kens and lesser 'pockets' on the Scheldt's south bank. An idea of
the conditions under which this enterprise was mounted can best
be given by another quote from *Royal Air Force 1939–1945*,
Vol. 3 :

The Canadian Army was joined in fierce and aqueous fray in and
about the town of Breskens, its stout-hearted infantry being sometimes up to their waists in water. Despite weather classified by the
meteorological experts as indifferent or bad, they were afforded the
fullest possible air support . . . The flooded and waterlogged nature
of the ground made attacks by any arm other than infantry, supported by the air force, out of the question. Here a new technique,
which gave excellent results, was tried for the first time. A smoke
screen was laid by the guns, immediately in front of the assaulting
troops. As soon as it was formed, aircraft of the Second Tactical Air
Force began to operate on the enemy's side of the screen, bombing
gun-pits and diving on slit trenches until the very last moment when,
through the murk and smoke, loomed purposeful figures with fixed,
determined bayonets.

On 7th October the West Riding Squadron flew no less than
seven missions of this nature; but 'Friday the 13th was a record
day for the number of sorties flown by the Airfield and our share
was eight attacks on Cab Rank work'. They were all under 'V.C.P.'
control, and the targets were gun positions, dykes and strongpoints
in buildings. Next day :

A message was received saying that the Army were most satisfied
with the day's work and congratulated the Wing on its great effort.
The ground crews were not forgotten. Their share was an important
as the pilots' . . . In the evening some twenty-two of us met in the town
for the weekly supper. We had with us our old C.O., Squadron-Leader
J. C. Wells, D.F.C. and Bar, and our old friend Flight-Lieutenant
Roberts, D.F.C. The business of the evening was to consider a proposal for the Squadron to present to the Town of Brussels a uniform
for 'Manikin Piss'. If the Mayor will accept, Manikin will become a
Pilot-Officer of the R.A.F.

Then came Walcheren, the island fortress guarding the mouth
of the Scheldt and the final impediment to the use of Antwerp.
With most of it below sea-level, and the sea kept out only by a
rim of dunes, the first step was for Bomber Command to breach

the dyke near Westkapelle, flood the enemy field batteries and render movement difficult. After that the batteries became targets for Second T.A.F., which between 10th October and 8th November fired no less than 11,637 rockets against the island, not to mention bombs. The vital amphibious assault was begun on 1st November by Royal Marine Commandoes, in weather that made air support extremely doubtful. Yet it came. The official history records :

Rocket-firing Typhoons were airborne and close to the island asking for orders from the headquarters ship ten minutes before 'H Hour', though visibility at their bases was not more than 1,000 yards and the cloud base was 500 feet.

According to Coningham's S.A.S.O. their support would have been impossible but for the zero or minus altitude of the target island. But without this support a sea-borne landing in the face of heavily protected gun emplacements and control points might also have been impossible. An attack on one such headquarters pill-box, mounted on the wall above the beach, by four aircraft of 609 won special praise from the ground troops just 200 yards distant, to whom it had been causing 'considerable trouble', and immediately afterwards they captured the position. This little team comprised Flight-Lieutenant G. E. Hardy, D.F.C. (a Canadian recently acquired from a sister squadron), Flight-Sergeant E. L. Jacquemin (Belgian), and Warrant-Officers A. H. Billam and P. W. Lough. The O.C. 123 Wing received the following message from the A.O.C. :

The action of your Wing during the critical early stages of the landing contributed to the major success of the operation. All pilots are to be congratulated upon their remarkable skill in operating in appalling weather conditions and their very substantial contribution to the fulfillment of a hazardous operation.

After that 609 seemed suddenly to go back in time and space. Though on 30th October it had moved to Ursel (B.67, between Ghent and Bruges), from 7th till 11th November it was operating over Dunkirk, the last of the Channel ports to hold out. After four and a half years the Squadron letters 'PR' appeared again above that fateful place. This time the approach was from the landward, and instead of the departing B.E.F. it was the assaulting Czechs, of them one a future brother-in-law of the author, whom the Squadron had come to help. First target was a military headquarters: it was razed to the ground with rockets, then strafed with cannon, and the Czechs sent their congratulations. The next eight missions, each by eight aircraft, were against gun sites, including 88mm. The final target, for twelve aircraft, was the garrison's ration store in the centre of the town. The Squadron was led by its C.O., T. Y. ('Bob') Wallace, a tall and wiry South African, once of No. 1 Squadron with whom he won a D.F.M., and who in September had been raised from Flight- to Squadron command in succession to 'Cheval'. The war diary records:

Wally took the Squadron over the target at about 3,000 feet, but cloud was low and he did not attack and went round again. This time a lot of *flak* came up and Wally was hit. He made the attack and pulled out but at about 3,000 feet his starboard wing was seen to drop, and the aircraft out of control crashed and burst into flames on impact. The target was destroyed.

The Australian, Norman Merrett, who was flying No. 2, described the circumstances as 'suicidal', and it is said that after the war Wallace's mother visited the spot where her son was supposed to have crashed into the shore. On that very day the tail fin of a Typhoon became visible through the sands, and digging revealed that this was indeed Wally's plane, with the ill-fated South African still in his harness. Dunkirk had claimed yet another pilot of 609. The others from 1940 still rest on the bed of the ocean.

During the first part of November the activity of 123 Wing had been as intense, despite the shorter days, as during the hectic period of the Falaise pocket. Now, as the Army advanced to the line of the Maas, the squadrons continued to attack the enemy wherever he was found, even though the weather grew steadily worse and the number of sorties less. Again and again the close-support target was a farm house or even church, where the enemy was known to have set up a headquarters, strongpoint or observation post. Regrettable though the destruction of churches was, it is notable that when the fighting moved into Germany, the enemy did not hesitate to militarize his own. Second T.A.F., with its headquarters in Brussels across the road from that of the British Twenty-First Army Group, had become even more closely integrated with the ground forces – though if its members now wore khaki battledress instead of blue, the reason was less imitation than a desire not to be mistaken for the enemy! H.Q. Allied Expeditionary Air Forces, having served its purpose, was now disbanded and its chief, Air Chief Marshal Sir Trafford Leigh-Mallory, posted to command Allied Air Forces in the Far East, under Mountbatten. He set out, but never arrived. On 14th November this high officer, who since early 1941 had been successively the West Riding Squadron's A.O.C. and C.-in-C., as well as friend, lost his life when his aircraft crashed in the Alps.

On that same day Charles de Moulin, D.F.C., was promoted from a flight-commandership in 164 Squadron – itself now commanded by that indestructible Belgian, Mony Van Lierde – as the third Belgian C.O. of 609. 'Windmill Charlie', to use the English version of his name, must have been just a trifle embarrassed, on assuming this command, to find still manning the Squadron telephones the same Auxiliary ops. clerks, Corporals Barker and Hinchcliffe, who in 1941 had ordered him, as a tassel-capped Belgian AC2 apprentice, to sweep out the Dispersal hut. His term of command was to be the shortest ever – just three weeks. On 5th December, while leading 609 in bad weather to attack oil storage plants over the frontiers in Germany, he was hit by *flak* north-west of Arnhem, and went down trailing black smoke. Happily 609 had a Spitfire escort on this occasion, whose leader saw him do a final climb, jettison his rockets and hood, and bale out to become another prisoner-of-war. It was left to Pilot-Officer R. D. Harkness of New Zealand to reform the bemused Squadron, which unwittingly had followed its leader down.

At last it was the turn of Eric Roberts, D.F.C., to be given command of 609 – something he had hoped for for the last four months, and now (as he confided to his diary) 'an honour I hope to uphold to the very best of my ability. It's still a good squadron whatever anyone says and – we'll show 'em!' On 4th September he had been injured in a road accident, and on returning to flying some six weeks later was appointed to 183 Squadron, when he wrote: 'To get back in the air in a Typhoon was a joy almost in-

describable, and to fire the guns at the Hun again was like heaven.'
In three months he would be twenty-three.

Meanwhile, on 26th November, the Wing had moved up to
within twelve miles of the enemy occupying the other side of the
Maas, to Gilze-Rijen, west of Tilburg. The instruction for the
move had reached Flying-Officer Hills, Adjutant of 609, while
his pilots were attacking a Dutch 'Quisling' H.Q. at Otterloo, and
they were ordered to land at the new base afterwards. Wrote Hills
a trifle testily :

It meant that all pilots' kit had to be packed, and in the usual
manner of pilots, it was in a terrible state. As a result the kit lorry
did not set off till 16.00 hours. The dog Blitz and the Goat were left
behind.

Only temporarily, of course. Gilze, which had suffered the loss
of so many Dornier 217s at the hands of the long-ranging Typhoons of 609 and 198 eleven months earlier, had been built by
the Luftwaffe as a permanent base, resembling the peace-time
bases of the R.A.F. Even hot showers were obtainable in the Mess,
and the Adjutant commented : 'Everyone is going static-minded.'
But not *that* static : the new C.O.'s first 'show' was to lead a dozen
609 Squadron Typhoons against a midget submarine base on the
south side of Schouwen Island, and a few days later he wrote :
'The high-ups cannot give us enough praise for the success of our
prang on the Human Torpedoes. Evidently all the jobs were destroyed, as well as stores on the jetties.' But Norman Merrett, now
a flight commander in 164, and a pilot of 198 Squadron were lost
this day.

A week earlier 123 Wing had been visited once again by General
Eisenhower and staff. To quote 609's war diary :

He was shown round by Group-Captain Scott and examined the
rocket-firing Typhoons. Later he addressed the Squadron pilots and
gave them a 'strawberry'. A.O.C.s and other bigwigs were about the
place, and generally there was a 'flap on'.

By this time 'Ike' and 'Monty' had made plans for the last really
difficult operation of the war – the crossing of the Rhine – to take
place in mid-December. They were, however, forestalled when on
16th December Field-Marshal von Rundstedt, whom 609 had

failed to eliminate fourteen months earlier under Pat Thornton-Brown, launched his celebrated Ardennes offensive, designed to cut off the whole of the British and Canadian Armies, and quite a chunk of the Americans. Meteorologically the moment could not have been better chosen, for though on the 16th fourteen Me 109s twice flew over Gilze airfield without opposition, after that the air forces of both sides were virtually grounded for a week, and the Germans advanced at a rate of about twelve miles a day. No mail could be flown in, and the guards were doubled and trebled against enemy paratroops. On the 23rd Roberts wrote in his diary :

Two days ago the airfield gave a party for the local kids, who certainly hadn't seen that much food before, and about an hour ago the Hun sent us all a Xmas present in the shape of a V-2. I don't know how many were killed in the village, but there's hardly a pane of glass left in the end near the 'drome. The V-1s on their way to Antwerp have passed right over the 'drome in the last week, so he must have some new launching sites.

Then, early on New Year's Day, 1945, the Luftwaffe made its desperate attempt to destroy the aircraft of Second T.A.F., many of whose personnel were suffering from hangovers, on the ground. I had spent the night at the Brussels house of the de Selys family, and was watching a huge column of smoke rising from Evère airfield when Jean's sister announced breakfast. 'I've just seen a German aircraft,' she added. 'But presumably all these' – and she indicated a series of fighters that were whooshing past the window – 'are yours?' 'No,' I answered, 'I'm afraid they are all German.'

With a brief improvement in the weather, the advance of the German Army had in fact already ground to a halt on Christmas Day, and on 31st December – such must have been the prestige of the rocket Typhoons – 123 Wing was invited to Chièvres (A.84 in the American sector) – with the prospect of repeating its exploits at Falaise. In the event the weather clamped down again, the Wing was stuck there for three weeks, and Wing-Commander Walter Dring, its leader almost since D-Day, was killed landing from a weather recce, the purpose of which was to get his squadrons back to Gilze. On only five days in January was there any flying at all.

The two flight commanders were now an Australian, R. K. Gibson, and a tall gangling Canadian, J. D. Inches. Both were pre-D-Day veterans and close friends. But the former's days were numbered. In February the Army began pushing up to the Rhine through the wooded part of Germany on the western bank centred on Cleve, and while 83 Group maintained 'interdiction' patrols across the river, 84 Group, with co-operation from U.S. XXIX Tactical Air Command, temporarily under Second T.A.F., operated on the battlefield itself. It was not till mid-February that 84 Group, dragging itself from the winter morass, could do so at full strength, but on the 14th, 'the most perfect day for months', 123 Wing flew a record 152 sorties. The second of ten missions by 609 was led by Gibson, who shortly before take-off had asked the M.O. at breakfast if he could see him urgently. Doc Bell continues:

It surprised me, as he was a fit, hard character, and to my astonishment he related the following story. He had awoken suddenly that morning to find his Australian fiancée sitting on the end of his bed. He insisted that he saw her in great detail, spoke to her and was absolutely certain that he was not dreaming. When he reached out to touch her she disappeared. I tried to explain to him that the phenomenon was really a hallucination, but as frequently happens he insisted that she was really there.

An hour or so later he was hit by *flak* with all his rockets still aboard, and blew up in mid-air.

Don Inches was to go on flying for two more months, when he too was hit by *flak* and baled out of his burning aircraft over No Man's Land. Again I quote from the Doc, just to show one pilot's devotion to 609:

He had very badly burned legs and on landing sat and paddled in a stream. An old peasant saw him and directed him to our lines. He was given a lift back and quickly changed his burned uniform to prevent me seeing the damage. Only later in the evening while drinking in the Mess did I discover the details about what had happened, and insisted on examining him. He wept when he was told he had to go to hospital, so keen was he to stay with the Squadron.

Long before this, on 9th March, 609 had lost yet another C.O. – on a supposedly 'easy' mission against barges moored off the north coast of a Dutch island bearing the appropriately sinister name of

'Over Flakkee'. Group-Captain Johnny Baldwin, now D.S.O., D.F.C. and Bar, who had recently succeeded Desmond Scott as airfield commander, decided to 'go along for the trip', and here is part of the last entry in Eric Roberts' diary:

Because of the lowered cloud base I checked with Baldy as to whether to attack, and received the expected O.K. owing to the scarcity of *flak*. Turning west, I spotted the barges and led the boys down. At the bottom of the dive I saw a machine-gun on the barge I was aiming at open up and almost immediately felt the engine hit. This is it! Panic! Or not so much panic as a feeling of futility at getting hacked down on such a 'stopgap' show. The motor stopped when I had climbed up to 1,500 feet, and I jettisoned the hood to select a spot for landing. With the windscreen covered with oil and glycol, I put my head out of the side to see, forgetting I was still doing 160 plus! Then I called up Baldy to say I had been hit and was force-landing. At about 150 feet I was horrified to see not only a line of telegraph posts ahead, but the chosen field full of anti-glider posts. A small prayer was offered up to God and Messrs. Hawkers, and the old Typhoon just ploughed through all obstructions, snapping them off like pea-sticks. They also reduced my speed, which was just as well, as when I came to rest I was balancing on the edge of a dike with a ten-foot drop, and fifty yards from a substantial farm house. Out of this people swarmed, and within sixty seconds of touchdown I was seeking help and a hiding place, but all I got was a spreading of hands and cries of 'Deutsch! Deutsch!' Also, 'Kingy' was orbiting us, and as they seemed to resent this, I walked off down the road ... straight into the arms of two members of the Wehrmacht on cycles.

'Kingy' was Flight-Lieutenant G. J. King, who had succeeded Gibson as 'B' flight commander, and was a rarity inasmuch as he had previously fought against the Japs and downed six of them. But the loss of a third C.O. within four months, as well as popular flight commander and other pilots, was having its effect, and Doc Bell recalls that morale for once was low. He promptly adds, however, that things were soon put right – by L. W. F. ('Pinky') Stark, D.F.C. and Bar, A.F.C., the sixteenth and last C.O. of the war and the pilot who had once scored 609's 200th air-to-air victory:

He was small, baby-faced, with a wispy, downy moustache, but he lifted the Squadron by the bootlaces and made it the efficient fighting unit it had always been. He could not tolerate laziness and untidiness, and tongue-lashed anyone who exhibited these characteristics. He led them in the air with the same ruthless efficiency, and soon 609's record was the best in 123 Wing.

On the day of his arrival, 12th March, I happened to pay my second visit to the Squadron since leaving it, and the navigational morale of the N.C.O.-pilot of 609 whom Johnny Baldwin sent to fetch me from Brussels was low indeed, his method of route-finding being apparently to fly along roads so low that he could read the signposts. Even so, he was headed straight for enemy territory when, having fortunately brought a map, I suggested it was high time he turned to port. Later I mentioned the mattter jokingly to Johnny, who promptly gave the unfortunate pilot a 'raspberry'.

'Pinky' had arrived in time for the great airborne crossing of the Rhine on the 24th, and this time Second T.A.F. took part both in the planning and execution. In preparation for it the Wing moved four days earlier to Kluis – B.91, south of Nijmegen – where once again it went under canvas. On the 'big day' Adjutant Hills wrote in the war diary :

1,000 Dakotas are to drop paratroops and many gliders will be in operation, with hundreds of fighters as escorts. The Squadron's job is to keep the *flak* down to give them a chance.

He added that everyone expected a number of casualties and was prepared for the worst. With Wesel the British Second Army's chief objective across the river, the Squadron sector of operations was between there and Bocholt. At 10.00 hours, and again at noon, it took off at full strength, then split into three sections each of four aircraft for separate attacks on the *flak* positions. Only the C.O. ('Pinky' Stark), a Canadian (Don Inches), a Belgian (A. F. Crekillie) and a New Zealander (A. D. Scott) flew on both occasions. 'Johnnie' Johnson, returning from a Spitfire sweep, spotted some of the Typhoons engaged on this 'unenviable and dangerous task', and paused to watch their technique, adding, 'These pilots had plenty of guts and we admired them.'

Happily, after all, 609 sustained no casualties and the Army sent a 'strawberry', saying the work of the Typhoons had reduced their own casualties by at least 10 per cent. The greatest danger, in fact, seems to have been the risk of collision with the many other types of aircraft congesting the air, 'Pinky' himself having a near miss with a Spitfire.

By 1st April the Ruhr had been encircled and the German forces inside it trapped. Subsequently, 609 played its part in the liberation, at last, of Arnhem – 'if,' wrote Hills, 'the total destruction of that town can be so called.' And whereas formerly a major task had been the interdiction of road, rail and water transport to prevent the enemy bringing reinforcements and supplies to the front, the preoccupation now was to prevent him evacuating men and material from northern Holland for use elsewhere. Emphasis was on railways, with one particularly satisfactory result on 10th April, when a section of 609 led by Group-Captain Baldwin blew up an ammunition train.

By mid-April part of the Canadian Army was advancing towards Emden in German Friesland, and the R.A.F. historians record :

Here the support of the fighter-bombers of No. 84 Group was so effective as to call forth the praise of the commander of the troops in the field, who was especially impressed by the assault delivered on 12th April by Typhoons against the village of Friesoythe, which they set on fire with rockets.

It was there, while leading 609's attack, that Don Inches * was hit and baled out from his burning plane. But to continue effective support in Germany it was necessary to be stationed in that country, and on the 17th, after five months in Holland, the Wing was ordered to Plantlunne – B.103 near Lingen on the Ems. ('We are not pleased,' wrote the Adjutant.) From there, finally, the Typhoons ranged in quest of shipping as far as Heligoland.

But the war was all but over. On 30th April Hitler committed suicide, and on 4th May the German forces in Holland, Denmark and North-West Germany surrendered to Montgomery. A day or two later the Squadron made a low-level flight over Emden, fascinated by the *flak* guns, now pointing silently upwards as if in salutation.

* Inches (Canada), Harkness (New Zealand) and King (Britain) were awarded the D.F.C. after the war.

On the night of VE-Day, 8th May, No. 123 Wing – like service units all over Europe – made Whoopee. The victory bonfires were the largest and most numerous anyone had seen. Thousands of coloured Very lights soared into the air, a photograph of Adolf Hitler was ceremoniously burned, and a blazing pine-wood nearly set off a bomb dump which would have blown most of the celebrants to Hades.

But as the flames and the cheering finally died away, there was a feeling of anti-climax, almost sadness, in 609 Squadron. Suddenly its *raison d'être* had ceased to be. The purpose that for years had united young men from a dozen different countries in friendship, mutual endeavour and loyalty to the Squadron of the White Rose, had been achieved. Flying together, fighting together, being gay and sometimes irresponsible together – it was a way of life that had provided a happiness and fulfilment that few would ever experience again, even if for so many it had also been a way of death. Since May 1944, when 609 first operated under Second T.A.F., it had lost thirty pilots – the largest number in any year since the war began. Of these – so far as I can determine – twenty were killed, six became prisoners of war, two evaded capture in enemy territory, and the fate of the other two seems unrecorded. Of the pilots who had been on Squadron strength on D-Day, just two – C. H. T. Cables and the New Zealander R. D. Harkness – seem to have flown each month and survived till VE-Day. Two others – K. H. ('Heinie') Adams and A. H. ('Lord') Billam – had spanned both dates, yet been away owing to sickness or injury. Several more – like Georges Jaspis and Paulo Cooreman of Belgium, Argentine-born 'Pancho' Pagnam, R. E. Bavinton of Australia and M. I. Seguin of Canada – had joined 609 still earlier and become 'tour-expired' before the end. Two officers who during the last year had preserved the spirit of continuity as much as anyone – bar the Goat, who on VE-Day received his final promotion to Air Commodore – were the M.O., George Bell, and the Adjutant, S. E. Hills, whose signature appears on twelve monthly issues of the war diary, counter-signed by seven successive squadron commanders.

Perhaps the crowning achievement of the last of these, 'Pinky' Stark, was not to lead 609 through the last weeks of war but in the first months of peace – to maintain the discipline of practice flying

on aircraft that were already becoming obsolete; to take it to Fair-
wood Common in South Wales to learn a type of gunnery that no
pilot had ever dreamt of using, and back again to B.116 – Wun-
storf near Hanover. There the road that had started at Yeadon
in 1936 with a few wooden huts and one small canvas-covered
hangar, ended at a Luftwaffe aerodrome worthy of the Thousand-
Year Reich. Dining hall with orchestra dais, beer cellar with vomi-
torium, officers' private suites, skittle alley and swimming pool,
sick quarters (as the Doc noted approvingly) complete with operating theatre and X-ray unit – such were among the amenities. In
the end the wooden huts had prevailed, and instead of a thousand
years Hitler's Reich had lasted twelve. To quote George Bell once
more about the pilots he had served so long as friend and doctor :

Now their only rivalry was in the skittle alley. They had come a
long way from blasting radar stations with rockets to throwing balls
at wooden pins.

The Belgian and Commonwealth pilots had begun to melt
away soon after taking part in the great victory air parade over
Holland and northern Germany on 15th May, either to join their
own national squadrons or be demobilized at home. New pilots
arrived for training, and the Squadron that 'Pinky' led on 15th
September over The Hague to celebrate the fifth anniversary of
Battle of Britain Day was all-British for the first time since the days
of Geoffrey Ambler.

Four days later the first incarnation of No. 609 (West Riding)
Squadron ended in a riotous party which I was privileged to
attend. Next day its pilots flew to Lasham in Hampshire, surrendered their Typhoons, and with cries of 'Good-bye, old chum, be
seeing you !' went their separate ways, in most cases never to meet
again.

Years later I asked 'Pinky' what happened to the Goat.

'Oh, he flew back too, and a farmer promised to look after him.
I last saw him grazing peacefully at Lasham.'

He had served his Squadron well, and deserved his rest.

EPILOGUE

Nor shall this peace sleep with her; but as when
The bird of wonder dies, the maiden phoenix,
Her ashes new-create another heir
As great in admiration as herself.

SHAKESPEARE, *Henry VIII*

THE second incarnation of No. 609 (West Riding) Squadron
began on 10th May, 1946, at Church Fenton. Shortly afterwards
it moved back for its second childhood to its original birthplace,
Yeadon, and re-occupied the same Officers' Mess, Airmen's Mess
and other wooden buildings which it had vacated seven, but seemingly seven times seven, years before. Gone was the international
team of warriors that might have served as the prototype for a
United Nations air force. The Squadron was back where it started,
composed of part-time Yorkshire volunteers, with a commanding
officer, Squadron-Leader P. H. Womersley, D.F.C., who had been
almost the last Auxiliary officer to join it in 1939, and trained with
Michael Appleby, David Crook and Gordon Mitchell, before he
himself diverged to Coastal Command.

The problem that confronted Pat Womersley in 1946 was probably as great as, though virtually the opposite of, the one that confronted Harald Peake in 1936. Then it had consisted in recruiting
and training a team of aircrew and servicing staff in time to help
defend the country in a war that loomed inevitably ahead, though
helped by the sense of unity, purpose and sacrifice that the threat
of it inspired. With that war won, people were sick of hardship,
discipline and uniforms, and the problem now was how to utilize

some of the war-time skills and experience in a Squadron whose future was both vague and unassured. For though the 'cold war' was soon to provide a new and lasting military crisis, the recent dropping of two atomic bombs had made the notion of a territorial air force seem archaic to say the least. Already in 1944, after watching Hawker Tempests shooting down V-1s, Mr. Duncan Sandys had said to their leader, Wing-Commander R. P. Beamont, late of 609, that 'we were wasting our time in this flying business – in a few years' time all this sort of thing would be done by rockets.' * It was as good as predicting the end of manned air forces, and although a quarter of a century later manned military aircraft are still flying in virtually every country, in the years following the end of World War II there were many people who agreed with him.

In retrospect it is ironical that the twenty squadrons (before the War there were twenty-one but after the War there were twenty, 503 Squadron RAuxAF having been incorporated into 616 Squadron RAuxAF) of the now *Royal* Auxiliary Air Force were recreated by a Labour government in 1946, when their efficiency was lacking and their value doubtful, and were abolished by a Conservative government (usually considered more friendly to British military and civil aviation) eleven years later, when once again they had reached a standard comparable with the professionals and a value potentially as great. Again they were raised on a 'county-regimental' basis, as a separate force parallel with the R.A.F., by the Territorial Associations. Now called Territorial and Auxiliary Forces Associations, each of these now had a Chairman and a Vice-Chairman, one of them an ex-Army, the other an ex-Air Force officer. Happily for 609 the Vice-Chairman of the West Riding Association, and Chairman of its Air Committee, was none other than Air Vice-Marshal Geoffrey Ambler, who had led the original Squadron to war in 1939. When he became its Honorary Air Commodore as well, the rights and special interests of 609's 'citizen airmen' were doubly safeguarded.

Starting again from scratch the Auxiliary squadrons were at first, of course, non-operational, and until they became so were put into Reserve Command along with the R.A.F.V.R., the Uni-

*From *Phoenix Into Ashes*, by Roland Beamont, C.B.E., D.S.O.*, D.F.C.* William Kimber 1968.

versity Air Squadrons and the A.T.C., all of which had also been
revived, though without the same status and privileges. Indeed
the attraction of belonging to such exclusive 'clubs' as the Auxiliary
squadrons was evidently still powerful, and within a year, despite
war-weariness, 609 had already nearly reached establishment
numbers. Arthur Hudson, one of its officers for six years and its
commander for four (he also supplied the apt quotations from the
Bard to mark this Epilogue's beginning and end), lists some of the
other motives that swayed the applicants :

Some, a declining number, were influenced still by patriotism – men
who could not bear to think of the war having been fought in vain,
and who felt it was just as important to win the peace. Others had a
liking for the service but not for service life, or missed service
camaraderie but wanted a home life, too. Amongst the aircrew were
many who had flying in their blood and could not bear to give it up,
but did not want to make it a whole-time job; while amongst the
ground crew were many of all trades who had acquired new skills
and wished to preserve and practise them. Lastly there was the de-
pendable 'hard core' – men who came in at or near the beginning,
and served until the end. To these, whether they were air or ground
crew, 609 was not only a magic number but a way of life.

Foremost amongst them was S. H. ('Darkie') Hanson, who like
one or two others had joined before the war, and in this book was
last heard of as a sergeant in 1944. As he joined once more in the
rank of Aircraftman 2, his life must have seemed like a game of
Snakes and Ladders; but this time he ended up as Flight-
Lieutenant Hanson, M.B.E., 609 Squadron's Engineer Officer. If
ever one man was the linchpin of a squadron throughout its history,
it was he.

Till National Service started, all aircrew were men who had
been pilots or navigators during the war. Yet though 609 was again
gazetted as a fighter squadron, with one exception none had been
a fighter pilot before. The exception was the first post-war flight
commander – the same Wing-Commander R. P. Beamont, late
R.A.F., who had led it to war-time fame on Typhoons. Later a test
pilot with the English Electric Company at Warton, Lancs., there
was nothing he loved more than to fly over to Yeadon at week-ends
and transfer into a Mosquito XXXII of 609. 'It was,' he tells me,

'a dangerous aircraft'—which, coming from the first man to fly the Canberra, the Lightning and the ill-fated TSR-2, might cause his contemporary pilots of 609 some retrospective shivering, were it not that most of them already shivered at the time. They were equipped with this aircraft because 609's initial post-war prospective role was that of a night-fighter squadron. Progress, however, was slow. To quote a later flight commander, T. P. Hodgson:

Enthusiasm for flying covered the whole range from not interested to dead keen . . . It is also probably more difficult to turn an experienced pilot into a fighter pilot than to train the latter from scratch.

He and Hudson also stress the disadvantages of Yeadon itself as a base, despite its link with the Squadron' past. One was that 609 developed in isolation, there being no other air force unit on the station to provide the spur of healthy competition. Another was that even its longer runway was then only 950 yards, with a steep fall at the end – adequate for the Hawker Hinds of pre-war days, but not for converting pilots to the twin-engined De Havilland Mosquito. The C.O., his Flight Commander, Regular Adjutant and Regular Training Officer – they and they alone were allowed to take this aircraft off and land it there. All other flying had to take place from Linton-on-Ouse, which meant ferrying pilots and a skeleton ground crew there and back each flying day. The result was that flying hours were drastically curtailed, and most ground crews never saw their aircraft flying, which was hardly a stimulus to their morale.

Thus during the first years of its second childhood the performance of the West Riding Squadron was poor, to say the least. Heavy recruiting had been followed by poor attendance and marked inefficiency as more and more members became disillusioned or plain fed up. In dark corners even the dread word Disbandment was heard. If the Squadron was to justify its name and reputation, something drastic had soon to be done.

From the flying point of view things went somewhat better after April 1948, when the Squadron reverted to a day-fighter role, equipped once more with Spitfires. The Spitfire LF XVI was of course a highly sophisticated aeroplane compared with the old Mark I with which 609 had fought the Battle of Britain, but it was

better adapted than the Mosquito to Yeadon, and though first
solos on the type were still flown at Linton, flying restrictions were
otherwise lifted as pilots grew more proficient. But personnel continued to include far too much 'dead wood'. Arthur Hudson, whose
influence and example made him the natural successor as C.O. to
Womersley at the end of 1949, puts October of that year as the
moment of crisis, when the following procedure, for which he was
largely responsible, was adopted :

Any officer or airman who had not attended for two months received a letter giving him one more month to mend his ways. If
no heed was taken, he received another letter informing him that
his services would no longer be required, and that his discharge
would be requested in one month's time. A man who failed to attend
for four consecutive months, surely, was a broken reed !

And it was Hudson who reaped the whirlwind. As Squadron
commander he was shaken to find himself in charge of a unit about
one quarter its previous size. In fact only the backing of the Honorary Air Commodore, Geoffrey Ambler – who eleven years earlier
had himself set a precedent for 'dead wood' pruning – plus the
appreciation by the A.O.C. 64 Group that the measures were
necessary, gave him the heart to persevere. And the policy paid
off. Small though the Squadron was for a while, each remaining
member was worth his salt. The 'hard core' now provided a foundation on which something new could be built. In future the
Squadron's selection board became so 'choosy' that to join 609 at
all became difficult, and the calibre of the applicants rose accordingly.

The policy applied to officer and aircrew candidates as much as
to airmen. Some fully qualified pilots, with excellent flying records,
were turned down simply because flying ability alone was not
enough. It was necessary for the applicant to convince the C.O.
and his board that he was a type who would give to the Squadron
as much as the Squadron gave to him. 'A pilot seeking a cheap
way of scrounging some flying was severely discouraged,' Hudson
adds. Following are the reactions of a candidate who had once
belonged to Leeds University Air Squadron, started training in the
R.A.F. towards the end of the war, and applied to join 609 as a
pilot in December 1951 :

The man who vetted aspiring members was not at first the C.O. – that came later – but a well-built, kindly but business-like senior N.C.O., with a magnificent R.A.F. handlebar moustache. On his verdict much depended, and it seemed impossible that I, whose experience was virtually limited to flying instruction in the peaceful open skies of South Africa seven years before, could ever be accepted as a potential pilot of a Spitfire, still less a Meteor, with which 609 at that time was being re-equipped, or confront the obvious impossibility of finding one's way about the murk of the West Riding after learning one's navigation over the High Veldt, with visibility never less than eighty miles and a single railway line as a constant landmark. But accepted I was, and thus started the happiest six and a half years of my life. How kindly the N.C.O. was I was to discover in later years of close friendship.

The N.C.O. was of course 'Darkie' Hanson, and the approved candidate David Shaw (the Elder), later the Squadron's twenty-first and last C.O. in the final year of its life.

Arthur Hudson had made his mark. I am told by an independent witness that under his leadership 609 had the best attendance record and the best air-to-air firing record of any Auxiliary squadron in the country. Yet even he had only become a fighter pilot after joining 609. Territorial Artillery officer already in 1937, in mid-war he remustered to the R.A.F., and in 1942 received his elementary flying training at the hands, strangely enough, of one of 609's original Auxiliary officers and Battle of Britain survivors, Jarvis Blayney, who reports:

He was a natural pilot. I think he went solo in less time than any other pupil at No. 4 E.F.T.S.

On D-Day, as leader of an Albemarle squadron, he had the unenviable task of landing some of the first assault troops in Normandy; and he did the same at Arnhem, where he was shot down, and at the airborne crossing of the Rhine. There must be few pilots who to a D.F.C. won during the war added an A.F.C. won during the ensuing peace, as he did.

Two events now prepared the way for the West Riding Squadron's final period of glory. In October 1950, leaving behind a rear link in the shape of its sister units, No. 2609 R.A.F. Regiment Squadron and No. 3609 Fighter Control Unit, No. 609

Fighter Squadron moved once more to Church Fenton, this time
for good. Then, after that year's autumn exercises, it entered the jet
age by converting first to Vampires, and immediately afterwards
via the two-seater Meteor VII to the fighter Meteor IV. Already,
some time back, the Royal Auxiliary Air Force squadrons had been
re-integrated with Fighter Command.

Church Fenton was also the permanent base of two Regular
squadrons, Nos. 19 and 41. The latter, which 609 had last met in
1939, was replaced in 1952 by 72 Squadron, on whose aircraft
at this same airfield some West Riding pilots had flown their first
Spitfire solos shortly before the war. The presence of these Regular
squadrons provided a splendid tonic to morale and efficiency. They
made their Auxiliary comrades welcome, and showed no trace of
jealousy even when the latter – by some freak of allocation that
caused eyebrows to be raised in certain quarters – began to re-
equip with jets when they themselves still flew piston-engined
Hornets. But this was only momentary, and as 609 advanced its
standard there developed a good-natured rivalry that could not
have been more healthy.

Both the above developments were not unconnected with
another event which had almost as galvanizing an impact on the
Government's attitude to air defence as 'Munich' had had in 1938
– namely the outbreak of the Korean war. Just as 609 was getting
the feel of its new jet fighters, it and the other Auxiliary squadrons
were suddenly, in April 1951, called up for three months' continuous training, which was like an extended war-time course at
an Operational Training Unit. It meant learning to fly as a complete unit – so far impossible, even with piston-engined aircraft,
owing to lack of a full muster of air and ground crew with adequate
collective training; and it also meant learning to fight as such. Thus
the first month was spent boosting individual performance both
in the air and on the ground, the second month in making the
result collective, and the third in creating a combatant unit, with
teeth : the C.O. was sent on a Fighter Leadership course, and his
Squadron to Acklington to learn sophisticated gunnery.

There (says Peter Hodgson) it was let into the secrets of the gyro
gun sight, level, high and vertical quarter attacks, not to mention
the tell-tale recorder camera which precluded cheating and induced

competition as to who could get the best shots at minimum range and maximum deflection (a true measure, too, of a pilot's flying abilities). There was also live firing on a flag towed by some expendable chap on a punishment posting, but after a while supplies ran out and we had to start towing ourselves – and heaven help anyone who came back with the flag and the towing aircraft on one picture!

By the end of the call-up 609 was once more a unit capable of operating, if need be, on its own steam without the Regular stiffening normally needed by an Auxiliary, part-time squadron in peacetime. 'Morale was at a peak,' adds Hodgson – 'we were good and we knew it.' A product of both Oxford and Cranwell, he himself was the youngest of the Squadron's ex-wartime or ex-Regular pilots, and also one of its most devoted and colourful members. Known as 'The Ox' because of his great size and strength – he had represented Yorkshire many times at rugger – he also ran a pre-war vintage SS Jaguar, in which he was wont to race others members of the Bradford contingent home after a day's flying.

A high-light of the call-up was a visit by the C.-in-C. Fighter Command, Air Marshal Sir Basil Embry, which started inauspiciously. Hudson recalls:

As he wished to meet all officers and aircrew, we recalled the Meteors when Air Traffic announced his approach, and the last to come in, flown by Sergeant Pilot X, joined circuit just ahead of the Great Man, who was flying his own Devon. X then proceeded to park his aeroplane in a little heap, wheels up, right on the intersection of the two runways, and it was consequently necessary to keep Sir Basil orbiting while the débris was removed. At last he landed and was introduced by the Station Commander to the three squadron C.O.s, lined up in order of seniority. 'Is it yours?' he asked each of the other two, and of course got a negative answer. When he came to me there was no one else left, and unable to contain himself any longer he burst out laughing, at the same time trying rather unsuccessfully to shake his head in a disparaging manner. No further reference was made to the incident until after he had met the officers and aircrew. Then, when we were alone for a moment, he said, 'It was the fat sergeant pilot, wasn't it? What hard luck for you!' Needless to say he was right – of such stuff are great personalities made.

Indeed, any initial bad impression of 609 was doubtless corrected when, striding into the crew room and glaring at the assembled company, he said : 'Well, I'm the b . . . who had you called up for three months – what do you say to that?' Quick as a flash came a voice from the back of the room : 'You should have made it six, Sir.'

The call-up had certainly proved a boon, and as a reward for its improved performance the Squadron was promoted to the more advancer Meteor VIII, and the Church Fenton Station Commander, Group Captain 'Black' Smith, announced his intention of flying a wing of three squadrons, two Regular and one Auxiliary, on an equal footing, with each squadron commander taking turns to lead it.

It was an unprecedented and fantastic notion, and showed how far the week-end flyers had progressed since the days when their ability to fly even a military biplane had been called in question. Any fighter pilot of the Battle of Britain era would have gaped not only at the speeds at which his jet-age successor flew, but at his technical sophistication. Professional or amateur, he was expected to have the ability to fly, land and intercept *at any time of the day or night, and in any weather conditions.* It presupposed, as Hodgson says, efficient use of radar and radio aids, and of the standard operational procedures of aircraft recovery by Q.G.H. (radar-controlled descent through cloud) and G.C.A. (radar-contolled talk-down and landing).

This Air Traffic Control was itself shared by a section of 609 part-timers, who operated whenever the Squadron was flying, both at home and during summer camps abroad. Its officers, mostly ex-pilots and navigators, were given the impressive title of 'High Intensity Jet Aircraft Controllers', and were assisted by a staff of 'Movement Control Clerical SD'. As one of them, Stephen Lerche, who started with 609 as a pilot says:

The set-up was a far cry from the days of an insignificant hut on the edge of a Fighter Command airfield manned by a motley mob of sketchily trained ex-store bashers and the like, presided over by a Duty Pilot equipped with a doubtful radio, a Very pistol and a soul full of hope ...

... and probably only there as a punishment from the C.O. of his squadron! So precise was the new system, adds Lerche, that 'the accident rate *pro rata* was phenomenally low', implying that 'with the steep rise in fighter aircraft cost – ten times in less than that numbers of years' – this was just as well. He also recalls that it was an Auxiliary officer who first coined the expression 'Cockpit-side Manner' to indicate the professional standard of assistance to pilots now expected of and given by, *inter alia*, Auxiliary controllers.

Thus Church Fenton's two Regular squadrons, and one Auxiliary squadron, together with their Air Traffic Control sections, became complementary and interchangeable, the 'pros' giving the 'amateurs' every assistance within their power.

It was almost (says Hudson) as if the stature of the Regulars depended on the standard achieved by their Auxiliary colleagues. They often even adjusted their working hours to enable them to fly with us at week-ends.

As before the war these younger professional men were sometimes a little envious of the continuity and pride of unit enjoyed by a group of officers and airmen with common local roots during years of part-time service together. Not that it was all *that* part-time. Besides week-ends, Monday evenings were given up to dusk and night flying, and Thursday evenings to the assessment of camera-gun films and ground training in general. In addition there were the summer camps and (from 1951 onwards) the annual autumn Fighter Command exercises, during both of which the Squadron was virtually 'mobilized'. Finally it took its turn in providing aircraft and pilots at Readiness to help in the task of investigation unidentified aircraft approaching the British coast or for other search requirements. In a word, it was operational.

Even so, it was not good enough – or so thought Flight-Lieutenant R. E. (Bob) Windle, its new Regular training officer and a former member of the R.A.F. Formation Aerobatic Team. Hodgson comments:

Flying discipline was tightened up, and the standard of instrument flying made much more exacting. Take-off, climb, high-speed runs, maximum-rate turns at speed, maximum deceleration, Q.G.H., G.C.A., landings – all had to be carried out blind within prescribed limits of time, speed and altitude.

If the pilot passed such a test, he was awarded an 'Instrument Rating', related to his experience and ability, and of which he was no doubt as proud as he had once been of his 'wings'. Bob Windle's background being what it was, it was not even so very surprising that 609 sought and achieved the highest goal of all – a Formation Aerobatic Team of its own. Initially this comprised Bob as leader, Arthur Hudson and Jimmy Heath as Nos. 2 and 3, and Frank Reacroft in the 'box'. When Bob and Arthur left the Squadron, Frank became the leader and 'Young' Dave Shaw and Malcolm Hargreaves joined it.

Formation aerobatics are the ultimate in flying ability, especially when allied to the sheer physical strength needed to haul a heavy jet about the sky with no servo-assisted controls. It is the tops, the terminus – you can't get any better. Suffice it to say that 609's F.A.T., with some rather elderly gentlemen included, became so well respected that the R.A.F. sometimes used it for air shows in preference to their own.

Flight-Lieutenant Hodgson speaking, and having also been a member of the team, he ought to know. With engaging immodesty he adds that nothing so conduced to the Squadron's prestige as an aerobatic breakaway just before landing at an overseas station for a summer camp. 'It got the local herberts looking.'

The summer camps were at once a reward for service past and an opportunity for refinement in competition with other units not usually met with. From 1950 to 1956 609 went four times to Germany and twice to Malta. At the first camp, Sylt, when it still had Spitfires, it met 601 Squadron, then commanded by Paul Richey, 609's C.O. in 1942. The second camp was at R.A.F. Celle, near Hanover, where it raised its standard of dog-fighting during many a combat with the Venoms of 16 Squadron. In 1953, for the only time since 1942, it spent a night at Biggin Hill on its way to R.A.F. Takali, Malta. If by then the Yorkshire amateurs had anything parochial about them left, they lost it on finding themselves dropping down to refuel at Marseilles, flying high over the Mediterranean, or landing for the night (on the way back) in Tunisia. Once Ramsgate and Thorney Island had seemed the outer limit of adventure for summer camps, and strangely amongst those waiting to meet the Squadron was its first Adjutant and flying instructor, Norman Odbert, now Station Commander at Luqa.

In Malta the emphasis was on air-firing, and the Squadron was even allotted part of the Navy for a shipping strike. The ground staff had of course been flown there too.

Take-offs at 05.00 in the cool of the morning; long lazy afternoons on the rocks of St. Paul's Bay, or in the blue, blue, clear water; the ancient cities of Valetta and Medina. Counting the colour-stained target flags and suddenly realizing that your last week's score of twenty has this week crept up to thirty. It proves we are working as well. But what a wonderful way of earning a summer holiday in the sun!

So 'Big Dave Shaw recalls nostalgically. Already a flight commander, he was called that to distinguish him from his namesake, 'Young' Dave Shaw. The latter and Malcolm Hargreaves had had the distinction of being the first two pilots to reach 609 by the National Service route. The third, Malcolm Slingsby, has recorded the gamut of training that the few National Service men accepted for aircrew training underwent. Starting in February 1952 on ancient Tiger Moths at *Initial* Flying Training School at dear old Digby, he progressed to Chipmunks at *Basic* F.T.S. at Desford, to Oxfords at *Advanced* F.T.S. at Pershore, and then to Vampires at *Jet Advanced* Flying School at Merryfield, and with only three months of his National Service still to run, reached 609 Squadron in November 1953 to convert to Meteors, with an Operational Conversion course at R.A.F. Stradishall still to follow.

Needless to say, the authorities did not incur the expense of so much training without a *quid pro quo*, and before it started the candidate had to sign an agreement to the effect that, if he qualified, he would serve four more years part-time. For this purpose he could nominate in advance the squadron he would like to join. There followed an interview with its C.O., and if accepted he was then 'pre-selected' for that squadron. Malcolm Slingsby chose 609 both because of its reputation and its proximity to his Bradford home, and Arthur Hudson remembers selecting him from quite a number of applicants.

Thus a month after his National Service ended this 'conscript' was back as an Auxiliary, and that summer flew a Meteor VIII in close formation with the other pilots of 609 en route to summer camp in Germany. In the end the Squadron had no officers more loyal than the seven younger ones who reached it in this manner. Their devotion was even 'posthumous'. Under the brilliant chairmanship of 'Young' Dave Shaw, they did as much as anyone to organize the 1968 Reunion, where this book began.

Arthur Hudson, after leading 609 for a record four years and taking it to its first three overseas camps, in December 1953 handed over to Squadron-Leader E. 'Tommy' Evans, the only Regular officer to command the Squadron in peace-time, and already knowing and known to it after a spell as administrative officer at Church Fenton. From all accounts he was a fine leader, and under him 609 reaped the harvest that Hudson had helped to sow. And the harvest was a pretty bumper one – no less than the Esher Trophy, awarded annually since the nineteen-twenties, apart from the war years, to the most efficient of the Auxiliary squadrons, now twenty in number. To win it required aggregate highest marks under such headings as recruitment and attendance, trade tests taken and passed, aircraft serviceability, flying hours, flying ability, gunnery and performance on annual R.A.F. exercises, as well as degree of improvement since the previous year. In the last two years of Hudson's reign 609 had once been third and once runner-up. Now, under Evans, it was runner-up again in 1954, and in 1955 finally won the trophy, which was flown up from Biggin Hill by its last owners, No. 615 (County of Surrey) Squadron, ceremonially escorted by four Meteors of 609. Then, at a gala parade attended by families and friends from all over Yorkshire, it was formally presented to the Squadron by Major-General The [11th] Earl of Scarbrough, Lord Lieutenant of York and the West Riding. The 10th Earl, who as Chairman of the West Riding Territorial Association twenty years earlier had been largely responsible for the Squadron's original creation, would have been pleased.

The 1954 camp had been at Oldenburg, near Bremen, where 609 is said to have shaken the local 2nd T.A.F. Wing, equipped with F.86 Sabres, by the intensity of its flying, which caused an R.A.F. padre, who was present, to remark ten years later: '609? They were in the air every blessed minute of the day!' Slingsby recalls the air-to-ground firing on the Meppen Ranges, once used for testing the V-1, and the exhilaration of diving down on the small white targets.

All witnesses agree that the new C.O. commanded his Squadron's leisure as deftly as its work, and he had the reputation of being able to down a bigger steak than any of his followers. Half way through the camp there was a week-end at Hamburg. 'Never has so much bare skin been seen for so long by so many,' comments Frank Reacroft, who the following year was awarded the Queen's Commendation for what he himself called 'an air-to-air bump with Jack Wroe', but officially for 'Valuable Services in the Air'. And the 1955 camp was again at Celle, where as before the main hazard to be avoided was the Iron Curtain, just five minutes flying time to the east.

Just before this camp there took place the final irony. Eighteen months before its death the West Riding Squadron was presented with something it had waited for since birth : a Town Head-quarters – something that the older Auxiliary squadrons had pos-sessed since the nineteen-twenties, and to be used not only for social purposes but also for ground instruction. Its name was 'Wheat-field', it was situated in Headingley, Leeds, and in size, furnishings and amenities was worthy of the Squadron that took it over after 'Bee', R. P. Beamont, had performed the opening ceremony. I went there once, and was impressed. There were all the familiar portraits and battle scenes, the trophies, the possessions. At last, it seemed, 609 had found a place to hang up it soul.

Malta 1956. I'm in charge this time. Will it be the same as three years ago? Much of it is. That half-built house near the airfield is now three-quarters built. Charlie's bar is still operating. There is still no overshoot at either end of the runway, and the landing of our Sector Commander demonstrates in spectacular, if non-fatal man-ner that something should have been done about it. Fortunately the sherry from Gibraltar is rescued undamaged . . .

'Big' Dave Shaw, 609's last C.O., reminiscing about the last summer camp. He also has an anecdote about his Squadron's return :

The Station Commander at Church Fenton had pointed out to me the convention that a Royal Air Force Officer always wears a hat with civilian clothes. He would be happy if I would bring that sartorial custom to the attention of my officers. I did so, and included our Honorary Air Commodore, Geoffrey Ambler, who was no better behaved in this respect. Arriving back from Malta, scruffy in sweat-soaked khaki drill, we were welcomed home by the Station Commander, immaculate in Sunday Afternoon Casuals, and smartly hatted. We were also welcomed by our Air Commodore, equally immaculate except for his head, which was covered by the most battered and disreputable piece of old felt imaginable. Fortunately the Station Commander had a sense of humour.

N.B. Two years earlier the Station Commander had been Johnnie Wells, the Squadron's eleventh C.O., who died shortly before the 1968 Reunion.

*

> Can such things be
> And overcome us like a summer's cloud
> Without our special wonder?
>> *Shakespeare, Macbeth*

The sands were running out, and the New Year's Ball that carried 609 Squadron into 1957 was disturbed by rumour. 'Suez' had come and gone, and the Auxiliary squadrons had been alerted for the last time. Did the political failure of that enterprise influence the decision to scrap them? On 6th January, 1957, Peter Hodgson and Malcolm Slingsby took off for some routine 'dog-fighting' with camera guns:

As the sun set, Peter and I enjoyed the last few minutes of our flight in the after-glow, chasing each other high above the Humber Estuary, and returned to Church Fenton full of spirits, little thinking that we had just flown our very last sortie with 609 Squadron. The following Sunday, January 12th, we found our aircraft lined up in two neat rows, all with their gun ports off, some with their guns already stripped, and not one of our faithful and hard-working ground crew to be seen. We walked over to the crew room, to be greeted by a group of other pilots, long-faced and glum. Then Flight-Lieutenant Paddy White, Regular flying instructor, came to meet us and said, quite simply, 'Sorry, chaps, no flying today – we've been scrubbed.'

That evening, at Town Headquarters, Squadron-Leader David

Shaw sadly but officially announced to the whole of the assembled 609 (West Riding) Squadron that, by decision of the Government, it would no longer exist. In retrospect he adds :

Men do not often weep, but that evening more tears were shed than contained. Such a blow was beyond belief, but it was true. Attitudes varied; my own was summed up on the tiny plate that decorates the clock presented to me by all the Squadron members : Disbandment with Dignity.

The blow had been semi-pending since 1954, and one reason it had not fallen before was the public opposition to it. So why did it happen? As Defence Minister Mr. Harold Macmillan had said it was a measure of economy. Yet it was to *save* the taxpayer's money that Trenchard had sold the whole idea of a citizen air force to the Government in 1924! Was it now really economical to pour so much training, expertise and public spirit down the drain? Perhaps the new generation of swept-wing fighters were too expensive to be risked in amateur hands. But was the accident rate higher amongst Auxiliary squadrons than elsewhere? In 15 years of peace-time flying 609 had just one fatality, and one of its pilots, Malcolm Hargreaves, is today a senior First Officer in B.O.A.C., flying V.C. 10s. The Editor of *The Aeroplane* wrote :

It is hard to imagine the poverty of imagination that lies behind the decision to disband the Auxiliaries . . . In these days when financial reward and material gain . . . are alleged to be the only springs of conduct and employment, is there nobody in high places who realizes that the spirit behind the Auxiliary Air Force is priceless? . . . Nothing could be madder than to discourage those who wish to allocate their spare time to serving their country.

Yet for all the protests the Royal Auxiliary Air Force was not reprieved. On Sunday, 11th of February, 1957, Squadron-Leader David Shaw, Flight-Lieutenant Frank Reacroft and Flight-Lieutenant Jimmy Heath in Meteor VIIIs, accompanied by Flying-Officer Malcolm Hargreaves flying a *Yorkshire Post* photographer in a Meteor VII, were given special dispensation to take-off and fly over the principal cities of Yorkshire in a farewell salute from the Squadron of the White Rose. And on 4th March the full Squadron went on parade at Church Fenton for the last time. As it marched past the saluting base, the Huntsman of the Bramham Moor Hunt sounded on his horn first the 'Tally Ho!', then the 'Gone Away'. And that was it.

On that day the trainee pilots who today inhabit Church Fenton were little children. Yet today, says Malcolm Slingsby, their sleep is still occasionally disturbed as the raucous voices of a few 'old men' grouped around a piano float out into the night across the silent runways, singing:

> We're the 609 West Riding Squadron,
> The occasional Air Force are we;
> We only fly Saturdays and Sundays
> When the poor hard-worked Regulars are free.
> If ever you've flown in a Meteor
> You'll know just how fast they can go,
> When you roll 'em and land 'em and roll 'em –
>   TALLY HO! . . . 609 . . . TALLY HO!

THE COMMANDING OFFICERS OF
No. 609 (WEST RIDING) SQUADRON

ROYAL AUXILIARY AIR FORCE

Squadron-Leader H. Peake	10. 2.1936
Squadron-Leader G. H. Ambler, A.F.C.	8.12.1938
Squadron-Leader M. T. Avent	28.12.1939
Squadron-Leader H. S. Darley, D.S.O.	28. 6.1940
Squadron-Leader M. Lister Robinson, D.S.O., D.F.C.	4.10.1940
Squadron-Leader G. K. Gilroy, D.F.C. & Bar	29. 7.1941
Squadron-Leader P. H. M. Richey, D.F.C. & Bar	1. 6.1942
Squadron-Leader R. P. Beamont, D.S.O., D.F.C. & Bar	3.10.1942
Squadron-Leader A. Ingle, D.F.C., A.F.C.	5. 5.1943
Squadron-Leader P. G. Thornton-Brown, D.F.C.	18. 8.1943
Squadron-Leader J. C. Wells, D.F.C.	29.12.1943
Squadron-Leader L. E. J. M. Geerts, D.F.C.	30. 6.1944
Squadron-Leader R. A. Lallemant, D.F.C. & Bar	14. 8.1944
Squadron-Leader T. Y. Wallace, D.F.M.	17. 9.1944
Squadron-Leader C. J. G. de Moulin, D.F.C.	14.11.1944
Squadron-Leader E. R. A. Roberts, D.F.C.	6.12.1944
Squadron-Leader L. W. F. Stark, D.F.C. & Bar, A.F.C.	16. 3.1945
Squadron-Leader P. H. Womersley, D.F.C. & Bar	10.5.1946
Squadron-Leader A. Hudson, D.F.C., A.F.C.	January 1950
Squadron-Leader E. T. Evans	December 1953
Squadron-Leader D. Shaw	January 1956

APPENDIX A–PERSONNEL

PERIOD I, 1936–45

Pilots who served with 609 Sqn with ranks held during time with the Sqn and fate. Year denotes year with Sqn.
(*Note: Commanding Officers are shown in capitals, pre-War Auxilliary officers are underlined*)

Name	Country	Year	Fate
Flt Sgt R K Adam	Brit	43–4	+ with Sqn 31 Jul 44
Fg Off K H Adams	Brit	43–5	
Fg Off N Le C Agazarian	Brit	40–1	+ with 274 Sqn 16 May 41.
Sgt R W Aitken-Quack	Brit	43	POW with Sqn 1 Dec 43
Sqn Ldr G H AMBLER	Brit	38–39	died post-War
Plt Off H D F Amor	Brit	42	+ with Sqn 15 Dec 42
FS B W Andrews	USA	42	
WO T F Annear	NZ	44	
Plt Off M J Appleby	Brit	39–40	
Plt Off P Van Arenberg	Belg	41	died post-War
Flt Sgt R Ashworth	Brit	44	M with Sqn 29 Jul 44
Fg Off J G Astbury	Brit	42	
Flt Lt A J Atkinson	Brit	40–43	
Sqn Ldr M T AVENT	Brit	39–40	
Fg Off G D Ayre	Brit	38–40	+ with Sqn 30 May 40
Plt Off P A Baillon	Brit	40	+ with Sqn 28 Nov 40
Flt Lt J R Baldwin	Brit	42–3	+ post-War
Plt Off F H R Baraldi	Brit	40–1	died post-War
WO T W Barker	Brit	42–3	M with Sqn 1 Apr 43
Plt Off D A Barnham	Brit	41	died post-War
Flt Lt P H Barran	Brit	39–40	+ with Sqn 11 Jul 40
WO R E Bavington	Aus	43–4	
S/Lt D M Bay FAA	Brit	42	POW with 611 Sqn 13 May 43
Sqn Ldr R P BEAMONT	Brit	42–3	POW with 150 Wg 12 Oct 44
Sgt J M B Beard	Brit	39–40	
Flt Lt S G Beaumont	Brit	36–40	
Flt Sgt G C Bennett	Brit	39–41	M with Sqn 29 Apr 41
Fg Off Bennett	Brit	45	
Fg Off Y Du Monceau de Bergendael	Belg	41	died post-War

Name	Country	Year	Fate
Sgt W Berry	Brit	43	
Plt Off W H Bewg	Brit	42	+ with 182 Sqn 17 Aug 43
Plt Off A G H Billam	Brit	44–5	
Flt Lt J D Bisdee	Brit	39–41	
Sgt S N J P Blackwell	Rhod	42	
Flt Lt A Blanco	Belg	42–4	died post-War
Fg Off A J Blayney	Brit	39–40	
Flt Sgt L E Bliss	Brit	44	+ with Sqn 11 Jul 44
Sgt N Booth	Brit	43	+ with Sqn 9 Mar 43
Sgt R J Boyd	Brit	40–1	+ with 41 Sqn 6 Sep 43
Sgt Bradbury	Aus	42	
Plt Off Bradley	Brit	45	
Sgt K W Bramble	Brit	41	+ with Sqn 21 Jul 41
Sgt G F Breckon	NZ	41	POW with 72 Sqn 24 Jul 41
Sgt Bromhall	Brit	42	
Fg Off J De Bruyn	Belg	44–5	
Plt Off F J Bryan	Can	43	
Sgt Bryant	Brit	42	
Plt Off J D Buchanan	Can	43–4	+ with Sqn 27 Jul 44
Plt Off J R Buchanan	Brit	39–40	+ with Sqn 27 Jul 40
Fg Off G F De Beuger	Belg	44–5	+ post-War
Plt Off C H T Cables	Brit	44–5	died post-War
Fg Off M Cameron	Irish	43	
Flt Lt M L Carrick	Brit	44	+ with Sqn 18 Aug 44
Flt Lt E R Carruthers	Brit	45	+ with Sqn 8 Aug 45
? Castermanns	Belg	45	
Fg Off C G Chappell	Brit	40	
Sgt G A Chestnut	Can	41	+ with Sqn 11 Jun 41
Fg Off M P C Choron	French	41	+ with 340 Sqn 10 Apr 42
Flt Sgt D B Clarke	NZ	42	
FS J Collins	Brit	43	
Flt Lt P H M Cooreman	Belg	43–4	died post-War
WO W E Corbett	Aus	45	
Flt Lt D V C Cotes-Preedy	Brit	42	died post-War
Fg Off A F Crekillie	Belg	45	
Fg Off J Y R G Creteur	Belg	42	
Plt Off D M Crook	Brit	38–40	M with 8 OTU 18 Dec 44
Plt Off D L Cropper	Brit	41	+ with Sqn 16 Aug 41
Flt Lt J Curchin	Aus	40–1	M with Sqn 4 Jun 41
Flt Lt J Van Daele	Belg	44	+ with Sqn 28 Sep 44
Fg Off G J G Daix	Belg	43–4	M with Sqn 4 Jan 44
FS Dalton	Brit	45	
Sqn Ldr H S DARLEY	Brit	40	
Sgt Davey	Brit	42	

Name	Country	Year	Fate
Flt Lt I J Davies	Brit	43–4	+ with 198 Sqn 22 Jun 44
Sgt A R N Davis	Brit	42–3	M with Sqn 23 Dec 42
Fg Off J Dawson	Brit	38–40	M with Sqn 1 Jun 40
Sqn Ldr C DE MOULIN	Belg	43–5	POW with Sqn 5 Dec 44
Sgt A R Deschamps	Belg	44	died post-War
Flt Lt C F J Detal	Belg	43–4	+ with Sqn 23 Mar 44
WO Deveson-Summerfield	Brit	45	
Sgt G R Dickson	NZ	41	
Fg Off G E F Dieu	Belg	41	died post-War
Sgt N L Dixon	Brit	44–5	
Sgt W B Doig	Brit	41	
Sgt Dolan	Can	42	
Plt Off R Dopere	Belg	42	+ with Sqn 23 Oct 42
Fg Off P Drummond-Hay	Brit	36–40	M with Sqn 9 Jul 40
Flt Lt J C Dundas	Brit	38–40	M with Sqn 28 Nov 40
FS Dunman	Brit	45	
WO R Dunne	Brit	45	
Fg Off R A C Dupre	Mauritius	44–5	
WO Ecclestone	Brit	45	
Fg Off A R Edge	Brit	36–40	died post-War
Flt Sgt R O Ellis	Brit	43	+ with Sqn 17 Nov 43
Plt Off P Etienne	Can	42	
Fg Off G Evans	Can	41–3	died post-War
Sgt W J Evans	Brit	43	
Fg Off Farley	Brit	45	
Plt Off J H E Farmer	Brit	45	
Sgt A N Feary	Brit	40	+ with Sqn 7 Oct 40
Sgt Featherstone	Brit	42	
Flt Sgt L P Fidgin	Brit	44	+ with Sqn 13 May 44
Flt Sgt B L J Foley	Aus	43	
Sgt A M C Folkard	Brit	41	
Plt Off A La Force	Belg	44–5	
Flt Lt T H T Forshaw	Brit	40–1	
Fg Off J J M Fromont	Belg	44–5	died post-War
Sgt K A Galloway	Can	41	
Plt Off J D Gardner	Brit	40	
Plt Off J W Garton	Brit	40	+ with 54 Sqn 9 Jul 40
Plt Off G N Gaunt	Brit	36–40	+ with Sqn 15 Sep 40
Sqn Ldr L E J M GEERTS	Belg	43–4	died post-War
Flt Lt R K Gibson	Aus	43–5	+ with Sqn 14 Feb 45
Fg Off J C Gilbert	Brit	37–40	+ with Sqn 31 May 40
Plt Off H L Gilbert	Brit	42	died post-War
WO C M Gill	Brit	45	
Sqn Ldr G K GILROY	Brit	41–2	

Name	Country	Year	Fate
Fg Off T H R Goblet	Belg	45	POW with Sqn 3 Mar 45; + post-War
*Flt Lt G W Golledge	Brit	39	
Fg Off H McD Goodwin	Brit	40	+ with Sqn 14 Aug 40
WO A Gracie	Aus	45	
Flt Lt J P Le Grand	Belg	43–4	
Fg Off R D Grant	Brit	43–4	POW with Sqn 14 Aug 44
Sgt W Greenfield	Brit	41	
Plt Off R G C de H de Grunne	Belg	41	M with Sqn 21 May 41
Plt Off J M Gueuffen	Belg	43	POW with Sqn 4 Oct 43
Flt Lt E Haabjoern	Norway	43	+ post-War
Flt Sgt A Haddon	Brit	41–3	M with Sqn 14 Feb 43
Fg Off R A Hagger	Brit	42	
WO F S Hammond	Brit	44–5	POW with Sqn 19 Mar 45
Fg Off E L Hancock	Brit	40	
Flt Lt G E A Hardy	Can	44	
Plt Off R D Harkness	NZ	44–5	
WO D C Hellens	Brit	45	
Fg Off B De Hemptinne	Belg	41	+ with 122 Sqn 5 May 42
Plt Off L L Henrion	Belg	43–4	M with Sqn 29 Jan 44
Sgt G P Hickman	Brit	40–1	POW with 92 Sqn 20 Sep 41; shot by Gestapo Dec 44
Plt Off S J Hill	Brit	40–1	+ with Sqn 18 Jun 41
Fg Off R H Holmes	Brit	43–4	+ with Sqn 27 Jun 44
Flt Lt F J Howell	Brit	39–41	+ post-War
Fg Off A L T M Hue	Belg	43–4	
Plt Off J A Hughes-Rees	Brit	40–2	Died in Egypt 30 Apr 43
Fg Off W Humble	Brit	36–7	
Flt Lt J S Humphreys	NZ	43	died post-War
Flt Lt J D Inches	Can	43–5	
Sqn Ldr A INGLE	Brit	43	POW with 124 Wg 11 Sep 43.
Sgt J G Innes	Rhod	41–2	M with Sqn 25 Apr 42
Sgt H W Jackson	Brit	43	+ with Sqn 29 Mar 43
Plt Off E L R Jacquemin	Belg	44	
Plt Off G L R C Jaspis	Belg	43–4	
(rank unknown) Jospe	Belg	45	
Plt Off J L Kemp	Brit	39–40	
Plt Off V C Keogh	USA	40	+ with 71 Sqn 15 Feb 41
Flt Sgt T L Kerr	Brit	45	
Plt Off King	?	42	
Flt Lt G J King	Brit	45	+ post-War
Sgt W M Krebs	NZ	41	+ with 485 Sqn 26 Mar 42

Name	Country	Year	Fate
Sgt K N Laing	Can	41	POW with Sqn 15 Nov 41
Sqn Ldr R A LALLEMANT	Belg	41–4	
WO Lane	?	?	
WO W T Lang	Aus	45	
Sgt L Lawrence-Smith	Brit	41	
WO Lee	Brit	45	
Sgt W C F Leicester	NZ	41	
Plt Off T D L Leslie	Brit	42–3	+ with Sqn 11 Sep 43
Fg Off R Van Lierde	Belg	42–3	died post-War
Plt Off W Van Lierde	Belg	41	
WO F D Linacre	Aus	45	
Flt Lt A G H Lindsell	Brit	42	+ with 181 Sqn 27 Sep 42
Fg Off B W Little	Brit	37–40	
Flt Lt J M P De Selys Longchamps	Belg	41–3	+ with 3 Sqn 16 Aug 43
Flt Sgt P W Lough	Brit	44	
Flt Lt J H G McArthur	Brit	40	died post-War
Sgt J N McConnell	NZ	41–2	M with 601 Sqn 15 Jun 42
Sgt W G McConnachie	NZ	42	
Plt Off J G McLaughlin	Aus	43	POW with Sqn 14 Jan 44
Flt Sgt H W McMann	Can	43	
Sgt P H A MacSherry	Can	41	+ with Sqn 27 Mar 41
Plt Off W McKenzie	Brit	41	+ with 118 Sqn 9 Mar 42
Plt Off R I P MacKenzie	Brit	41	died post-War
Plt Off R F G Malengreau	Belg	41–2	
Plt Off A Mamedorf	USA	40	+ with 133 Sqn 8 Oct 41
WO Mander	Brit	45	
Plt Off G K E Martin	Aus	43–4	
Flt Lt H M Mason	NZ	44	+ post-War
*Flt Lt A W S Matheson	Aus	36–38	+ with 1485 Flt 18 Jul 43
Plt Off J A Mathys	Belg	44–5	
Sgt R T D Mercer	Brit	40–1	+ with Sqn 9 May 41
Fg Off N L Merrett	Aus	43–4	+ with 164 Sqn 23 Dec 44
Plt Off C W Miller	Can	43	+ with Sqn 21 Dec 43
Plt Off R F G Miller	Brit	40	+ with Sqn 27 Sep 40
Sgt T L Mincher	Brit	42	
Plt Off G T M Mitchell	Brit	38–40	+ with Sqn 9 Jul 40
Plt Off G E Moberley	Brit	38	
Plt Off J E J Morai	Belg	41	died post-War
Flt Lt Morgan	Brit	41	
Fg Off J Morgan	Brit	45	
Sgt Morrison	NZ	42	
Flt Lt L J Mountjoy	Brit	45	

Name	Country	Year	Fate
Plt Off G A Y F F X Muller	Belg	41	POW with 122 Sqn 17 May 42
Fg Off P J Nankivell	Brit	42–3	+ with Sqn 7 Feb 43
Plt Off P A Nash	Brit	41–2	+ with 249 Sqn 17 May 42
Plt Off M L Van Neste	Belg	43	M with Sqn 30 Apr 43
Fg Off J C Newberry	Brit	40	
Plt Off J R Newsome	Brit	39	
Fg Off J Niblett	Brit	43–4	+ with 198 Sqn 2 Jun 44
Flt Lt D M Nicholls	Brit	43	
Fg Off P R Nickols	Brit	36–9	
Plt Off A Nitelet	Belg	41	
Fg Off T Nowierski	Polish	40–1	died post-War
*Flt Lt N C Odbert	Brit	36–8	
Flt Lt J H M Offenberg	Belg	41–2	+ with Sqn 22 Jan 42
Plt Off A K Ogilvie	Can	40–1	POW with Sqn 4 Jul 41
Fg Off Z Olenski	Polish	40–1	died post-War
Plt Off C C A Ortmans	Belg	41–2	+ with 615 Sqn 1 Apr 43
Plt Off V M Ortmans	Belg	41–2	POW with Sqn 21 Oct 41; died post-War
Plt Off B M Osborn	Brit	41–2	Killed in car crash whilst with Sqn 1 May 42
Plt Off P Ostazewski-Ostoja	Polish	40–1	
Fg Off C N Overton	Brit	39–41	
Plt Off B G Pagnam	Arg	43–4	
Sgt A G Palmer	Brit	40–1	M with Sqn 21 Oct 41
Flt Sgt L B Papa	Brit	45	
Sgt R J Parthoens	Belg	44	+ with Sqn 9 Dec 44
Sgt H Patterson	Brit	41	
Sqn Ldr H PEAKE	Brit	36–8	died post-War
Flt Lt D Persse-Joynt	Brit	36–40	M with Sqn 31 May 40
FS R Payne	NZ	42	M with 450 Sqn 22 Nov 42
Fg Off R H Payne	Brit	42	
Flt Lt P E R Pike	Brit	44	
Plt Off A F J Polek	Polish	42	
Sgt E W Pollard	Brit	41	+ with Sqn 21 Aug 41
Flt Sgt P M Price	NZ	44	+ with Sqn 27 Jul 44
Fg Off P E Raw	Brit	42–3	+ with 183 Sqn 21 Mar 44
FS Ray	Brit	45	
Fg Off F J Reahil	Brit	43	M with 268 Sqn 18 Jun 44
Fg Off G Remy	Belg	45	
Plt Off M H G Rendall	Brit	45	+ with Sqn 13 Apr 45
Plt Off J G F Renier	Belg	42–3	
WO G M Reynolds	Brit	44–5	

Name	Country	Year	Fate
Sqn Ldr P H M RICHEY	Brit	41–2	Died post-War
FS Riddoch	Brit	45	
Plt Off T C Rigler	Brit	41–2	Died post-War
Sqn Ldr E R A ROBERTS	Brit	43–5	POW with Sqn 9 Mar 45
Sqn Ldr M L ROBINSON	Brit	40–1	+ as OC Tangmere Wg 10 Apr 42
Flt Lt R J H Roelandt	Belg	41–4	+ with Sqn 26 Aug 44
Flt Lt A S Ross	USA	43–4	
Sgt S T Rouse	Brit	40–1	+ with 227 Sqn 15 Mar 45
Fg Off C A Rowland	Brit	43–4	+ with Sqn 29 Jun 44
Flt Lt R A Royston	Brit	45	
Fg Off I B N Russell	USA	39–40	+ with Sqn 1 Jun 40
Plt Off J E Rylands	Brit	37–8	
Sgt Sabourin	Can	42	
Fg Off L H Sagar	Brit	36–9	
Plt Off W B Sanders	Brit	41	
Sgt A C De Saxce	French	41–2	+ with 341 Sqn 10 Apr 45
Plt Off J E Van Schaick	Brit	41–2	+ with 59 OTU 20 Feb 43
Plt Off A D Scott	NZ	44–5	
Plt Off E G A Seghers	Belg	41	+ with 91 Sqn 26 Jul 44
Plt Off M J Seguin	Can	44–5	
Fg Off M H Shelton	Brit	43–4	+ with Sqn 29 Feb 44
Fg Off H T Skett	Brit	42–3	
Plt Off G W W Smith	NZ	41	
Flt Lt L E Smith	Brit	43	
WO S E Smith	Aus	45	+ with Sqn 23 Apr 45
Fg Off P L Soesman	Belg	43–4	M with Sqn 11 May 44
Fg Off J J Solak	Polish	42	
Flt Sgt A H E De Blommart de Soye	Belg	45	+ with Sqn 13 Apr 45
WO S H Spallin	Can	42	M with Sqn 5 Nov 42
Flt Lt F X E De Spirlet	Belg	41–2	+ with Sqn 26 Jun 42
Sgt Stanley	Brit	42	
Plt Off M E Staples	Brit	40	+ with 604 Sqn 9 Nov 41
Sqn Ldr L W F STARK	Brit	43–5	
WO J K Stellin	NZ	44	+ with Sqn 19 Aug 44
Plt Off G Stevens	Brit	42–3	
Flt Lt J A Stewart	Brit	44	POW with Sqn 13 May 44
Sgt W Stock	Can	41	died post-War
WO F L Taylor	Brit	44	+ with Sqn 15 Aug 44
Sqn Ldr P G THORNTON-BROWN	Brit	43	+ with Sqn 21 Dec 43
Fg Off J D Thorogood	Brit	44	+ post-War
Plt Off E G Titley	Brit	40	+ with 5 OTU 17 Jul 43

Name	Country	Year	Fate
Plt Off E Q Tobin	USA	40	+ with 71 Sqn 7 Sep 41
Plt Off T Turek	Polish	42–3	
Sgt H F Wade	Brit	41	
Sgt W H Walker	Brit	40	
Sqn Ldr T Y WALLACE	S African	44	+ with Sqn 11 Nov 44
Plt Off G L Watelet	Belg	43	
Fg Off J D F Wathieu	Belg	44–5	died post-War
Flt Lt W F Watts	Brit	43	
Sqn Ldr J C WELLS	Brit	42–3	died post-War
Sgt West	Can	43	
Fg Off R Wilmet	Belg	41	+ with 349 Sqn 28 Apr 43
Sgt Wilkinson	Brit	41	
Sgt A L Wilson	Can	41	
Sgt J Wiseman	Brit	42–3	+ with Sqn 14 Feb 43
Plt Off P A Womersley	Brit	39	
Flt Lt R L Wood	Brit	43–4	M with Sqn 11 May 44
Sgt Young	Brit	41–2	
Flt Sgt J A A Zegers	Belg	43–4	+ with Sqn 3 Jan 44
Plt Off J Zurakowski	Polish	40–1	
Sgt E J Van Zuylen van Nijvelt	Belg	43	M with Sqn 6 Apr 43

* Denotes Regular Adjutant & flying instructor

The above total of 300 pilots came from the following countries:

Britain	170
Belgium	55
Canada	20
New Zealand	17
Australia	14
Poland	7
USA	6
France	2
Rhodesia	2
Argentine	1
Ireland	1
Mauritius	1
Norway	1
South Africa	1
Unknown	2

Casualties

Killed with 609 Sqn	53
Missing with 609 Sqn	20
POW with 609 Sqn	12
Killed/missing with other Sqns	31
POW with other Sqns	6

GROUND OFFICERS

Hon. Air Commodore: The 6th Earl of Harewood.

Non-flying Adjutants
Anderson, Fg Off R. M. D., '40
Dodgshun, Plt Off G. T., '38–'39 (Asst).
Hills, Fg Off S.E., '44–'45.
Lincoln, Flt Lt, *The Earl of*, '36–'38
Robson, Fg Off, '43–'44
Sudworth, Fg Off *A.G.*, 40.
Tidswell, Fg Off E. H., '40–'43

Medical Officers
Bell, Fg Off G. A., '44–'45.
Boyle, Flt Lt. McM., '37–'40.
Lawrence, Fg Off, '41.
McKechnie, Fg Off, '42–'43.
Scott, Fg Off, '41–'42.
Somerville, Fg Off, '42.

Engineer Officers
Abraham, WO C. L. W., B.E.M., '38–'43.
Jackson, Fg Off, '42–'43.
Harvey, Fg Off C., '39–'40.
Wilson, Fg Off, '40–'41.
Yates, Flt Lt T. A., '41–'42, '44–'45.

Accounts Officers
Robinson, Fg Off *G. G.*, '36–'38.
Sudworth, Fg Off *A. G.*, '38–'40.

Equipment Officer
Burges, Flt Lt R. F., '36–'39.

Intelligence Officers
MacKay, Fg Off R. J., '40–'41.
Rose, Fg Off E. J. B., '40.
Ziegler, Flt Lt F. H., '41–'44.

SENIOR AUXILIARY N.C.O.S

Albrecht, FS A. R.
Andrews, Sgt D. H.
Barber, Sgt J. D.
Binks, Sgt E.
Craven, Sgt A.
Fitzgerald, FS J. M.
Hanson, Sgt S. H.
Hartley, FS W.
Ingall, FS G. E.
Payne, FS J.

Priestley, Sgt O.
Rabbidge, FS A. P.
Simpson, Sgt H.
Stockdale, Sgt S. E.
Waite, FS E.
Walker, Sgt A. G.
Walling, Sgt R.
Wood, Sgt A. H.
Wright, FS A. C.

Brazier, Sgt Photog.

Cloves, FS Airframe Fitter

Coakes, WO Armament

Evans, FS Airframe Fitter

Faux, WO Discip.

Fearnside, Sgt Eng. Fitter

Ferr, Sgt

Hughes, FS Airframe Fitter

Redfearn, WO

Roberts, FS Eng. Fitter

Toner, Sgt Eng. Fitter

Tucker, FS

PERIOD II, 1946–1957

Honorary Air Commodore:

Air Vice-Marshal G. H. Ambler, C.B., C.B.E., A.F.C., D.L., LL.D.

AUXILIARY PILOTS

*Bailey, Flt Lt P., D.F.C.

Beamont, Flt Lt R. P., D.S.O.*,
  D.F.C.*

Butcher, Plt Off M.

Campbell, Flt Lt W. S. (Jock).
  Killed in accident whilst with the
  Sqn, 22 April 1956.

Cartwright, Fg Off D.

Cooper, P II T.

Crowter, Fg Off E.

Cullum, Fg Off D. (Charlie Brown)

Dobie, Flt Lt T. G.

Dransfield, Fg Off D.

Goulbourn, Fg Off D.

Graham, Fg Off A.R.

Greaves, Plt Off T.

Hargreaves, Fg Off M.

Heath, Fg Off J.

Hodgson, Flt Lt T. P. (The Ox)

HUDSON, Sqn Ldr A., D.F.C.,
  A.F.C., T.D., O.C. '49–'54

Leonard, Fg Off S.

*Lerche, Flt Lt S.

Lumb, P II E.

McAlpine, Fg Off A.

Marrable, Fg Off D.

Milner, Flt Lt A.J.M. (now Lord
  M.).

Mudd, Fg Off J.

Ogden, Plt Off A.J.

Reacroft, Flt Lt F.D.

Scull, Sgt C.

SHAW, Sqn Ldr D., O.C. (Big
  Dave) '56–'57.

Shaw, Fg Off D. R. (Young Dave).

Slayton, P II G.

Slevin, Plt Off J.

Slingsby, Fg Off E. M.

Viles, Flt Lt J. E.

Walker, Sgt J.

Walker, Sgt. (Whisky).

Ward, Flt Lt S.

WOMERSLEY, Sqn Ldr P. A.,
  D.F.C., O.C. '46–'49

Wroe, Fg Off J.

*Officers who served first as pilots, then in the special duty indicated.

AUXILIARY GROUND OFFICERS

Andrews, Fg Off D. H.	Adj.	Hanson, Flt Lt S. H., M.B.E.	Eng.
*Bailey, Flt Lt O., D.F.C.	Int.	Kinsley-Lawrence, Flt Lt	Med.
Bell, Flt Lt E. (Dinger) A.T.	Con.	*Lerche, Flt Lt S.	A.T.Con.
Bell, Flt Lt	Med.	McConnell, Flt Lt C. H.	Accounts
Brierley, Flt Lt D. S. C.	Int.	Martineau, Sqn Ldr	Padre
Coleman, Flt Lt J. L.,	Med.	Midgley, Flt Lt W.	Equip.
Dixon, Fg Off 'Lofty'	A.T.Con.	Monks, Flt Lt G.	A.T.Con.
Fidler, Flt Lt G., D.F.C.	A.T.Con.	Sharp, Sqn Ldr F. J.	Med.
Guild, Plt Off D.	Adj.	Shorten, Sqn Ldr R. D.	Padre

*Officers who served first as pilots, then in the special duty indicated.

REGULAR OFFICERS

(All Regular Adjutants and Training Officers were pilots and flew with the Squadron, but were not reckoned Squadron pilots as such.)

Barnes, Flt Lt B. F.	Adj & Tr.O.	Murton, Flt Lt P.G.	Adj.
Booth, Flt Lt C.	Eng.	Oakley, Flt Lt	Eng.(1st)
Brittain, Flt Lt H. G., D.F.C., A. F. C	Adj.	Peaker, Flt Lt B.	Eng.
EVANS, Sqn Ldr/ E. T.	O.C. '54–'56	Smart, Flt Lt M.	Tr.O.
Fox, Flt Lt R.	Tr.O.	Starnes, Flt Lt R.	Adj.
Godfrey, Flt Lt A.	Tr.O.	Thomas, Flt Lt D.	Tr.O.
Jones, WO J.	Eng.	Thompson, Flt Lt P.D., D.F.C., D.F.M.	Adj.(1st)
Massey, Flt Lt L.	Eng.	White, Flt Lt 'Paddy'	Tr.O.
Mills, Flt Lt R.	Eng.	Windle, Flt Lt R.E., A.F.C.	Tr.O.
Moran, Flt Lt 'Spike'	Tr.O. (1st)		

SENIOR AUXILIARY N.C.O.S

Bryant, FS S.	Sanderson, Sen. Technician R.
Clapham, Sgt D.	Scott, FS P.
Davies, Sgt J. R.	Thomson, FS S.
Golphin, FS	Titherington, Sgt V.
Myers, Sgt H.	Wynyard, Sgt A..
Nash, Sgt	

OUTSTANDING REGULAR N.C.O.S

Carns, FS J.	Spencer, Chief Technician W.
Pratt, Sgt. H.	Veitch, Sgt. E.

Note: Any inaccuracies or omissions in the above lists are regretted.

APPENDIX B—AWARDS

(Previous decorations in brackets)

D.S.O.

Darley, Sqn Ldr H. S. Oct. 1940
Robinson, Sqn Ldr M. L. (D.F.C.)
  Aug. 1941

Beaumont, Sqn Ldr R. P. (D.F.C.
  & Bar) May 1943

D.F.C.

Russell, Fg Off I. B. N. (U.S.A.)
  June 1940
Howell, Flt Lt F. J. Oct. 1940
McArthur Flt Lt J. M. G. Oct. 1940
Dundas, Fg Off J. C. Oct. 1940
Robinson, Sqn Ldr M. L. Nov. 1940
Crook, Plt Off D. M. Nov. 1940
Curchin, Plt Off J. (Aus.) Nov. 1940
Nowierski, Fg Off T. (Pol)
  Nov. 1940
Dundas, Flt Lt J. C. (D.F.C.)
  Jan. 1941
Offenberg, Plt Off J. (Belg.)
  June 1941
Bisdee, Fg Off J. D. July 1941
Ogilvie, Fg Off A. K. (Can.)
  July 1941
Richey, Flt Lt P. H. M. (D.F.C.)
  July 1941
Ortmans, Fg Off V. (Belg.)
  Sept 1941
Du Monceau de Bergendael, Plt Off
  Count Y. (Belg.) Apl. 1942
Gilroy, Sqn Ldr G. K. (D.F.C.)
  July 1942
Beamont, Sqn Ldr R. P. (D.F.C.)
  Jan. 1943
Baldwin, Fg Off J. R. Feb. 1943
Lallemant, Fg Off R. A. (Belg.)
  Mar. 1943
Atkinson, Flt Lt J. A. May 1943
Raw, Fg Off P. E. May 1943

De Selys Longchamps, Fg Off
  Baron J. M. P. (Belg.) May 1943
Van Lierde, Fg Off R. (Belg.)
  May 1943
Wells, Flt Lt J. C. July 1943
Ingle, Sqn Ldr A. (A.F.C.)
  Aug. 1943
Haabjoern, Flt Lt (Norw.)
  Aug. 1943
Davies, Fg Off I. J. Sept. 1943
Thornton-Brown, Sqn Ldr P. G.
  Jan. 1944
Stark, Plt Off L. W. E. c. Jan. 1944
Detal, Plt Off C. F. J. (Belg.)
  Jan. 1944
De Moulin, Fg Off C. J. G. (Belg.)
  c. Feb. 1944
Renier, Fg Off J. G. F. (Belg.)
  1943/44
Smith, Flt Lt L. E. Mar. 1944
Roberts, Flt Lt E. R. A. July 1944
Geerts, Sqn Ldr L. E. J. M. (Belg.)
  July 1944
Lallemant, Sqn Ldr R. A. (D.F.C.)
  (Belg.) Aug. 1944
Merrett, Fg Off N. L. (Aus)
  Aug. 1944
King, Flt Lt G. J. June 1945
Inches, Flt Lt J. D. (Can.) June 1945
Harkness, Fg Off R. D. (N.Z.)
  July 1945

D.F.M.

Hughes-Rees, Sgt J. A.	Aug. 1941	Rigler, Sgt T. C.	Sept. 1941
Palmer, Sgt A. G.	Aug. 1941	Van Schaick, Sgt J. E.	Dec. 1941

A.F.C.

Ambler, W/CG. II.   July 1940   Hudson, Sqn Ldr A. (D.F.C., T.D.)
1954

M.B.E.

Jackson, Flt Lt 1943
Hanson, Flt Lt S.H. 1957

B.E.M.

Abraham, FS C.L.W. 1942

Queen's Commendation

Reacroft, Flt Lt F.D. 1955

Croix de Guerre (*French*)

Robinson, Sqn Ldr M.L.	1941	Richey, Sqn Ldr P.H.M.	1942
Gilroy, Sqn Ldr G.K.	1941		

Choron, Fg Off M. (French) 1941

Croix de Guerre (Belgian)

Plus many Belgian pilots,   1941–45

APPENDIX C
609 SQUADRON AIRCRAFT LOSSES,
1938–56

+   denotes killed
W   denotes wounded
E   denotes evaded
I   denotes injured
P   denotes POW

Date	Ac & Serial	Code	Pilot	Fate	Details
18 June 39	Hind K6848		Plt Off J C Dundas LAC Hunter	- -	Engine cut out on formation take off from Yeadon and crashed into house at Victoria Avenue, Yeadon.
21 Nov 39	Spitfire L1060		Sgt R J Staples	-	Skidded on landing at Drem into L1082 and refueller, ac written off.
	Spitfire L1082		Plt Off J C Dundas	-	
7 Jan 40	Spitfire L1064		Plt Off I B N Russell	-	Undercarriage failure and abandoned; crashed near Crook of Alves near Kinloss.
15 May 40	Spitfire L1007 Spitfire L1085		Fg Off G V Proudman	-	Engine cut out and landed on top of L1085 at Drem; both ac caught fire.
30 May 40	Spitfire L1086		Fg Off G D Ayre	+	Became lost returning from patrol and crashed in bad visibility near Great Oakley, Essex, 1420 hrs.
30 May 40	Spitfire L1063		Fg Off J C Dundas	-	Force-landed after combat near Frinton On Sea, Essex after 1420 hrs. Ac slightly damaged.
31 May 40	Spitfire N3202		Flt Lt D Persse-Joynt	M	Missing from patrol 1345–1535 hrs.
31 May 40	Spitfire L1091		Fg Off J C Gilbert	+	Shot down near Dunkirk 1855–2130 hrs.
31 May 40	Spitfire L1097		Sgt G C Bennett	W	Ditched 2 miles off Dover after combat, 1855–2130 hrs.
1 Jun 40	Spitfire L1058		Fg Off I B N Russell DFC	+	Shot down by Bf 110s near Dunkirk, 1415–1615 hrs.
1 Jun 40	Spitfire N3222		Fg Off J Dawson	M	Missing from patrol, 1810–2030 hrs.
9 Jul 40	Spitfire R6637	PR-Q	Fg Off P Drummond-Hay	M	Shot down by Lt Egon Mayer, I/JG 2 off Portland, 1828–2152 hrs
„	Spitfire N3203		Plt Off G T M Mitchell	-	Force-landed after combat with Bf 109s, 1828–2152 hrs.

Date	Aircraft	Code	Pilot		Details
11 Jul 40	Spitfire L1069		Flt Lt P H Barran	+	Shot down by Oblt Ludwig Franzisket, III/JG 27 off Portland, 0815 hrs.
11 Jul 40	Spitfire L1095		Plt Off G T M Mitchell	M	Shot down by Oblt Max Dobislav, 9/JG 27 off Portland, 0815 hrs.
15 Jul 40	Spitfire P9497		Plt Off J Curchin	-	Crashed landing at Warmwell.
18 Jul 40	Spitfire R6636	PR-F	Fg Off A R Edge	-	Shot down by Ju 88 off Swanage and crash-landed on Studland Beach at 1515 hrs; ac damaged.
„	Spitfire R6634		Flt Lt F J Howell	-	Shot down by Ju 88 4 miles south of Poole, 1515 hrs; pilot baled out.
26 Jul 40	Spitfire K9815		Fg Off J C Newberry	-	Force-landed due to engine failure at Piddlehinton, Dorset; ac caught fire.
27 Jul 40	Spitfire N3023		Plt Off J R Buchanan	+	Shot down by Oblt Gert Framm, Staffel Kapitaen 2/JG 27 over Weymouth Bay, 1020 hrs.
8 Aug 40	Spitfire P9322		Plt Off M J Appleby	-	Damaged in combat with Bf 110 of V(Z)/LG 1, off Isle of Wight.
11 Aug 40	Spitfire R6918	PR-D	Plt Off J C Dundas	-	Ac damaged in combat off Swanage, 1035 hrs.
12 Aug 40	Spitfire K9841		Plt Off N Le C Agazarian	-	Ac damaged in combat off Swanage, 1238 hrs.
„	Spitfire K9997		Plt Off H McD Goodwin	-	Damaged in combat with Bf 110s off Isle of Wight, 1230 hrs.
12 Aug 40	Spitfire R6692		Fg Off J C Newberry	-	Damaged in combat with Ju 88 over Channel, 1250 hrs.
13 Aug 40	Spitfire R6690	PR-A	Plt Off J C Dundas	-	Damaged in combat over Channel, 1625 hrs.
14 Aug 40	Spitfire N3024	PR-H	Fg Off H McD Goodwin	+	Shot down into sea off Bournemouth, 1730 hrs.

351

Date	Ac & Serial	Code	Pilot	Fate	Details
,,	Spitfire R6961		Plt Off J C Dundas	-	Damaged in combat with Ju 88, 5 miles SW Warmwell, 1740 hrs.
24 Aug 40	Spitfire L1082		Plt Off A Mamedorf	-	Severely damaged in combat with Bf 110 (Bf 109?) over Ryde, 1650 hrs.
,,	Spitfire X4104		Flt Lt F J Howell	-	Damaged in combat with Bf 110 over Ryde, 1650 hrs.
25 Aug 40	Spitfire R6986		Plt Off P Ostaszewski	W	Badly damaged in combat with Bf 110 over Swanage, 1730 hrs.
,,	Spitfire R6961		Plt Off D M Crook	-	Damaged in combat with Bf 110 over Swanage, 1730 hrs.
7 Sep 40	Spitfire N3280		Plt Off A K Ogilvie	-	Damaged in combat south of London, 1735 hrs.
,,	Spitfire N3113		Fg Off J D Bisdee	-	Damaged in combat south of London, 1730 hrs.
7 Sep 40	Spitfire R6915		Plt Off N LeC Agazarian	-	Damaged in combat with He 111 south of London, 1800 hrs.
15 Sep 40	Spitfire K9997		Plt Off E Q Tobin	-	Crash-landed at Middle Wallop, 1230 hrs.
15 Sep 40	Spitfire R6690	PR-A	Plt Off G N Gaunt	+	Shot down by Bf 110 and crashed at Castle Hill Farm, Addington Village, Kent, 1230 hrs.
15 Sep 40	Spitfire R6922		Fg Off J C Dundas	-	Damaged in combat with Do 17 over Rye, 1510 hrs.
25 Sep 40	Spitfire L1008		Sgt J A Hughes-Rees	-	Crash-landed near Glastonbury due to engine trouble, 1200 hrs.
,,	Spitfire N3280		Plt Off A K Ogilvie	-	Damaged in combat with Bf 109 south of Bristol, 1200 hrs.

Date	Aircraft	Code	Pilot		Notes
26 Sep 40	Spitfire N3288		Plt Off A K Ogilvie	-	Damaged in combat with He 111 over Christchurch, 1635 hrs.
,,	Spitfire R6979		Sqn Ldr H S Darley	-	Damaged in combat over Christchurch, 1640 hrs.
27 Sep 40	Spitfire X4107		Plt Off R F G Miller	+	Collided with Bf 110 C–4, wk nr 3297 coded 3U+FT of 9/ZG 76 over Cheselbourne at 1145 hrs and crashed near Piddletrenthide, Dorset.
,,	Spitfire X4234		Plt Off M E Staples	-	Damaged in combat over Poole, 1215 hrs.
30 Sep 40	Spitfire R6915		Plt Off N LeC Agazarian	-	Damaged in combat with He 111 north of Warmwell, 1730 hrs.
5 Oct 40	Spitfire N3223	PR-M	Fg Off T Nowierski	-	Abandoned over Salisbury Plain due to undercarriage problems & crashed at Chisenbury, Wilts 1815 hrs.
7 Oct 40	Spitfire N3238		Sgt A N Feary	+	Shot down in combat with Bf 109. Pilot tried to return to Warmwell but baled out too low. Ac crashed at 1630 hrs at Watercombe Farm, Warmwell.
7 Oct 40	Spitfire X4472		Flt Lt F J Howell	-	Crash-landed at Shaftesbury at 1630 hrs after combat with Bf 109 over Yeovil.
7 Oct 40	Spitfire N3231		Plt Off M E Staples	W	Shot down by Bf 109 over Yeovil; pilot baled out burned over Blandford Forum & ac crashed at Wynford Eagle, Dorset 1630 hrs.
,,	Spitfire R6915	PR-O	Fg Off J C Dundas	W	Damaged in combat with Bf 110 over Dorchester, force-landed Warmwell at 1635 hrs.

Date	Ac & Serial	Code	Pilot	Fate	Details
15 Oct 40	Spitfire P9503		Fg Off J C Dundas	-	Damaged by Bf 109 over Southampton, 1240 hrs.
27 Oct 40	Spitfire P9503		Plt Off P A Baillon	-	Shot down in combat with Ju 88 over Andover; pilot baled out and ac crashed at Upavon airfield.
28 Nov 40	Spitfire X4586		Flt Lt J C Dundas DFC	M	Shot down by Lt Rudi Pflanz, Stab/JG 2, 2 miles SW of Isle of Wight, 1615 hrs.
,,	Spitfire R6631	PR-O	Plt Off P A Baillon	+	Shot down by Major Helmut Wick, Stab/JG 2, 1615 hrs.Body washed ashore 5 Jan 41 at Ste Martin de Varonville and buried at Ste Marcouf.
13 Feb 41	Spitfire X4773		Fg Off T Nowierski	-	Damaged in combat with Ju 88 off Plymouth, 1705 hrs.
24 Feb 41	Spitfire X4598		Sgt R T D Mercer	-	Hit bomb crater landing at Biggin Hill and overturned; ac written off.
19 Mar 41	Spitfire P7830		Plt Off A K Ogilvie	-	Damaged in combat with Bf 109 of I(S)/LG 2 overChannel, 1625 hrs.
27 Mar 41	Spitfire P7785		Sgt P H A MacSherry	+	Crashed at St Martin's Plain, Kent, 1630 hrs whilst trying to land at Hawkinge.
16 Apr 41	Drone PR-?		Plt Off S J Hill	-	Crashed near Biggin Hill airfield boundary.
29 Apr 41	Spitfire P7669		FS G C Bennett	M	Shot down by Bf 109s over Channel, 0820 hrs.
,,	Spitfire P7542		Flt Lt J Curchin	-	Damaged by Bf 109s over Channel, 0820 hrs.
,,	Spitfire P7538		Sgt E G A Seghers	-	Damaged by Bf 109s over Channel, 0820 hrs.

Date	Aircraft	Code	Pilot		Notes
8 May 41	Spitfire P7734		Sgt R T D Mercer	-	Damaged by Bf 109s over Channel, 1120 hrs.
„	Spitfire P8264		Flt Lt J Curchin	-	Damaged by Bf 109s over Channel, 1120 hrs.
9 May 41	Spitfire P7305		Sgt R T D Mercer	+	Damaged by Bf 109s and is believed to have hit a mine attempting to force-land on the beach at St Margaret's Bay, Kent.
16 May 41	Spitfire P7602		Sgt A G Palmer	-	Force-landed at Detling after combat with Bf 109s near Dover.
17 May 41	Spitfire P8241	PR-A	Plt Off J A Atkinson	-	Force-landed at Rochester after combat with Bf 109s near Dover.
21 May 41	Spitfire P7436	PR-M	Plt Off R C C De Grunne	M	Shot down in combat with Bf 109s near Dover, 1715 hrs. Flt Lt J D Bisdee thought possible structural failure was responsible.
„	Spitfire P8098	PR-Z	Sgt R Boyd	-	Force-landed at Manston out of fuel.
„	Spitfire P7917	PR-F	Sgt A G Palmer	-	Force-landed at Kingsdown, Kent out of fuel.
15 May 41	Spitfire P7600		Plt Off F X E De Spirlet	-	Damaged in combat with Bf 109s over the Channel, 1900 hrs.
28 May 41	Spitfire P7834		Plt Off R E J Wilmet	-	Damaged in combat with Bf 109s over the Channel, 1830 hrs.
4 Jun 41	Spitfire P8204		Flt Lt J Curchin DFC	M	Probably collided with Bf 109 F–2, wk nr 6707 coded <3–+ of Stab I/JG 53 flown by Fw Heinrich Ruehl over the Straits of Dover, 2030 hrs.
11 Jun 41	Spitfire P8654	PR-L	Sgt G A Chestnut	+	Damaged by Bf 109 NW of Dunkirk, crashed into cliffs at Ramsgate, 1705 hrs.

Date	Ac & Serial	Code	Pilot	Fate	Details
18 Jun 41	Spitfire W3211	PR-H	Plt Off S J Hill	+	Shot down by Bf 109 and crashed 5 miles west of Dover.
22 Jun 41	Spitfire W3197	PR-T	Plt Off F X E De Spirlet	W	Shot down by Bf 109s off Dover at 1500 hrs, pilot baled out and rescued.
23 Jun 41	Spitfire W3215	PR-D	Sgt T C Rigler	-	Damaged by Bf 109s off Dover, 1500 hrs.
,,	Spitfire W3207	PR-F	Plt Off R E J Wilmet	-	Damaged by Bf 109 over the Pas de Calais; crashed at Hawkinge.
4 Jul 41	Spitfire X4664		Fg Off A K Ogilvie DFC	P	Shot down by Bf 109s of JG 26, pilot baled out wounded near St Omer.
6 Jul 41	Spitfire W3179	PR-K	Plt Off R F G Malengreau	-	Damaged by Bf 109 near Gravelines; crash-landed near Deal.
7 Jul 41	Spitfire W3115		Sgt G Evans	W	Shot down by Bf 109 over the Pas de Calais, pilot baled out wounded 2 miles off Boulogne and later rescued.
8 Jul 41	Spitfire W3313	PR-K	Flt Lt P H M Richey	-	Force-landed near Manston out of fuel.
,,	Spitfire W3239	PR-N	Sgt J A Hughes-Rees	W	Shot down in combat with Bf 109 and ditched over the Goodwin Sands, 0630 hrs.
21 Jul 41	Spitfire W3307		Sgt K W Bramble	+	Shot down in combat with Bf 109s near Lille, pilot buried Merville.
,,	Spitfire W3372	PR-L	Sgt J E Van Schaick	-	Badly damaged in combat with Bf 109s near Lille Landed at Manston.
31 Jul 41	Spitfire PR-T		Sgt E W Pollard	-	Damaged in combat, landed Manston.
,,	Spitfire W3187		Sgt R Boyd	-	Shot down by flak and baled out west of Calais; rescued later.
2 Aug 41	Spitfire PR-M		Sgt G A Y F F X Mueller	-	Ran out of fuel and force-landed near Chatham.

Date	Aircraft	Code	Pilot		Remarks
7 Aug 41	Spitfire W3603		Sgt R Boyd	-	Ran out of fuel and force-landed near Sandwich.
"	Spitfire W3240	PR-G	Flt Lt P H M Richey	-	Damaged in combat over Pas de Calais, force-landed Manston.
9 Aug 41	Spitfire W3254		Plt Off A Nitelet	E	Shot down by Lt Karl Borris, 6/JG 26 and crashed at Fauquemberges, 1730 hrs. Pilot badly wounded.
16 Aug 41	Spitfire P8745		Plt Off D L Cropper	+	Shot down by Stab/JG 2 over Cap Gris Nez, 1845 hrs. Pilot buried Pihen Les Guines.
19 Aug 41	Spitfire W3241	PR-D	Plt Off V M Ortmans	-	Shot down by Bf 109; pilot baled out mid-way between Dunkirk and Dover and rescued.
21 Aug 41	Spitfire W3651		Sgt E W Pollard	+	Shot down in combat south of Dunkirk, pilot buried Dunkirk.
27 Aug 41	Spitfire		Sgt A M C Folkard	W	Wounded in eye by cannon shell splinters.
27 Aug 41	Spitfire	PR-R	Sgt T C Rigler	-	Taxied into 92 Sqn Spitfire.
3 Sep 41	Spitfire W3368	PR-P	Plt Off G A Y F F X Mueller	-	Overshot and crashed into a barbed wire emplacement after practice night flying, 1030 hrs. Ac written off.
4 Sep 41	Spitfire	PR-L	Plt Off W B Sanders	-	Damaged in tail in combat and crash-landed at Detling. Ac written off.
17 Sep 41	Spitfire W3767		Plt Off J A Atkinson	-	Shot down in combat and baled out mid-Channel; rescued later.
"	Spitfire W3236	PR-M	Flt Lt J H M Offenberg	-	Damaged in combat.
"	Spitfire	PR-D	Plt Off V M Ortmans	-	Damaged in combat.
21 Sep 41	Spitfire W3315	PR-U	Plt Off W B Sanders	I	Ran out of petrol during final approach and crashed at Gravesend.

357

Date	Ac & Serial	Code	Pilot	Fate	Details
27 Sep 41	Spitfire W3625		Plt Off V M Ortmans	-	Ran out of fuel due to combat and baled out 5 miles off Dover; rescued later.
3 Oct 41	Spitfire	PR-U	Plt Off G E F Dieu	-	Taxied into van at Gravesend, ac written off.
21 Oct 41	Spitfire W3850		Fg Off V M Ortmans	P	Shot down in combat with Fw 190s north of Le Touquet, 1145 hrs.
"	Spitfire AD136	PR-K	Sgt A G Palmer DFM	M	Shot down in combat with Bf 109s off Le Touquet, 1145 hrs.
"	Spitfire W3236	PR-M	S/Lt M Choron	-	Damaged in combat with Bf 109s of JG 26 west of Boulogne, force-landed Rye, 1710 hrs.
15 Nov 41	Spitfire AD507	PR-N	Sgt K Laing	P	Shot down by flak over the Pas de Calais.
15 Dec 41	Spitfire W3574		Fg Off R F G Malengreau	-	Believed landed with wheels up on this day
10 Jan 42	Spitfire R6882	PR-V	Sgt B W Andrews	-	Broke up in air and abandoned 2 miles SE of East Stoke.
15 Jan 42	Spitfire AB859	PR-Y	Plt Off T C Rigler	W	Damaged by flak whilst attacking shipping off the Dutch Coast.
22 Jan 42	Spitfire AB188		Flt Lt J H M Offenberg	+	Collided with Spitfire AD229 of 92 Sqn flown by Sgt Godfrey De Renzi and crashed near Digby, Lincs, 1530 hrs.
14 Apr 42	Spitfire AB787	PR-H	Sgt J A Wilson	-	Selected undercarriage up too early.
19 Apr 42	Spitfire BL324	PR-K	Plt Off R A Lallemant	-	Engine cut on take off from West Malling and undercarriage collapsed.
24 Apr 42	Spitfire		Sgt Featherstone	-	Suffered engine vibration on training flight; pilot baled out near Kirton in Lindsey.

Date	Aircraft	Code	Pilot		Notes
25 Apr 42	Spitfire AD205		Sgt J G Innes	M	Shot down in combat with Bf 109s in Crotose/Le Treport area, 1545–1735 hrs. Believed crashed 8 miles west of Cayeaux.
„	Spitfire		Plt Off J M P De Selys-Longchamps	-	Damaged in combat and landed at West Malling.
29 May 42	Typhoon R7647		Plt Off J M P De Selys-Longchamps	-	Engine caught fire SE of March, Cambs; pilot baled out and ac crashed at Sutton Village near Ely, 1815 hrs.
10 Jun 42	Typhoon R7628	PR-R	Plt Off R Van Lierde	-	Belly landed at Duxford.
26 Jun 42	Typhoon R7817	PR-D	Plt Off R A Lallemant	-	Collided on take off at Duxford with R7710 when tyre burst, 0615 rs hrs. Ac destroyed.
„	Typhoon R7710	PR-E	Flt Lt F X E De Spirlet	+	Collided with above.
30 Jul 42	Typhoon R7816		Plt Off H L Gilbert	-	Crashed in forced landing at Catwater Farm, Cambs.
1 Aug 42	Typhoon R7883	PR-E	Plt Off R E J Wilmet	-	Belly landed at Duxford and not repaired.
23 Oct 42	Typhoon R8812	PR-K	Plt Off R Dopere	+	Crashed in bad weather at Ashburnham Pottery, Ashburnham near Hastings, Sussex, 1550 hrs.
30 Oct 42	Typhoon R7845		Plt Off R H Payne	-	Crash-landed at Biggin Hill 1340 hrs after tyre burst on take off.
31 Oct 42	Typhoon R7708	PR-V	Plt Off R H Payne	-	Shot down by friendly AA fire and ditched in Pegwell Bay.
5 Nov 42	Typhoon R7818	PR-Y	WO S H Spallin	M	Hit balloon cable at Dover and crashed into Channel, 1210 hrs.

Date	Ac & Serial	Code	Pilot	Fate	Details
24 Nov 42	Typhoon R8333		Fg Off R J H Roelandt	-	Hit bird and damaged in forced landing at Manston, 1130 hrs.
15 Dec 42	Typhoon R7689	PR-B	Plt Off H D F Amor	+	Shot down by Uffz Josef Zirngibl, 1/JG 26, 2 miles east of Dover, 1557 hrs. Body washed ashore and buried at Margate.
,,	Typhoon R8899	PR-X	Sgt T S Turek	-	Hit tree during Rhubarb to Roulers, 1310–1410 hrs.
23 Dec 42	Typhoon R8837		Sgt A R N Davis	M	Shot down by Uffz Heinrich Schnell, 3/JG 26, 20 km north of Cap Gris Nez. RAF sources say crashed 1110 hrs, 15 miles south of North Foreland.
18 Jan 43	Typhoon R8815	PR-C	Fg Off R A Lallemant	-	Force-landed Swingate.
,,	Typhoon R8898	PR-F	Fg Off G Evans	-	Take off accident, Bradwell Bay.
7 Feb 43	Typhoon R8838	PR-N	Fg Off P J Nankivell	+	Shot down by Fw 190 and crashed near Staden, Belgium, 1410 hrs.
14 Feb 43	Typhoon R7872	PR-S	Sgt J Wiseman	M	Shot down by Fw 190 of III/JG 2 over Dover Straits, 1100–1110 hrs.
,,	Typhoon DN294	PR-O	FS A Haddon	M	Shot down by Fw 190 of III/JG 2 over Dover Straits, 1100–1110 hrs.
2 Mar 43	Typhoon DN300	PR-W	Fg Off H T Skett	-	Damaged by flak, ac written off.
9 Mar 43	Typhoon DN481	PR-N	Sgt N Booth	+	Broke up during unauthorised aerobatics and crashed near Great Knell Farm, Ash, 1450 hrs.
9 Mar 43	Typhoon R8810	PR-R	Sqn Ldr R P Beamont DFC	I	Suffered engine failure and crash-landed near Deal, 1745 hrs. Ac used for spares.

Date	Aircraft	Code	Pilot		Remarks
25 Mar 43	Typhoon DN560	PR-R	Fg Off J R Baldwin	W	Shot down by Fw 190 10 miles east of Ramsgate, 1815 hrs.
29 Mar 43	Typhoon R8888	PR-Y	Sgt H W Jackson	+	Hit house trying to force-land at Manston, 1545 hrs.
1 Apr 43	Typhoon DN619	PR-P	WO T W Barker	M	Shot down by flak 3 miles north of Dunkirk.
6 Apr 43	Typhoon DN416		Sgt E J Van Zuylen	M	Suffered engine failure and ditched off Dover, 1200 hrs.
16 Apr 43	Typhoon R7855	PR-D	Sgt R W Aitken-Quack	-	Crashed in forced landing at Manston.
30 Apr 43	Typhoon R8883	PR-K	Plt Off M L Van Neste	M	Dived into sea 3 miles ESE of Dover, 0645 hrs.
27 May 43	Hurricane AG265		Sgt R E Bavinton	-	Undercarriage collapsed on landing at Manston.
1 Jun 43	Typhoon DN360	PR-A	Flt Lt E Haabjoern	-	Damaged by flak off Vlissingen and crash landed at Manston, 0605 hrs. Ac written off.
"	Typhoon R7752	PR-G	Sqn Ldr A Ingle DFC	-	Damaged by flak off Vlissingen and crash-landed at Manston, 0550 hrs.
10 Jun 43	Typhoon DN582	PR-P	Sgt F S Bryant	-	Crashed in forced-landing after engine failure.
8 Jul 43	Typhoon DN586	PR-N	Fg Off I J Davies	-	Engine cut on take off from Manston.
8 Aug 43	Typhoon JP390	PR-J	Flt Lt L E Smith	-	Badly damaged by flak and ditched off Deal, 1240 hrs. Possibly coded PR-C?
3 Sep 43	Typhoon EJ971	PR-X	FS A R Blanco	-	Landing in rain, skidded into hangar and damaged beyond repair.
4 Sep 43	Typhoon EK321		Sgt F J Bryant	-	Overshot landing at Lympne and overturned.
11 Sep 43	Typhoon JP678	PR-O	Plt Off T D L Leslie	+	Shot down by flak near Juvincourt, 1600 hrs.
13 Sep 43	Typhoon R8224	PR-H	WO R E Bavinton	-	Overstressed during aeros and not repaired.

361

Date	Ac & Serial	Code	Pilot	Fate	Details
20 Sep 43	Typhoon JP745	PR-L	Plt Off T S Turek	-	Damaged by flak and ditched off Dieppe; pilot rescued 2 days later.
26 Sep 43	Typhoon JP543	PR-A	Plt Off C J G De Moulin	-	Engine failure and ditched; pilot rescued later.
4 Oct 43	Typhoon JP750	PR-P	Plt Off J M J Gueuffen	P	Suffered engine failure and crashed near Fauville, 1445–? hrs.
17 Nov 43	Typhoon JR147		FS R O Ellis	P	Missing near Rouen, probably shot down by flak near Beaumont, 1505 hrs.
17 Nov 43	Typhoon JR191		Sgt G L Watelet	E	Shot down by Fw 190 near Beaumont Le Roger and crashed near Les Planches, 1545 hrs.
30 Nov 43	Typhoon JR332		Fg Off J Niblett	-	Became lost and force-landed near Teignmouth, 1500 hrs.
1 Dec 43	Typhoon JP924	PR-S	Sgt R W Aitken Quack	P	Shot down by Uffz Gerhard Guttmann, 15/JG 26, south of Valenciennes, 1315 hrs.
3 Dec 43	Typhoon JP748		Sgt J A A Zegers	-	Crashed in forced landing at Dungeness.
21 Dec 43	Typhoon R8845		Sqn Ldr P G Thornton-Brown	+	Shot down in error by P-47s in Abbeville area, 1100 hrs. Pilot buried Caumont.
,,	Typhoon JP674	PR-D	Fg Off C W Miller	+	Shot down in error by P-47s in Abbeville area, 1100 hrs. Pilot buried Amiens.
,,	Typhoon JR364		Fg Off A Ross	-	Damaged by P-47s.
3 Jan 44	Typhoon JP525	PR-B	FS J A A Zegers	+	Shot down by Uffz Gerhard Guttmann, 15/JG 26 north of Cambrai 1345 hrs. Pilot buried Grevelliers.
4 Jan 44	Typhoon JR374		Fg Off G J G Daix	M	Ditched off Ostende after possible engine failure.

Date	Aircraft	Code	Pilot		Remarks
14 Jan 44	Typhoon JR375	PR-B	Plt Off J G McLaughlin	P	Force-landed near Volkel.
29 Jan 44	Typhoon JP662	PR-A	Plt Off L L Henrion	M	Missing near Walcheren, 1315–? hrs.
2 Feb 44	Typhoon EK121	PR-U	Fg Off J A Stewart	-	Landed heavily and stalled, Manston.
29 Feb 44	Typhoon MN211		Fg Off M H Shelton	+	Shot down by flak near Douai on Ramrod 603. Pilot buried Cambrai.
23 Mar 44	Typhoon MN140		Flt Lt C F J Detal DFC	+	Spun into ground at North Seaton near Acklington, Northumberland, 1445 hrs.
25 Mar 44	Typhoon MN179		Flt Lt P E R Pike	I	Crashed at Acklington, Northumberland, 1455 hrs.
11 May 44	Typhoon MN496		Fg Off P L Soesman	M	Shot down by flak north of Caen and ditched into Channel, 1930 hrs.
"	Typhoon MN544		Flt Lt R L Wood	M	Shot down by flak off Cap D'Antifer.
"	Typhoon		FS R K Adam	-	Damaged by debris from MN544.
13 May 44	Typhoon MN414		Flt Lt J A Stewart	P	Shot down by flak near Fleury, 1040–? hrs.
"	Typhoon MN155		FS L P Fidgin	+	Shot down by flak near Rouen, pilot buried Beauvais.
30 May 44	Typhoon JR386		Fg Off J D Thorogood	E	Shot down by flak 15 miles NW of Formerie; pilot baled out and ac crashed at Flamet.
6 Jun 44	Typhoon MN697		WO G K E Martin	E	Shot down by flak N W of Caen.
17 Jun 44	Typhoon EJ912		?		Crashed in forced landing near Wantage.
27 Jun 44	Typhoon MN818		Fg Off R H Holmes	+	Shot down by flak at Alencon, pilot buried Le Mans.
29 Jun 44	Typhoon MN339		Fg Off C A Rowland	+	Shot down by Lt Guenther Heckmann, 8/JG 1 and crashed at Mezidon. Pilot buried St Aubin.

Date	Ac & Serial	Code	Pilot	Fate	Details
11 Jul 44	Typhoon R8972	PR-V	FS L E Bliss	+	Shot down by flak and crashed at Onchy; pilot buried Hottot-Les-Bouges.
27 Jul 44	Typhoon MN494	PR-E	Plt Off J D Buchanan	+	Shot down by flak near Tilly La Campagne. Pilot buried Banneville. Possibly coded PR-Z.
,,	Typhoon JP843		FS P M Price	+	Shot down by flak near Tilly La Campagne. Pilot buried Ranville.
29 Jul 44	Typhoon JP407		FS R Ashworth	M	Presumed shot down by flak near L'Aigle/Evroult.
31 Jul 44	Typhoon MN239		FS R K Adam	+	Crashed Caen/Falaise, pilot buried Banneville.
3 Aug 44	Typhoon MN322	PR-F	Fg Off P H M Cooreman	E	Shot down by flak behind enemy lines.
12 Aug 44	Typhoon MN630	PR-B	Flt Lt T Y Wallace DFM	-	Hit by JR379 (FS P W Lough) on runway at Martragny.
14 Aug 44	Typhoon JP966	PR-V	Plt Off R D Grant	P	Shot down near Falaise.
15 Aug 44	Typhoon JP659		WO F L Taylor	+	Shot down near Falaise, pilot buried Bayeux.
18 Aug 44	Typhoon JR125	PR-I	Flt Lt M L Carrick	+	Shot down near Trun, pilot buried Bailleul.
19 Aug 44	Typhoon JP975		WO J K Stellin	+	Shot down near Bernay; pilot buried St Maclou La Briere.
26 Aug 44	Typhoon MN142		Flt Lt R J H Roelandt	+	Shot down by flak near St Hellier; pilot buried Brettagne.
14 Sep 44	Typhoon PD505		Sqn Ldr R A Lallemant DFC	W	Damaged by flak and crash-landed at Merville and burned.
18 Sep 44	Typhoon MN954		Flt Lt J V Van Daele	+	Shot down by flak near Rotterdam. Pilot buried Altblasserdam

Date	Aircraft	Code	Pilot		Remarks
29 Oct 44	Typhoon JP494	PR-T	WO F S Hammond	-	Badly damaged by flak and force-landed near Bruges.
"	Typhoon MN268	PR-X	WO T F Annear	I	Crashed in forced landing near Estaires.
11 Nov 44	Typhoon MN205		Sqn Ldr T Y Wallace DFM	+	Shot down by flak and crashed on the beach at Dunkirk 1450-? hrs.
5 Dec 44	Typhoon PD470	PR-D	Sqn Ldr C J G De Moulin	P	Shot down by flak near Ede, 0930-? hrs.
9 Dec 44	Typhoon MN150		Sgt R J Parthoens	+	Lost control in cloud and crashed near Gorinchem.
2 Jan 45	Typhoon JR379	PR-L	Fg Off G F E H A De Beuger	-	Crashed on take off, 1110 hrs. Ac written off. Possibly coded PR-F.
8 Feb 45	Typhoon MN360	PR-D	Sgt J De Bruyn	-	Hit trees pulling out of dive and abandoned near Handel.
14 Feb 45	Typhoon RB311		Flt Lt R K Gibson	+	Shot down by flak near Kleve, crashed near Pfalzaldorf, 0930-? hrs.
25 Feb 45	Typhoon MN178	PR-V	Fg Off J D F Wathieu	-	Shot down by flak near Weeze.
3 Mar 45	Typhoon EK380		Fg Off T H R Goblet	P	Shot down by flak near Xanten.
9 Mar 45	Typhoon SW447		Sqn Ldr E R A Roberts DFC	P	Shot down by flak near Sommelsdijk.
10 Mar 45	Typhoon PD449	PR-A	WO G M Reynolds	-	Crash-landed at Gilze-Rijen.
18 Mar 45	Typhoon PD519	PR-I	WO G M Reynolds	-	Tyre burst on take off from Gilze Rijen and ac flicked over.
19 Mar 45	Typhoon JP858		WO F S Hammond	P	Suffered engine failure and force-landed NE of Deventer, Holland, 1130 hrs (possibly hit trees near Linde).
19 Mar 45	Typhoon SW499	PR-H	Plt Off K Adams	-	Crash-landed Gilze-Rijen 1135 hrs.

Date	Ac & Serial	Code	Pilot	Fate	Details
12 Apr 45	Typhoon PD593		Flt Lt J D Inches	W	Shot down by flak near Friesoythe.
13 Apr 45	Typhoon RB250	PR-A	FS A H E De Blommaert De Soye	+	Collided with MN434 and crashed near Grave Bridge, Holland, 1630 hrs.
" 16 Apr 45	Typhoon MN434	PR-K	Plt Off M H G Rendall	+	Collided with RB250.
16 Apr 45	Typhoon JR294	PR-K	Sgt A R A Deschamps	-	Badly damaged by flak and force-landed near Kampe.
23 Apr 45	Typhoon PD572	PR-O	WO S E Smith	+	Shot down by flak near Emden and crashed at Funten, Holland.
8 May 45	Typhoon SW497	PR-G	FS N J Dixon	-	Crashed in forced landing near Meppen.
5 Jul 45	Typhoon JR440		FS N R Dixon	-	Damaged in landing accident at B58.
8 Aug 45	Typhoon MN658		Flt Lt E R Carruthers	+	Crashed in bad weather 2 miles east of Schedehausen.
22 Aug 45	Typhoon JP375		WO R Dunne	I	Engine failure and force-landed near Wunsdorf.
20 Sep 45	Typhoon SW392		FS T L Kerr	-	Collided on ground at Wunsdorf with RB336, 0940 hrs. Ac written off.
23 Jul 48	Typhoon RB336		Flt Lt R A Royston	-	Collided on ground with SW392.
"	Spitfire TB625	RAJE	Flt Lt P W Thompson	-	Taxying accident with Anson NK715 at Manston, 1015 hrs.
2 May 49	Spitfire SM316		Pilot 2 J Mudd	-	Crashed after engine failure 1 mile south of Yeadon, 1935 hrs
22 Apr 56	Meteor WE895	H	Flt Lt W S Campbell	+	Crashed 4 miles SW of Selby

APPENDIX D
609 SQUADRON AIR COMBAT VICTORIES

Date	Pilot	Type	Details
27 Feb 40	Fg Off G D Ayre Plt Off J R Buchanan Fg Off D Persse-Joynt	He 111	Shot down 4–8 miles east of St Abbs Head, 1300 hrs. He 111 H–2 of 2/KG 26. Oblt Heinrich & crew POW
31 May 40	Plt Off C N Overton	He 111	Dunkirk area
,,	Fg Off I B N Russell	Bf 109	,,
,,	Plt Off C N Overton	Do 17	,,
,,	Plt Off P Drummond-Hay	He 111	,,
,,	Plt Off J R Buchanan	He 111	,,
,,	Plt Off J C Dundas	Do 17	,,
,,		Do 17	,,
9 Jul 40	Plt Off D M Crook	Ju 87	Off Portland, 1500 hrs. Ju 87 B of Stab I/St G 77. Hptm Freiherr von Dalwigk zu Lichtenfels (Gruppen Kommandeur) & gunner missing.
13 Jul 40	Fg Off J C Dundas	Bf 110	Portland Bill, 1500hrs.
,,	Plt Off R F G Miller	,,	,,
19 Jul 40	Fg Off J C Dundas	Bf 110	
8 Aug 40	Plt Off M J Appleby	,,	Off Isle of Wight, 1230 hrs.
,,	Plt Off J Curchin	,,	,,
,,	Sqn Ldr H S Darley	Ju 87	,,
,,	Flt Lt J H G McArthur	,,	,,
,,	,,	,,	,,

368

Date	Name	Type	Location/Notes
11 Aug 40	Plt Off N Le C Agazarian	Bf 110	15 miles south of Portland Bill, 1015 hrs.
,,	Fg Off J C Dundas	,,	Off Swanage, 1015 hrs.
,,	Plt Off J D Bisdee	,,	,,
,,	Flt Lt J H G McArthur	,,	15 miles SSE of Swanage, 1015 hrs.
12 Aug 40	Fg Off J C Dundas	Bf 110	East of the Isle of Wight, 1230 hrs.
,,	Plt Off H McD Goodwin	,,	,,
,,	Plt Off C N Overton	Bf 109	,,
,,	Fg Off D M Crook	,,	,,
,,	Sgt A N Feary	,,	,,
,,	Plt Off M E Staples	Bf 110	,,
,,	Plt Off N Le C Agazarian	,,	,,
13 Aug 40	Plt Off C N Overton	Ju 87	Lyme Bay, 1555 hrs.
,,	Fg Off J C Dundas	,,	Lyme Bay, 1600 hrs.
,,	Fg Off H McD Goodwin	,,	5 miles west of Portland, 1600 hrs.
,,	Plt Off R F G Miller	,,	5 miles west of Dorchester, 1600 hrs.
,,	Flt Lt F J Howell	,,	5 miles off Warmwell, 1600 hrs
,,	Fg Off T Nowierski	Bf 109	Off Weymouth, 1600 hrs. Bf 109 E–1, black 9+- of 5/JG 53 crashed into Weymouth Bay, Fw Pfannschmidt POW.
,,	Fg Off D M Crook	,,	Weymouth, 1600 hrs. Bf 109 E–1, black 10 of 5/JG 53. Crashed into Poole Harbour, Uffz Hohenfeldt POW.
,,	Flt Lt F J Howell	Ju 87	Lyme Bay.
,,	Plt Off M E Staples	,,	,,
,,	Sgt A N Feary	,,	Lyme Bay, 1615 hrs.

Date	Pilot	Type	Details
14 Aug 40	Fg Off J C Dundas	He 111	Romsey, 1700 hrs. He 111 P, wk nr 2898, G1+AA of Stab/KG 55 crashed East Dean, Hants. Oberst Stoeckl (Geschwader Kommodore) plus 2 killed, 2 POW.
,,	Fg Off D M Crook	,,	
,,	Sgt A N Feary	Ju 88	Near Middle Wallop.
15 Aug 40	Flt Lt F J Howell	Ju 88	Romsey, 1750 hrs. Possibly Bf 110 C of Stab II/ZG 76.
,,	Fg Off A R Edge	Bf 110	Crashed at Broadlands near Romsey, 1755 hrs. Uffz Rohrich & radio operator killed.
,,	Plt Off P Ostazewski	,,	Isle of Wight. Bf 110 C, M8+BP of 6/ZG 76. Crashed 1806 hrs at Ashey Down, Brading. Fw Birndorfer killed, radio operator wounded POW.
,,	Flt Lt J H G McArthur	,,	NW of Southampton.
,,	,,	,,	15 miles SSW of above kill.
25 Aug 40	Plt Off N Le C Agazarian	Bf 110	NW of Poole Harbour, 1710 hrs. Bf 110 C—4, 3M+KH of 1/ZG 2. Crashed at Priory Farm, East Holme, Dorset.
,,	Plt Off G Gaunt	,,	Uffz Becker and radio operator POW.
,,	Flt Lt J H G McArthur	,,	Warm well/Poole area, 1720 hrs.
,,	Sqn Ldr H S Darley	,,	2 miles off Warmwell, 1720 hrs.
,,	,,	Bf 109	4 miles off Warmwell, 1720 hrs.
,,	Plt Off E Q Tobin	Bf 110	Portsmouth/Bournemouth area.
,,	Plt Off J Curchin	Bf 109	5 miles off Portland, 1730 hrs.
,,	Flt Lt F J Howell	Bf 110	Portsmouth/Bournemouth area.
,,	Sgt A N Feary	,,	Coombe Keynes, 1745 hrs. Bf 110 C—4 of 1/ZG 2. Crashed Creech Barrow, Wareham, Oblt Goetz (Staffel Kapitaen) plus radio operator POW.

Date	Pilot	Type	Location
7 Sep 40	Plt Off J Curchin	Bf 109	Thames Estuary, 1740 hrs.
"	Fg Off T Nowierski	Do 17	
"	Flt Lt J H G McArthur	"	
"	Fg Off J D Bisdee	Bf 110	SW of London, 1800 hrs.
"	Flt Lt F J Howell	"	London, 1800 hrs.
"	Plt Off A K Ogilvie	Bf 109	"
15 Sep 40	Plt Off A K Ogilvie	Do 17	East of London, 1215 hrs. Do 17 Z, wk nr 2361, F1+FH of 1/KG 76. Claimed by numerous RAF fighters and crashed at Victoria Station. Oblt Zehbe and 2 killed, 2 POW.
"	Plt Off J Curchin		
"	Plt Off M J Appleby	"	Belly landed near Dungeness, 1210 hrs. Do 17 Z, wk nr 2555 F1+FS of 8/KG 76. Crash-landed at Castle Farm, Shoreham, Fw Heitsch plus 2 POW, one killed.
"	Plt Off E Q Tobin		
"	Fg Off J C Dundas		
"	Plt Off J Curchin	"	North of Hastings, 1530 hrs
"	Plt Off N Le C Agazarian		
"	Fg Off J C Dundas	Do 17	1530 hrs
"	Flt Lt F J Howell	"	"
24 Sep 40	Plt Off J Curchin	Bf 110	Off Isle of Wight, 1620 hrs
"	Sgt A N Feary	Do 17	Brightstone Bay, 1620 hrs
"	Plt Off M E Staples	"	Off Isle of Wight, 1620 hrs
"	Fg Off J C Dundas	Bf 109	Off Isle of Wight, 1620 hrs
25 Sep 40	Sgt J A Hughes Rees	Bf 110	Off Portishead Point, 1130 hrs.
"	Plt Off J Curchin	He 111	Force-landed near Swanage, 1130 hrs. He 111 H, wk nr 6305, G1+BH of 1/KG 55. Crash landed at Studland, Hptm Koethke and crew POW.

Date	Pilot	Type	Details
25 Sep 40	Flt Lt J H G McArthur	Bf 110	Bournemouth.
"	Fg Off J C Dundas	"	"
"	Plt Off N Le C Agazarian	He 111	Into a house east of Poole Harbour. He 111 P, wk nr 2803 G1 + LR of 7/KG 55. Crashed at Branksome Park, Poole, 1208 hrs. Oblt Scholz and crew killed.
	Plt Off J Curchin		
"	Fg Off T Nowierski	"	West of Bournemouth.
	Plt Off R F G Miller		
26 Sep 40	Plt Off N Le C Agazarian	Bf 109	Southampton, 1630 hrs.
"	Fg Off J C Dundas	"	"
"	Plt Off J Curchin	He 111	30 miles south of Southampton, 1630 hrs. Possibly He 111 H, wk nr 5314, G1+BL of 3/KG 55. Oblt Graf Schweinitz plus 4 missing.
27 Sep 40	Fg Off D M Crook	Bf 110	60 miles south of Weymouth, 1145 hrs
"	Fg Off J D Bisdee	"	Portland.
"	Fg Off J C Dundas	Bf 109	25 miles south of Portland, 1200 hrs
"	Plt Off N Le C Agazarian	Bf 110	Collided with Bf 110 C-4, wk nr 3297, 3U+FT of 9/ZG 26 which crashed at Dole Ash Farm, Piddletrenthide. Gefr Jackstedt POW, radio operator killed,
"	Plt Off R F G Miller		Portland
"	Plt Off A K Ogilvie	Bf 109	Off Swanage, 1130 hrs
30 Sep 40	Fg Off D M Crook	"	"
"	Plt Off M J Appleby	"	Weymouth, 1130 hrs

Date	Pilot	Aircraft	Details
30 Sep 40	Fg Off T Nowierski	Bf 109	Sydling St Nicholas, 1715 hrs. Bf 109 E–4, wk nr 4861 of 5/JG 2, crashed at Sydling St Nicholas, Gefr Dollinger killed.
7 Oct 40	Fg Off J D Bisdee	Bf 110	Cerne Abbas, 1550 hrs.
,,	Sqn Ldr M L Robinson	,,	North of Portland.
,,	,,	,,	Long Bredy. Bf 110 C–7, wk nr 3418, 3U+JP of 6/ZG 26. Ofw Herzog and radio operator killed.
,,	Flt Lt F J Howell	,,	10 miles NW of Portland, 1600 hrs.
,,	Fg Off J C Dundas	Bf 109	6 miles north of Warmwell, 1630 hrs.
15 Oct 40	,,	Bf 110	Christchurch Bay, 1240 hrs.
,,	Plt Off N Le C Agazarian	Bf 109	Poole area, 1240 hrs.
,,	Fg Off T Nowierski	,,	Lymington, 1245 hrs. Bf 109 E–1, wk nr 3279, white 10 of 4/JG 2. Crashed at Everton near Lymington, Gefr Pollach POW.
21 Oct 40	Flt Lt F J Howell	Ju 88	Milford on Sea, 1345 hrs. Ju 88 A–5, wk nr 8116, 9K+BH of 1/KG 51. Crashed 1347 hrs, Oblt Fabian and crew killed.
	Plt Off S J Hill		*100th kill.*
28 Nov 40	Flt Lt J C Dundas	Bf 109	Off Isle of Wight, 1615 hrs. Bf 109 E–4, wk nr 5344, <+ of Stab/JG 2. Maj Wick (Geschwader Kommodore) missing
2 Dec 40	Fg Off T Nowierski	Bf 110	Off Thorney Island
,,	Fg Off N Le C Agazarian		
8 May 41	Sqn Ldr M L Robinson	Bf 109	Off Calais, 1720 hrs.
,,	Flt Lt J Curchin	,,	,,
,,		,,	,,
,,	Sgt J A Hughes-Rees	,,	

Date	Pilot	Type	Details
8 May 41	Sgt T C Rigler	Bf 109	Off Calais, 1720 hrs
,,	,,	,,	,,
16 May 41	Plt Off S J Hill	Bf 109	Off Dover, 1615 hrs.
,,	Plt Off A K Ogilvie	,,	Off Dover, 1620 hrs.
21 May 41	Flt Lt J D Bisdee	Bf 109	10 miles off Deal, 1800 hrs
	Plt Off V M Ortmans		
4 Jun 41	Plt Off V M Ortmans	Bf 109	4 miles off Dover, 2010 hrs.
,,	Sgt T C Rigler	,,	2 miles south of Dover, 2010 hrs.
17 Jun 41	Fg Off A K Ogilvie	Bf 109	Exploded at Le Touquet, 1930 hrs.
,,	Flt Lt J D Bisdee	,,	Le Touquet, 1930 hrs.
,,	Fg Off F X E De Spirlet	,,	Off Le Touquet, 1945 hrs
21 Jun 41	Sgt R J Boyd	Bf 109	4 miles NE of Le Touquet, 1735 hrs.
,,	Fg Off A K Ogilvie	,,	Pilot baled out near Le Touquet, 1740 hrs.
22 Jun 41	Flt Lt J D Bisdee	Bf 109	Dunkirk, 1600 hrs.
,,	Sgt T C Rigler	,,	On the beach east of Dunkirk, 1600 hrs.
,,	Sgt T C Rigler	,,	In a field near Boubourg, 1600 hrs.
,,	Sgt T C Rigler	,,	Off Berck Sur Mer, 1600 hrs.
30 Jun 41	Flt Lt P H M Richey	Bf 109	Foret De Nieppe, 1820 hrs.
,,	Plt Off V M Ortmans	,,	Lille.
,,	Sgt J A Hughes Rees	,,	NW of St Omer, 1900 hrs.
3 Jul 41	Sqn Ldr M L Robinson	Bf 109	Hazebrouck, 1200 hrs

374

3 Jul 41	Sqn Ldr M L Robinson	Bf 109	Hazebrouck, 1200 hrs
7 Jul 41	Plt Off J H M Offenberg	Bf 109	Off Le Touquet 1045–1130 hrs
8 Jul 41	Sgt J A Hughes-Rees	Bf 109	Near Lens, 0620 hrs
9 Jul 41	Flt Lt J D Bisdee	Bf 109	Le Touquet beach, 1410 hrs
10 Jul 41	Sqn Ldr M L Robinson	Bf 109	Hardelot, 1216 hrs.
11 Jul 41	,,	Bf 109	Cassel/St Omer, 1445 hrs; pilot baled out.
,,	Sgt R J Boyd	,,	36 miles SE of Dunkirk, 1450 hrs.
,,	Plt Off E G A Seghers	,,	Cassel, 1500 hrs; pilot baled out.
,,	Gp Capt R Barwell	,,	Cassel/St Omer, 1445 hrs; wings broke off
12 Jul 41	Sqn Ldr M L Robinson	Bf 109	Off Cap Gris Nez, 1340 hrs.
14 Jul 41	Sqn Ldr M L Robinson	Bf 109	Inland from Le Touquet, 1000 hrs
23 Jul 41	Flt Lt P H M Richey	Bf 109	Foret De Nieppe, 2015 hrs; pilot baled out.
24 Jul 41	Sgt T C Rigler	Bf 109	Off Fecamp; pilot baled out.
9 Aug 41	Plt Off A Nitelet	Bf 109	Campagne, 1820 hrs.
16 Aug 41	Fg Off B De Hemptinne	Bf 109	Ambleteuse, 1830 hrs.
18 Aug 41	Plt Off Y Du Monceau de Bergandael	Bf 109	2 miles off Calais, 1820 hrs.
,,	Plt Off V M Ortmans	,,	5 miles north of Calais, 1825 hrs.
27 Aug 41	Fg Off M P C Choron	Bf 109	Off Gravelines, 0735 hrs.
29 Aug 41	Fg Off F X E De Spirlet	Bf 109	Inland from Gravelines, 0730 hrs.

Date	Pilot	Type	Details
17 Sep 41	Fg Off M P C Choron	Bf 109	8 miles off Cap Gris Nez, 1503 hrs.
27 Sep 41	Plt Off Y Du Monceau de Bergandael	Bf 109	5 miles off Mardyck, 1425–1500 hrs
13 Oct 41	Sgt P A Nash	Bf 109	20 miles west of Bethune, 1430 hrs.
21 Oct 41	Fg Off V M Ortmans	Fw 190	Off Boulogne/Hardelot, 1150–1210 hrs
27 Oct 41	Sqn Ldr G K Gilroy	Bf 109	Off Cap Gris Nez, 1500 hrs
„	„	„	„
7 Nov 41	Sgt P A Nash	Bf 109	3 miles off Le Touquet
„	Sgt J E Van Schaick	„	10 miles NE of Le Touquet
8 Nov 41	Sqn Ldr G K Gilroy	Bf 109	Le Touquet, 1145 hrs.
18 Nov 41	Plt Off D A Barnham	Fw 190	Off Dover, 1215 hrs.
18 Feb 42	Fg Off Y Du Monceau de Bergandael	Do 217	Off the Humber Estuary, 1437 hrs. Probably Do 217 E–4, wk nr 5342, U5+KR of 7/KG 2. Lt Palm and crew missing from an attack on the east coast of the UK.
8 Mar 42	Fg Off G E F Dieu	Fw 190	Off Dunkirk, 1630 hrs. Possibly Fw 190 A–1, wk nr 092, black 10 of 8/JG 26; Fw Weber killed.
„	Fg Off Y Du Monceaude Bergandael	„	10 miles off Cap Gris Nez, 1630 hrs. See above; 121 Sqn claimed 1.
15 Apr 42	Sqn Ldr G K Gilroy	Fw 190	10 miles SSW of St Inglevert, 1430 hrs. Probably from I/JG 26

Date	Pilot	Type	Details
25 Apr 42	Plt Off T C Rigler	Bf 109	Le Crotoy/Le Treport area. Possibly Bf 109 F–4, wk nr 7657, white 14 of 1/JG 2. Fw Steiner killed (also claimed by 118 and 124 Sqns).
15 Dec 42	Flt Sgt A Haddon	Fw 190	East of Ramsgate, 1600 hrs; pilot baled out.
16 Dec 42	Sgt T S Turek	Fw 190	On the beach at Boulogne, 1505 hrs.
19 Dec 42	Fg Off R A Lallemant	Fw 190	Off Deal, 1420 hrs. Probably Fw 190 A–4, wk nr 0712 of 10/JG 26; Oblt Muller (Staffel Kapitaen) killed.
20 Dec 42	Sgt T S Turek	Fw 190	Off Dungeness, 0905 hrs. Possibly from I/JG 26.
20 Jan 43	Fg Off R A Lallemant	Fw 190	Off Dungeness, 0915 hrs. Fw 190 A–4, wk nr 7037, black 8 of 8/JG 26. Crashed 3 kms west of Cap Gris Nez. 0925 hrs, Lt Kummerling killed.
"	Fg Off R Van Lierde	"	1250 hrs.
"	Fg Off J R Baldwin	Bf 109	Off Dover. Bf 109 G–4, wk nr 16141, brown 11 of 6/JG 26. Lt Wenzel (Staffel Fuehrer) missing.
"	"	"	Off Dover. Bf 109 G–4, wk nr 16102, brown 7 of 6/JG 26. Uffz Budde POW
"	"	"	Off Dover. Bf 109 G–4, wk nr 16113, brown 12 of 6/JG 26. Uffz Marquardt POW.
"	Fg Off A J Atkinson	Fw 190	5 miles east of Dover, 1435 hrs.
21 Jan 43	Fg Off P J Nankivell	Fw 190	10 miles east of Deal, 0840 hrs. Possibly Fw 190 A–4, wk nr 0692 of II/JG 26. Shot down off Calais, Uffz Kaufmann killed.
5 Feb 43	"	Fw 190	30 miles south of Beachy Head, 0940 hrs. Possibly Fw 190 A–4, wk nr 2435, black 1 of 10/JG 26. Uffz Buttner killed

Date	Pilot	Type	Details
10 Feb 43	Flt Lt J C Wells	Fw 190	Off St Margarets Bay, 1655 hrs. Fw 190 A–4, wk nr 5655, brown 14 of I/JG 2. Uffz Leber killed
14 Feb 43	Fg Off R A Lallemant	Fw 190	Off Dover, 1155 hrs. III/JG 2 lost Fw 190 A–4, wk nr 0733, Uffz Armbruster killed; Fw 190 A–4, wk nr 2421, Lt Deuerling killed: Fw 190 A–4, wk nr 7177, Uffz Bischoff killed. 800–1000 yds off Dover, 1200 hrs. See above.
„	Fg Off J H P De Selys Longchamps	„	Off Calais, 1200 hrs. See above.
„	Fg Off R H Payne	„	Off Calais, 1210 hrs.
16 Feb 43	Flt Lt J C Wells	Bf 109	Off South Foreland, 1655 hrs.
26 Feb 43	Fg Off A J Atkinson	Fw 190	2 miles west of Boulogne; possibly Fw 190 A–4, wk nr 0674 of 8/JG 26, Oblt Thiessen killed.
3 Mar 43	Fg Off J R Baldwin	Fw 190	Off Cap Gris Nez, 1000 hrs.
12 Mar 43	Plt Off L W F Stark	Fw 190	Dunkirk/Mardyck area, 1020 hrs. Probably Fw 190 A–5, wk nr 0829 of 10/JG 54. Crashed 10–20 kms off Dunkirk, Fw Boesch missing.
26 Mar 43	Plt Off R Van Lierde	Ju 52	Chievres, 1220 hrs. Ju 52 3/m wk nr 3230 of Ueberfuhrungskommando Luftzeuggruppe 3 (UKdo LzGr 3), Ath. Fw Benthark and crew all killed.
7 Apr 43	Sgt T D L Leslie	Do 217	Off Cap Gris Nez, 1350 hrs.

Date	Name	Type	Remarks
9 Apr 43	Flt Lt E Haabjoern	Fw 190	Off Boulogne, 1915 hrs. Possibly Fw 190 A–4, wk nr 5612 of III/JG 26, crashed in the sea off Boulogne, Lt Spieler killed.
14 May 43	Plt Off R Van Lierde	He 111	Off Ostend, 0020 hrs.
1 Jun 43	Fg Off I J Davies	Fw 190	Broadstairs/Ostend. Only loss Fw 190 A–5, wk nr 2529 green R of 5/SKG 10. Crashed near Manston, Uffz Zuegenruecker killed.
,,	,,	,,	Broadstairs/Ostend
,,	,,	,,	Broadstairs/Ostend
,,	Flt Lt J C Wells	,,	Off Ramsgate, 1310 hrs
,,	,,	,,	Off Ramsgate, 1315 hrs
30 Jul 43	Plt Off R Van Lierde	Bf 109	Off Zandvoort, 1110 hrs. Possibly Bf 109 G–4, wk nr 16180 of III/JG 54, crashed near Falberg, Uffz Hunginger killed or Bf 109 G–4, wk nr 14971 of III/JG 54, crashed near Amerongen, Fw Hermann wounded
,,	Flt Lt E Haabjoern	,,	Off Zaandvoort, 1115 hrs; see above
28 Aug 43	Sqn Ldr P G Thornton-Brown	Fw 190	St Clair/Verneuil. 10/JG 26 lost 2 ac near Evreux: Fw 190 A–6, wk nr 550442, Lt Mayer killed and Fw 190 A–6, wk nr 530393, Uffz Schmid killed.
,,	Flt Lt J R Baldwin	,,	,,
11 Sep 43	Fg Off A S Ross	Hs 126	Sissonnes, 1400 hrs.
,,	Fg Off F J Reahill	e/a	Chateau Thierry. Possibly Ar 96 B–1, wk nr 4255, RB+VC of 3/SG 101. Crashed near Chery les Pouilly, Uffz Huppertz killed.
,,	Plt Off T D L Leslie	Fi 156	Juvincourt

Date	Pilot	Type	Details
4 Oct 43	Flt Lt J R Baldwin	Bf 109	Juvincourt/Laon. Possibly Bf 109 G–6, wk nr 20640 of 7/JG 2, crashed near Creil, Uffz Baudisch killed or Bf 109 G–6, wk nr 27065 of 7/JG 2, force-landed near Compeigne, Uffz Sonntag wounded.
"	Sgt L L Henrion	Bf 110	Florennes
"	Fg Off C J G De Moulin	"	"
5 Oct 43	Fg Off L W F Stark	Ju 88	*200th kill*. Possibly Ju 88 A–4, wk nr 144105 of IV/KG 6. Shot down by fighters near Sevry, Uffz Moeckel and crew killed.
"	Fg Off R Van Lierde	"	See above.
16 Oct 43	Plt Off C F J Detal	Me 410	Bretigny
	Flt Lt L E Smith		
"	Flt Lt J R Baldwin	Ju 88	Probably Ju 88 A–14, wk nr 144375 of IV/KG 6. Shot down by fighters near Chevannes, Uffz Trocka and crew killed or Ju 88 A–14, wk nr 1735 of IV/KG 6. Shot down by fighters near Mennesy, Ogefr Guzi and one killed, 2 wounded.
	Sqn Ldr P G Thornton Brown		
	Sqn Ldr P G Thornton Brown.		
"	Flt Lt L E Smith	"	See above
2 Nov 43	Plt Off G L R C Jaspis	Bu 133	15 miles NE Paris. Probably Bu 131 wk nr 0184, RO+NA of 6/SG 101. Crashed at Chateau de La Fortune, Lt Badewitz plus one killed.

Date	Crew	Aircraft	Notes
2 Nov 43	Fg Off L W F Stark	Ju 88	15 miles NE Paris. Probably Ju 88 A–4, wk nr 4472 of IV/KG 6. Shot down by fighters near Marles/Coulommiers, Uffz Boettger and crew killed.
"		Ju 88	
30 Nov 43	Fg Off R Van Lierde	Bf 110	Hasselt
1 Dec 43	WO G K E Martin	Bf 109	Alsemberg. Fw 190 A–6, wk nr 530127 of Stab/JG 2 crashed near Brussels?
4 Dec 43	Plt Off C F J Detal	Do 217	Eindhoven, 1500 hrs. 3/KG 2 lost 4 ac, 7/KG 2 one ac during attack by 198 and 609 Sqns
"	"	"	"
2 Jan 44	Fg Off L E J M Geerts	Fw 190	WNW of Charleville
3 Jan 44	Plt Off C F J Detal	Fw 190	North of Cambrai, 1345 hrs
4 Jan 44	Plt Off C F J Detal	Do 217	Gilze Rijen. 7/KG 2 lost 2 ac, 10/KG 2 lost one.
"	Fg Off L W F Stark	"	
"	Fg Off L E J M Geerts	"	
"	Fg Off I J Davies	"	
"	Fg Off W F Watts	"	
10 Jan 44	Fg Off G L R C Jaspis	Ju 88	Melsbroeck
27 Jan 44	Fg Off C F J Detal	Bf 109	Probably Bf 109 wk nr 410296 of 6/JG 2, Uffz Raub killed
"	"	Bf 110	Brussels/Evere. Probably wk nr 4770 of ERLA, Brussels, Uffz Drost wounded
"	Fg Off L W F Stark	Goeland	Brussels. Probably Fw 58 wk nr 3581 of Flugsbereitschaft Lg Kdo, all killed.

Date	Pilot	Type	Details
30 Jan 44	Fg Off C J G De Moulin	Fw 190	
"	Fg Off L W F Stark	"	
"		"	
26 Feb 44	Plt Off G L R C Jaspis	Ju 88	Charleroi/Fruges
29 Feb 44	Sqn Ldr J C Wells Flt Lt L E Smith Fg Off C J G De Moulin WO G K E Martin WO J D Buchanan	Ju 188	Near Cambrai. Ju 188 A, 3E+AB of Stab I/KG 6. Crashed 1330 hrs at Sebancourt. Major Fuhrhopp and crew killed.
29 Feb 44	Sqn Ldr J C Wells Flt Lt L E Smith Fg Off G Jaspis Flt Lt J P Le Grand WO G K E Martin WO J D Buchanan	Ju 188	"
23 Jun 44	Flt Lt E R A Roberts	Bf 109	Lisieux-Evreux area

382

INDEX